EARLY 20TH CENTURY

STANLEY TOOLS

A PRICE GUIDE

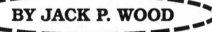

BY JACK P. WOOD

 Published by:
L-W Book Sales
P.O.Box 69
Gas City, IN 46933

ISBN# 0-89538-010-2

1909 Catalog Reprint
1926 Catalog Reprint

Layout: David Dilley

Table of Contents

Introduction

This book is a reprint of 1909 catalog and a 1926 catalog. As you will notice in the book we left all measurements and descriptions to better help you identify your tools. We do not claim to be experts in the tool collecting field. After many years in the publishing business we do feel that we know what is helpful to collectors. You will notice that the book is divided into two sections and each section is numbered separately as the original catalog. There is a separate price guide included in this book, which is only the opinion of the editor.

We Hope You Enjoy This Book!!

STANLEY
RULE AND LEVEL
COMPANY
CARPENTERS & MECHANICS TOOLS

WORKS AND GENERAL OFFICES
NEW BRITAIN CONN.
U. S. A.

CABLE ADDRESS
"STARULECO"
NEW BRITAIN

CABLE ADDRESS
"STARULECO"
NEW YORK

NEW YORK OFFICE AND WAREHOUSE
107 CHAMBERS STREET

NO. 102

Introduction

In publishing this catalogue it has been our purpose to present to the users and sellers of our tools a hand-book giving specifications, information and prices of the various tools made by this Company, and in which will be found a complete new set of illustrations and several new lines of goods.

This Company has long been engaged in the designing and manufacture of Carpenters' Tools, and especially Boxwood Rules, Levels and Planes. It was organized in 1857, and for several years previous to that time the same business was carried on under other names, and today, is the largest producer in the world engaged exclusively in the manufacture of Carpenters' and Mechanics' Tools.

We are thus enabled to bring into the manufacture and offer tools which embody the experience and study of half a century devoted to their design, both as regards the results which may be obtained with them and the best methods of manufacture.

It has always been the policy of this Company to furnish the best quality of goods at the lowest price possible, quality considered, and the fact that we are today the largest manufacturers in our line, we feel is an endorsement of our policy.

Owing to our improved methods of manufacture, combined with increased output, it is now possible to sell many tools, which in the past have been too expensive to find their way into every "Tool Kit," at prices that make them available to all.

STANLEY TOOLS, long recognized as the STANDARD THE WORLD OVER, are sold in every civilized country and stocks are carried by all the leading Jobbers and Dealers in hardware.

We take this opportunity of stating that the designs of many of the special tools we show originated in the suggestions of our customers, and we are always pleased to receive suggestions from tool users.

Expressing our appreciation of the favor that has been shown for STANLEY TOOLS in the past, and assuring to all users our best endeavors to maintain their quality and workmanship, we solicit their continued patronage.

THE STANLEY RULE & LEVEL CO.

Index

Stanley Boxwood Rules

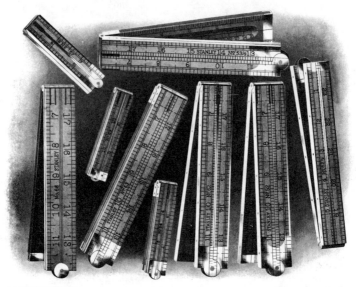

COPYRIGHT, 1909, BY THE STANLEY RULE AND LEVEL COMPANY   ILLUSTRATIONS OF NOS. 52, 53½, 57, 62, 62½, 63, 64, 68 AND 69

Stanley Boxwood Rules

STANLEY BOXWOOD RULES are of the highest quality both as regards workmanship, material and finish.

The value of the Rule consists not only in its being made of correct length and with accurate graduations, but also that it shall be so designed and made of such materials as to insure its remaining correct.

Our improved methods insure accuracy in manufacture, and as all the Boxwood used in Stanley Rules is sawed into shape and left to season for nearly two years before being made into finished Rules, it insures their remaining correct, and herein lies our claim for the superiority of the STANLEY RULE.

NO.	LENGTH	WIDTH	FOLD	JOINT	FRAME PLATES	GRADUATIONS			SPECIAL FEATURES	PACKED		CODE	PRICE DOZ. $	NO.
						INCHES	SCALES	MEASURE		IN BOX	WT. LBS.			
69	1 FT.	⅝ IN.	4	ROUND	MIDDLE	8 AND 16				12	½	STARULEMOS	1.75	69
65	1 "	" "	"	SQUARE	"	" "				6	¼	STARULEKUM	2.00	65
64	1 "	" "	"	"	EDGE	" "				6	⅜	STARULEKOL	2.75	64
65½	1 "	" "	"	"	BOUND	" "				6	½	STARULELAN	5.50	65½
55	1 "	" "	"	ARCH	MIDDLE	" "				6	⅜	STARULEHAL	2.50	55
56	1 "	" "	"	"	EDGE	" "				6	⅜	STARULEHEM	3.50	56
57	1 "	" "	"	"	BOUND	" "				6	½	STARULEHIN	6.25	57
61½	2 FT.	¾ "	"	SQUARE	MIDDLE	8, 10, 16			EXT. NARROW	6	⅝	STARULEJOS	3.25	61½
63½	2 "	" "	"	"	EDGE	8, 10, 16			" "	6	⅝	STARULEKIG	4.25	63½
62½	2 "	" "	"	"	BOUND	8, 10, 12, 16			" "	6	1	STARULEKAD	8.00	62½
68	2 "	1 "	"	ROUND	MIDDLE	8 AND 16				12	1¼	STARULEMIR	2.50	68
61	2 "	" "	"	SQUARE	"	8, 10, 12, 16				6	¾	STARULEJIX	3.00	61
63	2 "	" "	"	"	EDGE	" " " "	DRAFTING			6	¾	STARULEKEF	4.00	63
84	2 "	" "	"	"	HALF BOUND	" " " "	"			6	1	STARULERUP	6.50	84
62	2 "	" "	"	"	BOUND	" " " "	"			6	1⅛	STARULEJUB	8.00	62
51	2 "	" "	"	ARCH	MIDDLE	" " " "	"			6	¾	STARULEFUZ	3.50	51
53	2 "	" "	"	"	EDGE	" " " "	"			6	¾	STARULEGED	4.50	53
52	2 "	" "	"	"	HALF BOUND	" " " "	"			6	⅞	STARULEGAC	7.25	52
54	2 "	" "	"	"	BOUND	" " " "	"			6	1⅛	STARULEGOG	8.75	54
59	2 "	" "	"	D'B'L ARCH	BITTED	" " " "	"		EXT. STRONG	6	¾	STARULEJAS	5.25	59
60	2 "	" "	"	"	BOUND	" " " "	"		" "	6	1¼	STARULEJET	10.75	60
53½	2 "	" "	"	ARCH	EDGE	" " " "	"		INSIDE BEVEL	6	¾	STARULEGIF	8.00	53½

ANY RULE specified above can be furnished with Metric Graduations on both sides or with Metric on one side and Inches on the other; or can be furnished with "English Marking," that is, with the numbers reading from left to right, if so ordered.

OCTAGONAL SCALES (page 9) are used for laying out Eight Sided Work from 1 to 24 or 34 inches diameter. First outline on a Board a Square of the diameter desired, then on the Middle Scale marked M set off with a pair of dividers a number corresponding with the desired diameter, and from the MIDDLE of each side of the Square, prick this distance in each direction and saw off the Corners on the diagonal joining these points; or on the Edge Scale marked E, set off a corresponding number and prick on the side of the Square from each CORNER and saw off on the diagonal line joining these points.

Stanley Boxwood Rules

COPYRIGHT, 1909, BY THE STANLEY RULE AND LEVEL COMPANY

ILLUSTRATIONS OF NOS. 7, 18, 58, 66½, 70, 75, 78½ AND 94

Stanley Boxwood Rules

NO.	LENGTH	WIDTH	FOLD	JOINT	FRAME PLATES	GRADUATIONS			SPECIAL FEATURES	PACKED		CODE	PRICE DOZ: $	NO.
						INCHES	SCALES	MEASURE		IN BOX	WT. LBS.			
67	2 FT.	1⅜ IN	4	ROUND	MIDDLE	8 AND 16				6	⅞	STARULEMAN	3.50	67
70	2 "	" "	"	SQUARE	"		DRAFTING			6	1	STARULEMUT	4.00	70
72	2 "	" "	"	"	EDGE	8, 10, 16,	"			6	1	STARULENEZ	5.00	72
72½	2 "	" "	"	"	BOUND	" " "	"			6	1	STARULE NIB	9.00	72½
73	2 "	" "	"	ARCH	MIDDLE	" " "	"			6	1½	STARULENOC	5.00	73
75	2 "	" "	"	"	EDGE	" " "	"			6	1	STARULENUD	6.00	75
76	2 "	" "	"	"	BOUND	" " "	"			6	1⅜	STARULEPAP	10.00	76
77	2 "	" "	"	D'B'L ARCH	BITTED	" " "	"		EXT. STRONG	6	1⅛	STARULEPER	6.50	77
78	2 "	" "	"	" "	HALF BOUND	" " "	"		" "	6	1⅜	STARULEPIS	10.00	78
78½	2 "	" "	"	" "	BOUND	" " "	"			6	1⅜	STARULEPOT	12.00	78½
83	2 "	" "	"	ARCH	EDGE	8, 12, 16,	OCTAG'AL	100 OF FT	SLIDE	6	1⅝	STARULEROM	10.00	83
79	2 "	" "	"	SQUARE	"	12 AND 16	DRAFTING	BOARD		6	1¼	STARULEPUV	7.00	79
81	2 "	" "	"	ARCH	"	" "	"			6	1	STARULERED	8.00	81
82	2 "	" "	"	"	BOUND	" "	"			6	1	STARULERIL	12.00	82
7	2 "	"	"	SQUARE	EDGE	8 AND 16	"		BLINDMANS'	6	1½	STARULAFAC	11.00	7
29	2 "	"	2	ROUND	"	" "				6	1	STARULAKAN	2.75	29
18	2 "	1½	"	SQUARE	"	" "				12	1½	STARULAJEF	4.00	18
22	2 "	" "	"	"	BITTED	10, 12, 16,	OCTAG'AL	BOARD		6	1	STAR ULAJIG	5.00	22
1	2 "	" "	"	ARCH	"	8, 10, 16,	D'FT & OCT.		EXTRA THIN	6	1⅛	STARULADAR	4.50	1
4	2 "	" "	"	"	BOUND	8 AND 16	" "			6	¾	STARULADOX	6.50	4
5	2 "	" "	"	SQUARE	"	" " "	OCTAG'AL		SLIDE	6	1½	STARULADUZ	9.50	5
26	2 "	" "	"	"	BITTED	" " "	D'FT & OCT.	100 OF FT	GUNTER SLIDE	6	1⅜	STARULAJOL	7.00	26
27	2 "	" "	"	ARCH	"	" " "	" " "	" " " "		6	1⅜	STARULAJUM	10.00	27
12	2 "	" "	"	"	BOUND	" " "				6	1⅜	STARULAFOG	11.00	12
15	2 "	" "	"	"	EDGE	8, 10, 12, 16,				6	1¾	STARULAGUR	15.00	15
58	3 "	¾	6	"	BOUND	" " "			YARD INSIDE	6	¾	STARULEHOP	6.50	58
58½	3 "	1	4	MIDDLE		8 AND 16				6	1⅛	STARULEHUR	18.00	58½
66	3 "	" "	"	"		" "				6	1	STARULELIR	6.00	66
66½	3 "	" "	"	"	BOUND	" "				6	1	STARULELOS	6.00	66½
66¾	3 "	" "	"	SQUARE	EDGE				BLINDMANS'	6	1⅝	STARULELUT	15.00	66¾
8	3 "	" "	"	ARCH	BOUND				CARR. M'K'RS	6	1	STARULAFED	12.00	8
94	4 "	1½	"						D'BLE TONGUE	6	3	STARULEVUF	26.00	94
42	1 "	⅝	ENDS							12	1⅝	STARULECAB	4.00	42

ANY RULE specified above can be furnished with Metric Graduations on both sides, or with Metric on one side and Inches on the other; or can be furnished with "English Marking," that is, with the numbers reading from left to right, if so ordered. BOARD MEASURE RULES will give the contents in "Board Measure" of 1 inch boards of any ordinary dimensions.

Stanley Boxwood Caliper and Ivory Rules

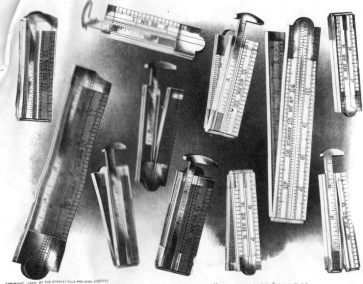

ILLUSTRATIONS OF NOS. 3, 32, 32½, 36, 36½, 38, 39, 40, 87, 88 AND 92

Stanley Boxwood Caliper Rules

NO.	LENGTH	WIDTH	FOLD	MATERIAL	JOINT	FRAME PLATES	INCHES	SCALES	MEASURE	CALIPER	IN BOX	WT. LBS.	CODE	PRICE DOZ. $	NO.
36	6 IN.	7/8 IN.	2	BOXWOOD	SQUARE		8,10,12,16			16 THS.	6	3/8	STARULARAT	4.50	36
14	6 "	7/8 "	"	"	"	BOUND	" " " "			"	6	1/2	STARULAGIN	8.00	14
13	6 "	1 1/8 "	"	"	"		8 AND 16			"	6	1/2	STARULAGAL	5.50	13
13 1/2	6 "	1 1/2 "	"	"	"		" "			"	6	3/4	STARULAGEM	6.50	13 1/2
3	1 FT.	5/8 "	4	"	"	BOUND	8,10,12,16			"	6	5/8	STARULADIT	12.00	3
32	1 "	1 "	"	"	ARCH	EDGE	" " " "			"	6	5/8	STARULAPED	7.00	32
32 1/2	1 "	1 "	"	"	"	BOUND	" " " "			"	6	3/4	STARULAPIL	10.00	32 1/2
36 1/2	1 "	1 3/8 "	2	"	SQUARE		" " " "			"	6	7/8	STARULAREX	6.50	36 1/2

Stanley Ivory Rules

NO.	LENGTH	WIDTH	FOLD	MATERIAL	JOINT	FRAME PLATES	INCHES	SCALES	TRIM'NGS	SPECIAL FEATURES	IN BOX	WT. LBS.	CODE	PRICE DOZ. $	NO.
40 1/2	6 IN.	5/8 IN.	2	IVORY	SQUARE	BOUND	8 AND 16		GER. SILV.	CALIPER	6	1/4	STARULASOR	24.00	40 1/2
38	6 "	7/8 "	"	"	"	"	8,10,12,16		" "	"	6	3/8	STARULAROB	15.00	38
40	1 FT.	5/8 "	4	"	"	"	8 AND 16		" "	"	12	3/4	STARULASIP	44.00	40
90	1 "	1/2 "	"	"	ROUND	MIDDLE	" "		" "	"	6	3/8	STARULETOR	10.00	90
92 1/2	1 "	5/8 "	"	"	SQUARE	"	" "		" "	"	6	1/2	STARULEVOD	14.00	92 1/2
92	1 "	" "	"	"	"	EDGE	" "		" "	"	6	1/2	STARULEVIC	17.00	92
88 1/2	1 "	" "	"	"	ARCH	"	" "		" "	"	6	1/2	STARULESUC	32.00	88 1/2
88	1 "	" "	"	"	"	BOUND	8,10,12,16		" "	"	6	3/4	STARULETUS	23.00	88
91	1 "	3/4 "	"	"	"	SQUARE EDGE	8,10,12,16		" "	CALIPER	6	1	STARULASAG	38.00	91
39	1 "	" "	"	"	"	"	" " " "		" "	"	6	1 1/8	STARULE SAT	54.00	39
85	2 FT.	" "	"	"	"	"	" " " "		" "	"	6	1 1/2	STARULESEX	64.00	85
86	2 "	" 1 "	"	"	ARCH	"	" " " "		DRAFTING	100THS OF FT.	6	1 1/8	STARULESOB	80.00	86
87	2 "	1 "	"	"	"	BOUND	" " " "		" "	" "	6	1	STARULETIP	92.00	87
89	2 "	1 "	"	"	"	"	" " " "		" "	INSIDE BEVEL	6		STARULE12	96.00	89
86 1/2	2 "	1 "	"	"	ARCH	EDGE	" " " "		" "	INSIDE BEVEL	6		STARULE12	96.00	86 1/2

ALL CALIPER RULES are regularly made with Caliper left hand, as shown in cuts on opposite page. When ordered with Caliper right hand, an additional charge of twenty-five cents per dozen, net, will be made. The Caliper of all Caliper Rules is regularly graduated in 16ths, but can be furnished in 32nds, without additional charge, if so ordered.

ANY RULE specified above can be furnished with Metric Graduations on both sides, or with Metric on one side and Inches on the other; or can be furnished with "English Marking," that is with the numbers reading from left to right, if so ordered.

Stanley Boxwood Rules

ILLUSTRATIONS OF NOS. 7, 18, 58, 66½, 70, 75, 78½ AND 94

Stanley Boxwood Rules

NO.	LENGTH	WIDTH	FOLD	JOINT	FRAME PLATES	GRADUATIONS INCHES	GRADUATIONS SCALES	GRADUATIONS MEASURE	SPECIAL FEATURES	PACKED IN BOX	PACKED WT. LBS.	CODE	PRICE DOZ. $	NO.
67	2 FT.	1⅜ IN	4	ROUND	MIDDLE	8THS AND 16THS				6	⅞	STARULEMAN	3.50	67
70	2 "	" "	"	SQUARE	"	" "	DRAFTING			6	1	STARULEMUT	4.00	70
72	2 "	" "	"	"	EDGE	8THS, 10THS, 16THS,	"			6	1	STARULENEZ	5.00	72
72½	2 "	" "	"	"	BOUND	" " "	"			6	1½	STARULENIB	9.00	72½
73	2 "	" "	"	ARCH	MIDDLE	" " "	"			6	1	STARULENOC	5.00	73
75	2 "	" "	"	"	EDGE	" " "	"			6	1	STARULENUD	6.00	75
76	2 "	" "	"	"	BOUND	" " "	"			6	1⅜	STARULEPAP	10.00	76
77	2 "	" "	"	D'B'L ARCH	BITTED	" " "	"		EXT. STRONG	6	1⅛	STARULEPER	6.50	77
78	2 "	" "	"	" "	HALF BOUND	" " "	"		" "	6	1⅜	STARULEPIS	10.00	78
78½	2 "	" "	"	" "	BOUND	" " "	"		" "	6	1⅝	STARULEPOT	12.00	78½
83	2 "	" "	"	ARCH	EDGE	8THS, 12THS, 16THS,	OCTAG'AL	100THS OF FT.	SLIDE	6	1¼	STARULEROM	10.00	83
79	2 "	" "	"	SQUARE	"	12THS AND 16THS	DRAFTING	BOARD		6	1	STARULEPUV	7.00	79
81	2 "	" "	"	ARCH	"	" "	"	"		6	1	STARULERED	8.00	81
82	2 "	" "	"	"	BOUND	" "	"	"		6	1½	STARULERIL	12.00	82
7	2 "	" "	"	SQUARE	EDGE	8THS AND 16THS			BLINDMANS'	6	1	STARULAFAC	11.00	7
29	2 "	" "	2	ROUND		" "				12	1½	STARULAKAN	2.75	29
18	2 "	1½ "	"	SQUARE		" "				6	1	STARULAJEF	4.00	18
22	2 "	" "	"	"	BITTED	10THS, 12THS, 16THS,	OCTAG'AL	BOARD		6	1	STARULAJIG	5.00	22
1	2 "	" "	"	ARCH	"	8THS AND 16THS	"			6	1⅛	STARULADAR	4.50	1
4	2 "	" "	"	"	"	8THS, 10THS, 16THS,	D'F'T & OCT.		EXTRA THIN	6	¾	STARULADOX	6.50	4
5	2 "	" "	"	"	BOUND	" " "	" "			6	1½	STARULADUZ	9.50	5
26	2 "	" "	"	SQUARE		" " "	OCTAG'AL		SLIDE	6	1⅜	STARULAJOL	7.00	26
27	2 "	" "	"	"	BITTED	" " "	D'F'T & OCT.	100THS OF FT.	GUNTER SLIDE	6	1⅜	STARULAJUM	10.00	27
12	2 "	" "	"	ARCH	"	" " "	" "	" " "	" "	6	1⅜	STARULAFOG	11.00	12
15	2 "	" "	"	"	BOUND	" " "	" "	" " "	" "	6	1¾	STARULAGUR	15.00	15
58	2 "	¾ "	6	"	EDGE	8THS, 10THS, 12THS, 16THS,				6	¾	STARULEHOP	6.50	58
58½	2 "	" "	"	"	BOUND	" " " "				6	1⅛	STARULEHUR	18.00	58½
66	3 "	1 "	4	"	MIDDLE	16THS			YARD INSIDE	6	1	STARULELIR	6.00	66
66½	3 "	" "	"	"	"	8THS AND 16THS				6	1	STARULELOS	6.00	66½
66¾	3 "	" "	"	"	BOUND	" "				6	1⅝	STARULELUT	15.00	66¾
8	3 "	" "	"	SQUARE	EDGE	" "			BLINDMANS'	6	1	STARULAFED	12.00	8
94	4 "	1½ "	"	ARCH	BOUND	" "			CARR. M'K'RS	6	3	STARULEVUF	26 00	94
42	1 "	⅝ "	ENDS			" "			D'BLE TONGUE	12	1⅝	STARULECAB	4.00	42

ANY RULE specified above can be furnished with Metric Graduations on both sides, or with Metric on one side and Inches on the other; or can be furnished with "English Marking," that is, with the numbers reading from left to right, if so ordered.

BOARD MEASURE RULES will give the contents in "Board Measure" of 1 inch boards of any ordinary dimensions.

Stanley Boxwood Caliper and Ivory Rules

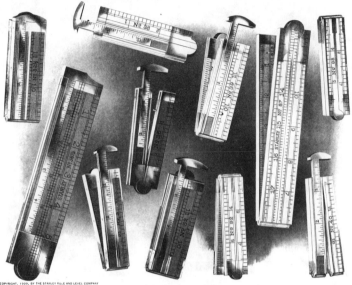

ILLUSTRATIONS OF NOS. 3, 32, 32½, 36, 36½, 38, 39, 40, 87, 88 AND 92

Stanley Boxwood Caliper Rules

| NO. | LENGTH | WIDTH | FOLD | MATERIAL | JOINT | FRAME PLATES | GRADUATIONS | | | | PACKED | | CODE | PRICE DOZ. $ | NO. |
							INCHES	SCALES	MEASURE	CALIPER	IN BOX	WT. LBS.			
36	6 IN.	⅞ IN.	2	BOXWOOD	SQUARE		THS THS THS 8, 10, 12, 16			16 THS.	6	⅜	STARULARAT	4.50	36
14	6 "	⅞ "	"	"	"	BOUND	" " " "			"	6	½	STARULAGIN	8.00	14
13	6 "	1⅛ "	"	"	"	"	THS THS 8 AND 16			"	6	½	STARULAGAL	5.50	13
13½	6 "	1½ "	"	"	"	"	" "			"	6	¾	STARULAGEM	6.50	13½
3	1 FT.	⅝ "	4	"	"	BOUND	" "			"	6	⅝	STARULADIT	12.00	3
32	1 "	1 "	"	"	ARCH	EDGE	8, 10, 12, 16			"	6	⅝	STARULAPED	7.00	32
32½	1 "	1 "	"	"	"	BOUND	" " " "			"	6	¾	STARULAPIL	10.00	32½
36½	1 "	1⅜ "	2	"	"	SQUARE	" " " "			"	6	⅞	STARULAREX	6.50	36½

Stanley Ivory Rules

| NO. | LENGTH | WIDTH | FOLD | MATERIAL | JOINT | FRAME PLATES | GRADUATIONS | | TRIM'NGS | SPECIAL FEATURES | PACKED | | CODE | PRICE DOZ. $ | NO. |
							INCHES	SCALES			IN BOX	WT. LBS.			
40½	6 IN.	⅝ IN.	2	IVORY	SQUARE	BOUND	THS THS 8 AND 16		GER. SILV.	CALIPER	6	¼	STARULASOR	24.00	40½
38	6 "	⅞ "	"	"	"	"	THS THS THS THS 8, 10, 12, 16		" "	"	6	⅜	STARULAROB	15.00	38
40	1 FT.	⅝ "	4	"	"	"	THS THS 8 AND 16		" "	"	6	⅝	STARULASIP	44.00	40
90	1 "	½ "	"	"	ROUND	MIDDLE	" "		" "		12	¾	STARULETOR	10.00	90
92½	1 "	⅝ "	"	"	SQUARE	"	" "		" "		6	⅜	STARULEVOD	14.00	92½
92	1 "	" "	"	"	"	EDGE	" "		" "		6	½	STARULEVIC	17.00	92
88½	1 "	" "	"	"	ARCH	"	" "		" "		6	½	STARULETAG	21.00	88½
88	1 "	" "	"	"	"	BOUND	" "		" "		6	½	STARULESUC	32.00	88
91	1 "	¾ "	"	"	SQUARE	EDGE	8, 10, 12, 16		" "		6	½	STARULETUS	23.00	91
39	1 "	⅞ "	"	"	"	"	" " " "		" "	CALIPER	6	¾	STARULASAG	38.00	39
85	2 FT.	" "	"	"	"	"	" " " "		" "		6	1	STARULE SAT	54.00	85
86	2 "	" "	"	"	ARCH	"	" " " "	DRAFTING	" "	100THS OF FT.	6	1⅛	STARULESEX	64.00	86
87	2 "	1 "	"	"	"	BOUND	" " " "	"	" "		6	1½	STARULESOB	80.00	87
89	2 "	1 "	"	"	D. ARCH	"	" " " "	"	" "		6	1⅝	STARULETIP	92.00	89
86½	2 "	1 "	"	"	ARCH	EDGE	" " " "		" "	INSIDE BEVEL	6	1	STARULESIZ	96.00	86½

ALL CALIPER RULES are regularly made with Caliper left hand, as shown in cuts on opposite page. When ordered with Caliper right hand, an additional charge of twenty-five cents per dozen, net, will be made. The Caliper of all Caliper Rules is regularly graduated in 16ths, but can be furnished in 32nds, without additional charge, if so ordered.
ANY RULE specified above can be furnished with Metric Graduations on both sides, or with Metric on one side and Inches on the other; or can be furnished with "English Marking," that is with the numbers reading from left to right, if so ordered.

Stanley Wood Plumbs and Levels

COPYRIGHT,-1909, BY THE STANLEY RULE AND LEVEL COMPANY
ILLUSTRATION OF NOS. 0 (TYPE NOS. 00, 01, 1) 3, 9, (TYPE NOS. 04, 011, 4, 5, 10, 11) 102, (TYPE NO. 103) 104, (TYPE NO. 1½)

Stanley Wood Plumbs and Levels

STANLEY WOOD PLUMBS AND LEVELS are made from thoroughly seasoned stock and are guaranteed.

All Stanley Wood Plumbs and Levels have the side groove, or "HAND-Y" grip feature, rightly so called, because of the feeling of security it gives the workman when handling these Levels in actual working or in climbing ladders, staging, etc.

All Wood Levels are fitted with Proved or Ground Level Glasses, and are non-adjustable or adjustable as specified. The Adjustable Level Glasses are set in a Metal Case, held in place by plaster, and are adjustable by means of the Screws and Spiral Springs at each end of the Level Glasses, merely by removing the Top Plate, as illustrated on the opposite page.

The Adjustable Plumb Glasses have Metal Cases, three pronged at bottom, which fit tightly into the body of Level and at the top have a tight fitting Metal Disc with a Slot and Set Screw, and are adjustable by removing the Screws of the Cover Plate. All Plumbs and Levels have Improved Settings to give a better view of the bubble when working overhead.

NO.	LENGTH	TYPE	MATERIAL	FINISH	TRIM	TOP PLATE	SIDE VIEWS	LEVEL GLASS	PACKED IN BOX	WT. LBS.	CODE	PRICE DOZ. $	NO.
102	1 to 16 in.	NON-ADJUST.	HARDWOOD	POLISHED		ARCH		PROVED	12	11	STALEVESAT	5.10	102
103	18 " 24 "	" "	"	"		"		"	12	23	STALEVESEX	6.40	103
104	12 " 18 "	" "	"	"		"		"	12	15	STALEVESIZ	7.60	104
1½	18 " 24 "	" "	MAHOGANY	"		"		"	12	21	STALEVACON	13.90	1½
1¾	12 " 18 "	" "	"	"	BRASS TIPS	"	BR. LIPS	"	12	18	STALEVACUP	14.70	1¾
00	18 " 24 "	" "	HARDWOOD	"		"		"	6	16½	STALEVABAB	8.75	00
0	24 " 30 "	" "	"	"		"		"	6	20	STALEVABEC	9.90	0
01	24 " 30 "	" "	MAHOGANY	"		SQUARE		"	6	20	STALEVABID	14.70	01
02	24 " 30 "	" "	HARDWOOD	"		"	" "	"	6	20	STALEVABOF	13.20	02
03	24 " 30 "	" "	"	"	" "	"		"	6	22	STALEVABUG	14.70	03
04	24 " 30 "	" "	"	"	" "	"	" "	"	6	22½	STALEVACAH	18.90	04
011	24 " 30 "	" "	ROSEWOOD	"	" "	"	" "	"	6	29	STALEVACEL	40.00	011
1	24 " 30 "	ADJUSTABLE	MAHOGANY	"		"		"	6	17½	STALEVACIM	19.80	1
2	24 " 30 "	"	HARDWOOD	"		"	" "	"	6	22	STALEVADAR	14.70	2
3	24 " 30 "	"	"	"	" "	"		"	6	22	STALEVADES	16.50	3
3*	18 " 24 "	"	"	"	" "	"		"	6	18½	STALEVADIT	16.50	3*
4	24 " 30 "	"	"	"	" "	"	" "	"	6	22½	STALEVADOX	19.20	4
5	24 " 30 "	"	"	"	" "	"	" "	"	6	24	STALEVADUZ	22.50	5
6	24 " 30 "	"	MAHOGANY	"		"	" "	"	6	19½	STALEVAFAC	23.70	6
9	24 " 30 "	"	"	"	" "	"	" "	"	6	21	STALEVAGAL	27.60	9
10	24 " 30 "	"	"	"	" "	"	" "	"	6	25½	STALEVAGEM	32.40	10
11	24 " 30 "	"	ROSEWOOD	"	" "	"	" "	"	6	29	STALEVAGIN	43.00	11

Levels Nos. 5 and 10 are Triple Stock. Levels Nos. 102 and 103 have no Plumbs.

Prices given for Levels cover any length in which that number is made. Length always increases by two inches.

The tables give the extreme lengths in which the various numbers are made. Assorted sizes are always sent unless otherwise ordered.

Stanley and "Victor" White Enamel "Zig Zag" and Blacksmiths' Rules

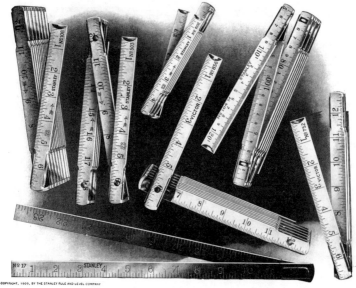

COPYRIGHT, 1909, BY THE STANLEY RULE AND LEVEL COMPANY

ILLUSTRATIONS OF NOS. 17, 104M, 108, 503, 602, 752 AND 856

Stanley and "Victor" White Enamel "Zig Zag" and Blacksmiths' Rules

WHITE ENAMEL "ZIG ZAG" RULES are more easily read than the YELLOW ENAMEL and are offered as a finer quality Rule.

							GRADUATIONS			PACKED				
NO.	LENGTH	WIDTH	FOLD	MATERIAL HARDWOOD	JOINT	TRIMMINGS	INCHES	SCALES	SPECIAL FEATURES	IN BOX	WT. LBS.	CODE	PRICE DOZ. $	NO.
Stanley White Enamel "Zig Zag" Rules														
602	2 FT	7/16 IN.	6	FLEXIBLE	CONCEALED	BRASS PLAT'D	16THS			6	3/8	STARULINAX	4.08	602
603	3 "	" "	9	"	"	" "	"			6	5/8	STARULINEZ	6.00	603
604	4 "	" "	12	"	"	" "	"			6	3/4	STARULINOC	8.04	604
102	2 FT	5/8 "	4	"	"	" "	"		SHIELD PLATES	6	1/2	STARULIDAB	2.40	102
103	3 "	" "	6	"	"	" "	"		" "	6	3/4	STARULIDEC	3.60	103
104	4 "	" "	8	"	"	" "	"		" "	6	1	STARULIDOF	4.80	104
104M	4 "	" "	8	"	"	" "	"	METRIC	" "	6	1	STARULIDUG	4.80	104M
105	5 "	" "	10	"	"	" "	"		" "	6	1 3/8	STARULIFEL	6.00	105
106	6 "	" "	12	"	"	" "	"		" "	6	1 1/2	STARULIFIM	7.20	106
108	8 "	" "	16	"	"	"	"		" "	6	1 7/8	STARULIFON	9.60	108
502	2 FT	" "	4	"	RIVET	" "	"			6	1/2	STARULILAD	2.28	502
503	3 "	" "	6	"	"	" "	"			6	3/4	STARULILEF	3.36	503
504	4 "	" "	8	"	"	" "	"			6	7/8	STARULILIG	4.44	504
504M	4 "	" "	8	"	"	" "	"	METRIC		6	7/8	STARULILOL	4.44	504M
505	5 "	" "	10	"	"	" "	"			6	1 1/4	STARULILUM	5.52	505
506	6 "	" "	12	"	"	" "	"			6	1 1/2	STARULIMAN	6.60	506
508	8 "	" "	16	"	"	" "	"			6	1 3/4	STARULIMOS	8.88	508
"Victor" White Enamel "Zig Zag" Rules														
752	2 FT	5/8 "	4	FLEXIBLE	CONCEALED	BLUED	16THS			12	7/8	STARULOFAB	2.28	752
753	3 "	" "	6	"	"	"	"			12	1 3/8	STARULOFEC	3.36	753
754	4 "	" "	8	"	"	"	"			12	1 7/8	STARULOFOD	4.44	754
755	5 "	" "	10	"	"	"	"			12	2 5/8	STARULOFUG	5.52	755
756	6 "	" "	12	"	"	"	"			12	2 7/8	STARULOGEL	6.60	756
758	8 "	" "	16	"	"	"	"			12	3 3/4	STARULOGEM	8.88	758
852	2 FT	" "	4	"	RIVET	"	"			12	7/8	STARULOLAL	2.04	852
853	3 "	" "	6	"	"	"	"			12	1 3/8	STARULOLEM	3.00	853
854	4 "	" "	8	"	"	"	"			12	1 3/4	STARULOLIN	3.96	854
855	5 "	" "	10	"	"	"	"			12	2 1/4	STARULONOP	4.92	855
856	6 "	" "	12	"	"	"	"			12	2 7/8	STARULONUR	6.00	856
858	8 "	" "	16	"	"	"	"			12	3 1/2	STARULOPAS	7.92	858
Blacksmiths' Rule														
17	2 FT	5/8 IN.	2	SPRING BR.	CONCEALED		BAND 16			6	1 3/8	STARULAJAD	6.00	17

Stanley and "Victor" Yellow Enamel "Zig Zag" Rules

COPYRIGHT, 1909, BY THE STANLEY RULE AND LEVEL COMPANY

ILLUSTRATIONS OF NOS. 02, 04M, 05, 204, 302, 406, 704 AND 808

Stanley and "Victor" Yellow Enamel "Zig Zag" Rules

STANLEY "ZIG ZAG" RULES are superior to the "VICTOR" in Finish, in having Patented Direction Arrows, and Shield Plates on the Concealed Joint type. All "Zig Zag" Rules have joints containing a stiff spring holding them rigid when open.

Stanley Yellow Enamel "Zig Zag" Rules

NO.	LENGTH	WIDTH	FOLD	MATERIAL HARDWOOD	JOINT	TRIMMINGS	GRADUATIONS		SPECIAL FEATURES	PACKED		CODE	PRICE DOZ. $	NO.
							INCHES	SCALES		IN BOX	WT. LBS.			
302	2 FT.	7/16 IN.	6	FLEXIBLE	CONCEALED	BRASS PLAT'D	16THS			6	3/8	STARULIHAC	3.70	302
303	3 "	" "	9	"	"	" "	"			6	5/8	STARULIHED	5.50	303
304	4 "	" "	12	"	"	" "	"			6	3/4	STARULIHIF	7.30	304
02	2 FT.	5/8 "	4	"	"	" "	"		SHIELD PLATES	6	1/2	STARULABAB	2.20	02
03	3 "	" "	6	"	"	" "	"		" "	6	3/4	STARULABEC	3.30	03
04	4 "	" "	8	"	"	" "	"		" "	6	1	STARULABID	4.40	04
04M	4 "	" "	8	"	"	" "	"	METRIC	" "	6	1	STARULABOF	4.40	04M
05	5 "	" "	10	"	"	" "	"		" "	6	1 3/8	STARULABUG	5.50	05
06	6 "	" "	12	"	"	" "	"		" "	6	1 1/2	STARULACEL	6.60	06
08	8 "	" "	16	"	"	" "	"		" "	6	1 7/8	STARULACON	8.80	08
402	2 FT.	" "	4	"	RIVET	" "	"			6	1/2	STARULIJAL	2.00	402
403	3 "	" "	6	"	"	" "	"			6	3/4	STARULIJEM	3.00	403
404	4 "	" "	8	"	"	" "	"			6	7/8	STARULIJIN	4.00	404
404M	4 "	" "	8	"	"	" "	"	METRIC		6	7/8	STARULIJOP	4.00	404M
405	5 "	" "	10	"	"	" "	"			6	1 1/8	STARULIJUR	5.00	405
406	6 "	" "	12	"	"	" "	"			6	1 1/2	STARULIKAS	6.00	406
408	8 "	" "	16	"	"	" "	"			6	1 3/4	STARULIKET	8.00	408
204	4 FT.	" "	8	"	CONCEALED	" "	"		EXTENSION	6	1 1/2	STARULIGAR	7.70	204
206	6 "	" "	12	"	"	" "	"		"	6	2	STARULIGES	9.90	206

"Victor" Yellow Enamel "Zig Zag" Rules

702	2 FT.	5/8 IN.	4	FLEXIBLE	CONCEALED	BLUED	16THS			12	7/8	STARULIPAF	2.00	702
703	3 "	" "	6	"	"	"	"			12	1 3/8	STARULIPEG	3.00	703
704	4 "	" "	8	"	"	"	"			12	1 7/8	STARULIPOL	4.00	704
705	5 "	" "	10	"	"	"	"			12	2 5/8	STARULIPUN	5.00	705
706	6 "	" "	12	"	"	"	"			12	2 7/8	STARULIRAP	6.00	706
708	8 "	" "	16	"	"	"	"			12	3 3/4	STARULIROT	8.00	708
802	2 FT.	" "	4	"	RIVET	"	"			12	7/8	STARULOHAR	1.80	802
803	3 "	" "	6	"	"	"	"			12	1 3/8	STARULOHES	2.70	803
804	4 "	" "	8	"	"	"	"			12	1 3/4	STARULOHIT	3.60	804
805	5 "	" "	10	"	"	"	"			12	2 1/4	STARULOHOX	4.50	805
806	6 "	" "	12	"	"	"	"			12	2 7/8	STARULOHUZ	5.40	806
808	8 "	" "	16	"	"	"	"			12	3 1/2	STARULOJOG	7.20	808

Stanley Boxwood Shrinkage, Extension and Miscellaneous Rules

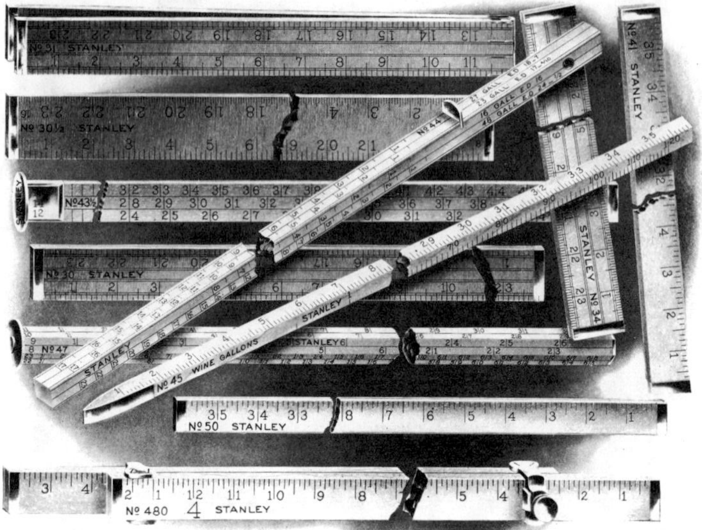

COPYRIGHT, 1909, BY THE STANLEY RULE AND LEVEL COMPANY

ILLUSTRATIONS OF NOS. 30, 30½, 31, 34, 41, 43½, 44, 45, 47, 50 AND 480

Stanley Boxwood Shrinkage, Extension and Miscellaneous Rules

NO.	LENGTH	WIDTH	MATERIAL	NAME	TRIM	GRADUATIONS INCHES	SCALES	MEASURE	SPECIAL FEATURES	PACKED IN BOX	WT. LBS.	CODE	PRICE DOZ. $	NO.
Stanley Boxwood Shrinkage Rules														
30½A	24⅛ IN.	1½ IN.	BOXWOOD	SHRINKAGE	BRASS	8THS, 10THS, 12THS, 16THS			SHRINKAGE 1/16 IN. PER FT.	6	1	STARULAKOS	18.00	30½A
30½B	24 2/12 "	" "	"	"	"	" " " "			1/12 " " "	6	"	STARULAKUT	18.00	30½B
30½C	24 2/10 "	" "	"	"	"	" " " "			1/10 " " "	6	"	STARULALAX	18.00	30½C
30½D	24 3/16 "	" "	"	"	"	" " " "			3/32 " " "	6	"	STARULALEZ	18.00	30½D
30½E	24¼ "	" "	"	"	"	" " " "			⅛ " " "	6	"	STARULALOC	18.00	30½E
30½F	24⅜ "	" "	"	"	"	" " " "			3/16 " " "	6	"	STARULALUD	18.00	30½F
30½G	24½ "	" "	"	"	"	" " " "			¼ " " "	6	"	STARULAMEG	18.00	30½G
31½A	24⅛ "	" "	"	"	"	" " " "			1/16 " " "	6	"	STARULAMUN	21.00	31½A
30	24¼ "	1¼ "	"	"	"	8THS AND 16THS			⅛ " " "	6	"	STARULAKIR	15.00	30
31	24¼ "	1 5/16 "	"	"	"	" " "			⅛ " " "	6	1⅜	STARULAMOL	18.00	31
Stanley Extension Rules														
240	2–4 FT.	1 IN.	MAPLE	EXTENSION	BRASS	8THS					⅝	STARULIGIT	8.00	240
360	3–6 "	" "	"	"	"	"					¾	STARULIHOG	9.00	360
480	4–8 "	" "	"	"	"	"					1	STARULIKIX	10.00	480
510	5–10 "	" "	"	"	"	"					1¼	STARULIMUT	12.00	510
612	6–12 "	" "	"	"	"	"					1⅜	STARULINUD	15.00	612
Stanley Miscellaneous Rules														
34	2 FT.	1 5/16 IN.	MAPLE	BENCH	BRASS	8THS AND 16THS				12	2½	STARULAPUP	4.00	34
80	3 "	1½ "	"	SADDLERS	CAP'D ENDS	" " "				12	3⅝	STARULERAZ	9.00	80
33	3 "	¾ "	"	YARD STICK		8THS	YARD ONE SIDE			12	2	STARULAPOM	2.00	33
50	3 "	" "	HICKORY	" "	" "	"	" " "			12	2	STARULEFOX	4.50	50
41	3 "	1 "	MAPLE	" "	BR. TIPS	"	" " "			12	2⅝	STARULASUS	3.50	41
46	2 "	⅞ "	"	B'D STICK	BR. CAPS	16 LINES	8 TO 23 FT.	BOARD	OCTAGONAL	6	2¾	STARULEDEL	16.00	46
46½	2 "	" "	"	" "	" "	" "	" " " "	"	SQUARE	6	3⅜	STARULEDIM	16.00	46½
47	3 "	" "	"	" "	" "	" "	" " " "	"	OCTAGONAL	6	3¾	STARULEDON	26.00	47
47½	3 "	" "	"	" "	" "	" "	" " " "	"	SQUARE	6	4⅝	STARULEDUP	26.00	47½
43½	3 "	1 "	HICKORY	" "	BR. HEAD	6 "	12 TO 22 "	"	FLAT	6	1¾	STARULECAC	15.00	43½
49	3 "	" "	"	" "	ST. HEAD	" "	" " " "	"	EXT. STRONG	6	1⅞	STARULEFIT	22.00	49
48	3 "	¾ "	"	B'D CANE	BR. HEAD	8 "	9 TO 16 "	"	OCTAGONAL	6	3⅛	STARULEFAR	21.00	48
48½	3 "	¾ "	"	LOG CANE	" "	7 "	12 TO 22 "	LOG	DOYLE REVIS'D	6	3⅛	STARULEFES	26.00	48½
71	4 "	1¼ "	MAPLE	WOOD	BR. CAPS	8THS	10THS FT.	WOOD		6	6	STARULENAX	16.00	71
44	16½ IN.	⅝ "	"	WANTAGE	BRASS LIP	8 LINES			16 TO 48 GAL.	12	2⅛	STARULECID	7.00	44
37	16½ "	" "	"	"	" "	12 "			16 " 200 "	12	2⅛	STARULARIZ	10.00	37
45	3 FT.	½ "	"	GAUGING	BRASS TIP				120 "	12	3⅛	STARULECOF	7.00	45
45½	4 "	⅝ "	"	"	" "		WANTAGE TABLE		180 "	12	4¼	STARULECUG	18.00	45½

SHRINKAGE RULES NOS. 30½ and 31½ can be furnished graduated only in 8ths and 16ths without extra charge. Shrinkage Rule No. 31½ is two fold and made for the same shrinkages as No. 30½. See pages 123 and 124 for Code of various lengths

Stanley Duplex, "Victor" and Masons' Wood Plumbs and Levels

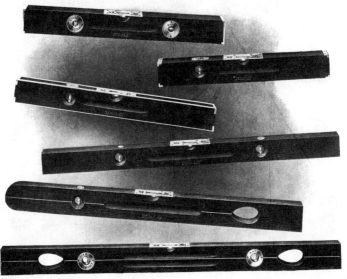

COPYRIGHT, 190?, BY THE STANLEY RULE AND LEVEL COMPANY
ILLUSTRATIONS OF NOS. 8, ·TYPE NOS. 7½, 20· 18, ·TYPE NO. 19· 21, 30, ·TYPE NOS. 25, 50· 35, 45½, ·TYPE NO. 45·

Stanley Duplex Wood Plumbs and Levels

STANLEY DUPLEX WOOD PLUMBS AND LEVELS are made with Adjustable Level and Plumb Glasses, as described on page 19. An additional Level Glass is set in the side at the opposite end to the Plumb Glass for a better observation of the Level Glass SIDEWISE. Both of these Glasses are protected by Brass Discs, can be seen from either side, and are inserted in the Level with the least possible removal of the wood from the stock. LEVEL NO. 50 IS OF TRIPLE STOCK.

NO.	LENGTH	TYPE	MATERIAL	FINISH	TRIM	TOP PLATE	SIDE VIEWS	LEVEL GLASS	PACKED		CODE	PRICE DOZ. $	NO.
									IN BOX	WT. LBS.			
25	24 TO 30 IN.	ADJUSTABLE	MAHOGANY	POLISHED	BRASS TIPS	SQUARE		BR. LIPS	PROVED	6	22	STALEVAHOZ	26.00	25
30	24 " 30 "	"	HARDWOOD	"	" "	"		"	"	6	24	STALEVAHUB	20.00	30
50	24 " 30 "	"	"	"	"	"		"	" "	6	24	STALEVEGOZ	26.00	50

Stanley "Victor" Plumbs and Levels

NO.	LENGTH	TYPE	MATERIAL	FINISH	TRIM	TOP PLATE	SIDE VIEWS	LEVEL GLASS	PACKED		CODE	PRICE DOZ. $	NO.
									IN BOX	WT. LBS.			
17	24 TO 30 IN.	ADJUSTABLE	HARDWOOD	POLISHED		SQUARE		PROVED	1	3¼	STALEVAGOP	18.00	17
18	24 " 30 "	"	"	"	BRASS TIPS	"		"	1	3½	STALEVAGUR	21.00	18
19	24 " 30 "	"	ROSEWOOD	"	"	"	BR. LIPS	"	1	3¾	STALEVAHAS	42.00	19
21	24 " 30 "	"	MAHOGANY	"	BR. BOUND	"		"	1	3⅜	STALEVAHIX	48.00	21

Stanley Masons' Plumbs and Levels

NO.	LENGTH	TYPE	MATERIAL	FINISH	TRIM	TOP PLATE	SIDE VIEWS	LEVEL GLASS	PACKED		CODE	PRICE DOZ. $	NO.
									IN BOX	WT. LBS.			
7	36 IN.	NON-ADJUST.	HARDWOOD	POLISHED	BRASS TIPS	SQUARE		PROVED	6	26	STALEVAFED	21.60	7
7½	36 "	"	"	"	"	"		"	6	24	STALEVAFIF	18.90	7½
8	42 "	"	"	"	"	"		"	6	28	STALEVAFOG	21.60	8
20	42 "	ADJUSTABLE	"	"	"	"	BR. LIPS	"	6	20	STALEVAHET	30.00	20
35	42 "	"	SOFTWOOD	"	"	"	" "	"	6	32½	STALEVANER	21.00	35
45	48 "	"	"	"	1⅜ STOCK	"	" "	"	6	40	STALEVEGAS	36.00	45
45½	48 "	"	"	"	1 1/16 "	"	" "	"	6	30	STALEVEGET	36.00	45½

Prices given for Levels cover any length in which that number is made. Length always increases by two inches.
The tables give the extreme lengths in which the various numbers are made. Assorted sizes are always sent unless otherwise ordered.

Stanley Wood Plumbs and Levels with Ground Glasses

COPYRIGHT, 1929, BY THE STANLEY RULE AND LEVEL COMPANY

ILLUSTRATION OF NOS. 70 (TYPE NO. 80) 90, 95. (TYPE NO. 96) AND 98-6", 12", 18"

Stanley Wood Plumbs and Levels with Ground Glasses

STANLEY WOOD PLUMBS AND LEVELS WITH GROUND GLASSES are the highest type of Wood Level which have ever been placed before the mechanic. The demand for a Level of the highest grade originally induced us to manufacture this line and their sale has far exceeded our expectations.

The Glasses are adjustable as described and illustrated on pages 18 and 19.

NO.	LENGTH	TYPE	MATERIAL	FINISH	TRIM	TOP PLATE	SIDE VIEWS	LEVEL GLASS	PACKED IN BOX	WT. LBS.	CODE	PRICE DOZ. $	NO.
60	24 TO 30 IN.	ADJUSTABLE	MAHOGANY	POLISHED		SQUARE	BR. LIPS	GROUND	1	3¼	STALEVEGUB	35.00	60
90	24 " 30 "	"	"	"	BRASS TIPS	"	" "	"	1	3⅜	STALEVEJOS	39.00	90
95	24 " 30 "	"	"	"	BR. BOUND	"	" "	"	1	3½	STALEVEJUT	60.00	95
96	24 " 30 "	"	ROSEWOOD	"	"	"	" "	"	1	4⅞	STALEVEMAX	80.00	96

Stanley Machinists' Plumbs and Levels with Ground Glasses

NO.	LENGTH	TYPE	MATERIAL	FINISH	TRIM	TOP PLATE	SIDE VIEWS	LEVEL GLASS	PACKED IN BOX	WT. LBS.	CODE	PRICE DOZ. $	NO.
98	6 IN.	ADJUSTABLE	ROSEWOOD	POLISHED	BR. BOUND	SQUARE	BR. LIPS	GROUND	1	1⅛	STALEVENAZ	26.00	6"-98
98	9 "	"	"	"	" "	"	" "	"	1	1¾	STALEVENED	32.00	9"-98
98	12 "	"	"	"	" "	"	" "	"	1	2⅛	STALEVENIL	38.00	12"-98
98	18 "	"	"	"	" "	"	" "	"	1	2¾	STALEVENOM	50.00	18"-98

Stanley Masons' Plumbs and Levels with Ground Glasses

STANLEY MASONS' PLUMBS AND LEVELS WITH GROUND GLASSES have two Plumb Glasses reading the same way and enabling the workman to plumb work above or below him without turning the Level.

NO.	LENGTH	TYPE	MATERIAL	FINISH	TRIM	TOP PLATE	SIDE VIEWS	LEVEL GLASS	PACKED IN BOX	WT. LBS.	CODE	PRICE DOZ. $	NO.
70	36 IN.	ADJUSTABLE	MAHOGANY	POLISHED		SQUARE	BR. LIPS	GROUND	6	18½	STALEVEJAN	45.00	70
80	42 "	"	"	"		"	" "	"	6	24	STALEVEJIR	50.00	80

In ordering specify the lengths of the Levels desired.

Stanley Metallic Plumbs and Levels

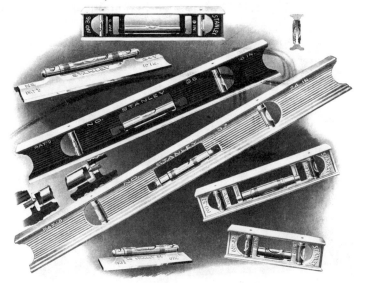

COPYRIGHT, 1909, BY THE STANLEY RULE AND LEVEL COMPANY

ILLUSTRATIONS OF NOS. 34—6″ AND 10″, 36—9″ AND 18″, 37—6″, 9″ AND 24″

Stanley Metallic Plumbs and Levels

STANLEY METALLIC PLUMBS AND LEVELS are so designed as to remain true under all ordinary conditions. Both the Plumb and Level Glasses are set in Metallic Cases. The bottom of each Case is machined so as to fit accurately on Supports in the body of the Level. The Case is held firmly on the Supports by means of Cone Centres which engage each end of the Case. The centre lines of the Case and the Cones are eccentric, and it is possible to adjust the Levels or to accurately insert new Glasses by placing paper between the Case and its Supports.

LEVELS No. 37 are Nickel Plated throughout and are fitted with GROUND GLASSES, protected by "Eclipse Covers."

Metallic Plumbs and Levels with Proved Glasses.

NO.	LENGTH	TYPE	MATERIAL	FINISH	LEVEL GLASS CASE			LEVEL GLASS	PACKED		CODE NO.36 G	CODE NO.36	PRICE DOZ. $	NO.
					MATERIAL	FINISH	COVER		IN BOX	WT. LBS.				
36	6 IN.	ADJUSTABLE	SPEC. IRON	JAPAN	METAL	NICKEL		PROVED	I	⅞	STALEVASAG	STALEVARAT	15.00	6″—36
36	9 "	"	" "	"	"	"		"	I	1¼	STALEVASEH	STALEVAREX	18.00	9″—36
36	12 "	"	" "	"	"	"		"	I	1⅞	STALEVASIP	STALEVARIZ	21.00	12″—36
36	18 "	"	" "	"	"	"		"	I	3	STALEVASOR	STALEVAROB	24.00	18″—36
36	24 "	"	" "	"	"	"		"	I	4¼	STALEVASUS	STALEVARUC	27.00	24″—36

Nickel Plated Metallic Plumbs and Levels with Ground Glasses and Eclipse Case Covers.

NO.	LENGTH	TYPE	MATERIAL	FINISH	LEVEL GLASS CASE			LEVEL GLASS	PACKED		CODE NO.37 G	CODE NO.37	PRICE DOZ. $	NO.
					MATERIAL	FINISH	COVER		IN BOX	WT. LBS.				
37	6 IN.	ADJUSTABLE	SPEC. IRON	NICKEL	METAL	NICKEL	ECLIPSE	GROUND	I	⅞	STALEVEDAC	STALEVECAR	24.00	6″—37
37	9 "	"	" "	"	"	"	"	"	I	1¼	STALEVEDED	STALEVECES	30.00	9″—37
37	12 "	"	" "	"	"	"	"	"	I	1⅞	STALEVEDIF	STALEVECIT	36.00	12″—37
37	18 "	"	" "	"	"	"	"	"	I	3	STALEVEDOG	STALEVECOX	42.00	18″—37
37	24 "	"	" "	"	"	"	"	"	I	4¼	STALEVEDUH	STALEVECUZ	48.00	24″—37

Stanley "Eclipse" Levels

STANLEY "ECLIPSE" LEVELS have the Glass in a Metallic Case and an outer Shell is fitted over this Case and when the Level is not in use can be turned so as to completely protect the Glass from damage. This shell is termed by us an "Eclipse Cover."

NO.	LENGTH	TYPE	MATERIAL	FINISH	LEVEL GLASS CASE			LEVEL GLASS	PACKED		CODE NO.34 V	CODE NO.34	PRICE DOZ. $	NO.
					MATERIAL	FINISH	COVER		IN BOX	WT. LBS.				
34	4 IN.	ADJUSTABLE	SPEC. IRON	NICKEL	METAL	NICKEL	ECLIPSE	GROUND	I	⅜	STALEVAMEG	STALEVALAX	15.00	4″—34
34	6 "	"	" "	"	"	"	"	"	I	¾	STALEVAMIH	STALEVALEZ	18.00	6″—34
34	8 "	"	" "	"	"	"	"	"	I	1⅛	STALEVAMOL	STALEVALOC	24.00	8″—34
34	10 "	"	" "	"	"	"	"	"	I	1¾	STALEVAMUN	STALEVALUD	30.00	10″—34

Levels marked Grooved or V bottoms for leveling shafting, etc. are furnished without extra charge if so ordered.

Stanley Level Sights, Pitch Adjusters, Bit and Square, Pocket Levels

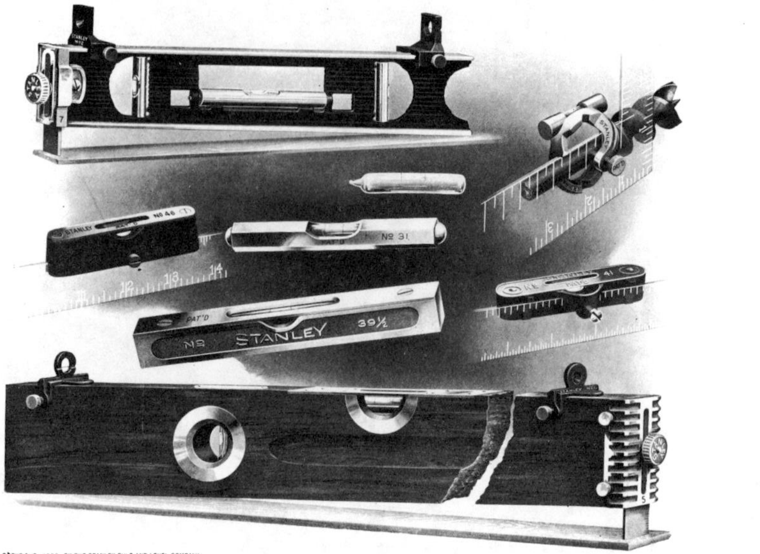

COPYRIGHT, 1909, BY THE STANLEY RULE AND LEVEL COMPANY

ILLUSTRATIONS OF NOS. 1, 2, 5, 7, 31, 39½, 41, 44, 46 AND LEVEL GLASS

2

Stanley Level Sights, Pitch Adjusters, Bit and Square, Pocket Levels

STANLEY IMPROVED LEVEL SIGHTS Nos. 1 and 2 can be attached to any Level and afford a convenient and accurate means for leveling at a distance. When not in use the Level Sights can be packed away in a small space for future use.

STANLEY PITCH ADJUSTERS Nos. 5 and 7 can be attached to any Wood or Iron Level and securely fastened in place by means of a Thumb Screw. The Bottom of the Frame should be set flush with the Bottom of the Level.

THE STANLEY BIT AND SQUARE LEVEL No. 44 has three pairs of V slots on the back edge of the Circular Frame. The Shank of a Bit will lie in these slots, either horizontal, vertical, or at an angle of 45 Degrees and the boring can be done with accuracy by observing the Level Glass while turning the Bit. It can also be attached to a Carpenter's Square, thus making an accurate Spirit Level when in a horizontal position. The Upright Arm of the Square will indicate an exact Plumb Line.

Stanley Improved Level Sights.

NO.	LENGTH	WIDTH	TYPE FOR	MATERIAL	FINISH	SPECIAL FEATURES	PACKED IN BOX	PACKED WT. LBS.	CODE	PRICE DOZ. $	NO.
1	1½ IN.	2 IN.	WOOD LEVELS	SPEC. IRON	GUN FINISH	FOR LONG DISTANCE LEVELING	1 PAIR	¼	STALEVOVAL	9.00	1
2	¾ "	1¼ "	IRON "	" "	" "	" " " "	1 PAIR	¼	STALEVOVIN	9.00	2

Stanley Pitch Adjusters.

NO.	LENGTH	WIDTH	TYPE FOR	MATERIAL	FINISH	SPECIAL FEATURES	PACKED IN BOX	PACKED WT. LBS.	CODE	PRICE DOZ. $	NO.
5	3 IN.	1¾ IN.	WOOD LEVELS	SPEC. IRON	NICKEL	MAXIMUM PITCH 1½ IN. PER FT.	1	⅝	STALEVOTOR	12.00	5
7	2¼ "	1⅛ "	IRON "	" "	"	" " " "	1	⅜	STALEVOTUS	12.00	7

Stanley Patent Bit and Square Level.

NO.	LENGTH	WIDTH	TYPE FOR	MATERIAL	FINISH	SPECIAL FEATURES	PACKED IN BOX	PACKED WT. LBS.	CODE	PRICE DOZ. $	NO.
44	1¾ IN.	1½ IN.	BIT & SQUARE	BRASS	POLISHED	WILL FIT ANY ORD'RY. BIT OR SQ.	1	⅛	STABESATIC	3.60	44

Stanley Hexagon Machinists and Pocket Levels.

NO.	LENGTH	TYPE	MATERIAL	FINISH	NAME	TOP PLATE	ENDS	LEVEL GLASS	PACKED IN BOX	PACKED WT. LBS.	CODE	PRICE DOZ. $	NO.
31	2 IN.	NON-ADJUST.	BRASS	NICKEL	HEXAGON		SPHERICAL	PROVED	6	¼	STALEVAJAD	3.90	2"—31
"	2½ "	" "	"	"	"		"	"	6	¼	STALEVAJIG	4.20	2½"—"
"	3 "	" "	"	"	"		"	"	6	½	STALEVAJOL	5.10	3" —"
"	3½ "	" "	"	"	"		"	"	6	⅝	STALEVAJUM	6.00	3½"—"
"	4 "	" "	"	"	"		"	"	6	¾	STALEVAKAN	7.20	4" —"
"	4½ "	" "	"	"	"		"	"	6	⅞	STALEVAKOS	7.80	4½"—"
38½	4 "	" "	SPEC. IRON	"	MACHINISTS	NICKEL	SQUARE	"	6	1⅝	STALEVEFAL	5.00	38½
39½	6 "	" "	" "	"	"	"	"	"	6	3½	STALEVEFEM	6.00	39½
40	3¼ "	" "	" "	JAPAN	POCKET	JAPAN	ROUNDED	"	12	1⅝	STALEVEFIN	1.56	40
41	3¼ "	" "	" "	"	"	BRASS	"	"	12	1⅝	STALEVEFOP	1.68	41
42	3¼ "	" "	BRASS	POLISHED	"	"	"	"	12	2	STALEVEFUS	5.70	42
46	3 "	" "	SPEC. IRON	JAPAN	"	"	"	"	12	2½	STALEVEGIX	2.28	46

Stanley Angle Divider, "Odd Jobs," and Leveling Stand

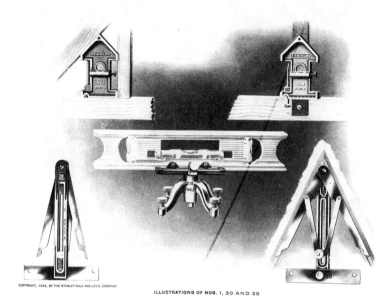

COPYRIGHT, 1909, BY THE STANLEY RULE AND LEVEL COMPANY

ILLUSTRATIONS OF NOS. 1, 30 AND 38

Stanley Angle Divider, "Odd Jobs" and Leveling Stand

THE STANLEY ANGLE DIVIDER No. 30 is a tool especially designed, as its name implies, for bisecting or dividing any angle, and for fitting mouldings or other woodwork into odd angles. The Angle is first measured accurately by adjusting the Angle Divider in the corner it is desired to fit. This Angle, owing to its construction, is always SYMMETRIC with the Central Shaft of the Angle Divider, and by laying this Central Shaft along the Moulding to be cut, the correct angle BISECTED is marked, and by reversing the Angle Divider, the other corresponding Angle can be marked. The Central Shaft is graduated on the back side for laying out—4, 6 or 8 sided work. By means of a removable "T" head, shown on the bottom, this Angle Divider can also be used as a Try or "T" Square.

STANLEY "ODD JOBS" TOOL No. 1 is Nickel Plated throughout and any user who has this tool to use can do all ordinary jobs with only a Saw, Hammer and a Plane in addition. This tool is sent out with a 12-inch graduated Rule inserted in it, and near one end of the Rule is an adjustable steel point for using tool as a Marking Gauge, etc. This addition greatly facilitates the use of this unique tool, already favorably known to mechanics, amateurs and housekeepers.

Stanley Angle Divider.

NO.	LENGTH	WIDTH	MATERIAL	FINISH	SPECIAL USES	PACKED IN BOX	WT. LBS.	CODE	PRICE DOZ. $	NO.
30	7⅜IN.	5 IN.	SPEC. IRON	NICKEL	TRY SQUARE & ANGLE BISECTOR	1	⅝	STAANGABAR	18.00	30

Stanley "Odd Jobs" Tool.

									PRICE DOZ. $	
1	4 IN.	2½ IN.	SPEC. IRON	NICKEL	10 TOOLS IN ONE	1	⅝	STAODDAJOB	9.00	1

Stanley Leveling Stand.

NO.	LENGTH	WIDTH	MATERIAL	FINISH	SPECIAL USES	PACKED IN BOX	WT. LBS.	CODE	EACH	NO.
38	4½IN.	3½ IN.	SPEC. IRON	NICKEL		1	1⅜	STALEVOWAN	1.20	38
39	12 "	3½ "	" "	"	DISTANCE LEVELING WITH NO.2 SIGHTS & NO.36-12 LEVEL	1	3½	STALEVOWET	3.70	39

Stanley Proved and Ground Level Glasses

PROVED LEVEL GLASSES									GROUND LEVEL GLASSES								
NO.	PACKED IN BOX	WT. LBS.	CODE	PRICE GRO. $	NO.	PACKED IN BOX	WT. LBS.	CODE	PRICE GRO. $	NO.	PACKED IN BOX	WT. LBS.	CODE	PRICE GRO. $	NO.	PACKED IN BOX	WT. LBS.	CODE	PRICE GRO. $
1"	12	⅛	STALEVONAL	9.48	3"	12	½	STALEVOPER	11.50	1"	12	¼	STALEVIFAR	60.00	3"	12	½	STALEVIRET	84.00
1¼"	12	⅛	STALEVONEM	9.60	3½"	12	½	STALEVOPIS	13.00	1¼"	12	¼	STALEVIFES	60.00	3½"	12	½	STALEVIRIX	90.00
1½"	12	¼	STALEVONIN	9.72	4"	12	⅝	STALEVOPOT	14.50	1½"	12	¼	STALEVIFIT	60.00	4"	12	⅝	STALEVIROZ	96.00
1¾"	12	¼	STALEVONOP	9.84	4½"	12	¾	STALEVOPUX	16.00	1¾"	12	¼	STALEVIFOX	60.00	4½"	12	¾	STALEVIRUB	108.00
2"	12	⅜	STALEVONUR	10.00	ASS'TD	12	½	STALEVOSAT	12.00	2"	12	¾	STALEVIFUZ	72.00	ASS'TD	12	½		
2½"	12	⅜	STALEVOPAP	10.50						2½"	12	¾	STALEVIRAS	78.00					

Stanley Try and Mitre Squares and "T" Bevels

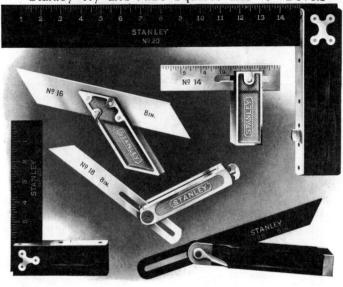

COPYRIGHT, 1909, BY THE STANLEY RULE AND LEVEL COMPANY

ILLUSTRATIONS OF NOS. 14, 16, 18, 20 AND 25

3

Stanley Try and Mitre Squares and "T" Bevels

STANLEY TRY AND MITRE SQUARES AND "T" BEVELS are of the highest quality made.
"T" BEVELS No. 25 can be furnished with Thumb Screws, in place of the Thumb Levers shown opposite, if so ordered.

NO.	BLADE LENGTH	MATERIAL	FINISH	MARKED	HANDLE LENGTH	MATERIAL	TRIM	FINISH	SPECIAL FEATURES	PACKED IN BOX	WT. LBS.	CODE	PRICE DOZ. $	NO.
Rosewood Handle Try Squares														
20	3 IN	STEEL	BLUE	8THS	2 7/8 IN	ROSEWOOD	BR. FACE PLATE	POLISHED	SQ. IN & OUT	6	3/4	STASQUILAC	2.35	3"—20
20	4	"	"	"	3 1/2	"	"	"	"	6	1 1/2	STASQUILED	2.52	4"—20
20	4 1/2	"	"	"	3 1/2	"	"	"	"	6	1 5/8	STASQUILIF	2.70	4 1/2"—20
20	5	"	"	"	3 1/2	"	"	"	"	6	1 3/4	STASQUILOG	2.88	5"—20
20	6	"	"	"	4 5/8	"	"	"	"	6	2	STASQUIMAS	3.60	6"—20
20	7	"	"	"	5 3/8	"	"	"	"	6	2 3/4	STASQUIMET	3.72	7"—20
20	7 1/2	"	"	"	5 3/8	"	"	"	"	6	2 7/8	STASQUIMIX	4.15	7 1/2"—20
20	8	"	"	"	5 3/8	"	"	"	"	6	3 1/8	STASQUIMOZ	4.25	8"—20
20	9	"	"	"	6	"	"	"	"	6	3 5/8	STASQUINER	5.10	9"—20
20	10	"	"	"	6	"	"	"	"	6	3 3/4	STASQUINIS	5.50	10"—20
20	12	"	"	"	7	"	"	"	"	6	4 3/4	STASQUINOT	6.70	12"—20
20	14	"	"	"	7	"	"	"	"	6	5	STASQUIRAT	7.80	14"—20
20	15	"	"	"	8 1/4	"	"	"	HANDLE REST	6	6 3/8	STASQUIREX	9.00	15"—20
20	16	"	"	"	8 1/4	"	"	"	"	6	7	STASQUIRIZ	10.56	16"—20
20	18	"	"	"	9 3/4	"	"	"	"	6	7 3/4	STASQUIRUC	11.40	18"—20
Sliding "T" Bevels														
25	6 IN	STEEL	BLUE		4 7/8 IN	ROSEWOOD	BRASS TIP	POLISHED	BR. LEV. FLUSH	6	1 1/4	STABEVAGOP	3.95	6"—25
25	8	"	"		5 7/8	"	"	"	"	6	1 3/4	STABEVAGUR	4.30	8"—25
25	10	"	"		7 7/8	"	"	"	"	6	2 1/4	STABEVARAT	4.65	10"—25
25	12	"	"		8 1/2	"	"	"	"	6	2 7/8	STABEVAREX	5.00	12"—25
25	14	"	"		10 1/4	"	"	"	"	6	3 1/2	STABEVARIZ	5.40	14"—25
Eureka Flush "T" Bevels														
18	6 IN	STEEL	NICKEL		4 1/4 IN	SPEC. IRON		NICKEL	END SCREW	6	2 3/8	STABEVAGAL	6.60	6"—18
18	8	"	"		5 1/8	"		"	"	6	2 7/8	STABEVAGEM	8.40	8"—18
18	10	"	"		6 1/4	"		"	"	6	3 1/2	STABEVAGIN	9.10	10"—18
Adjustable Try Squares														
14	4 IN	STEEL	NICKEL	8THS	2 3/4 IN	SPEC. IRON		NICKEL	SET SCREW	6	1 1/8	STASQUIBEL	4.10	4"—14
14	6	"	"		3 5/8	"		"	"	6	2 1/4	STASQUIBIM	4.95	6"—14
Improved Mitre Squares														
16	8 IN	STEEL	NICKEL		4 3/8 IN	SPEC. IRON		NICKEL	SET MITRE	6	4	STASQUIDAL	7.70	8"—16
16	10	"	"		5 1/8	"		"	"	6	4 5/8	STASQUIDEM	8.80	10"—16
16	12	"	"		5 5/8	"		"	"	6	4 3/4	STASQUIDIN	9.90	12"—16

Blades of Squares Nos. 20 and 14 are regularly graduated Inches, but can be graduated Metric, if so ordered.

Stanley Try and Mitre Squares

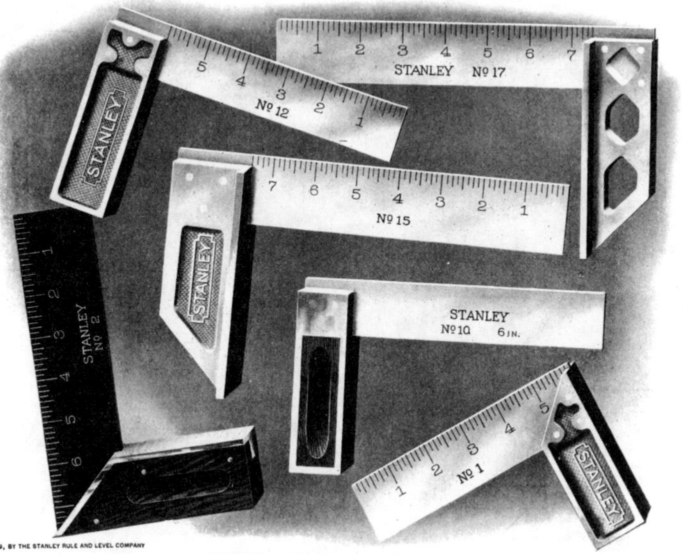

COPYRIGHT, 1909, BY THE STANLEY RULE AND LEVEL COMPANY

ILLUSTRATIONS OF NOS. 1, 2, 10, 12, 15 AND 17

Stanley Try and Mitre Squares

STANLEY TRY SQUARES AND IMPROVED MITRE TRY SQUARES are Square and true inside and out.

STANLEY "WINTERBOTTOM'S" COMBINED TRY AND MITRE SQUARES can be used with equal advantage and accuracy as a Try or Mitre Square. By simply changing the position of the Handle and bringing the Mitred Face at the top of the Handle against one edge of the work in hand, a perfect mitre or angle of 45 degrees can be struck from either edge of the Blade.

NO.	BLADE				HANDLE				SPECIAL FEATURES	PACKED		CODE	PRICE DOZ. $	NO.
	LENGTH	MATERIAL	FINISH	MARKED	LENGTH	MATERIAL	TRIM	FINISH		IN BOX	WT. LBS.			
Iron Handle Try Squares														
12	2 IN.	STEEL	NICKEL	8THS	2 IN.	SPEC. IRON		NICKEL	SQ. IN & OUT	6	⅞	STASQUANER	2.80	2"—12
12	4 "	"	"	"	3⅛ "	" "		"	" " " "	6	1⅞	STASQUANIS	3.40	4"—12
12	6 "	"	"	"	4⅜ "	" "		"	" " " "	6	2¼	STASQUANOT	3.95	6"—12
12	8 "	"	"	"	5⅛ "	" "		"	" " " "	6	4⅕	STASQUARAT	5.00	8"—12
12	10 "	"	"	"	6⅝ "	" "		"	" " " "	6	5⅛	STASQUAREX	6.40	10"—12
12	12 "	"	"	"	8 "	" "		"	" " " "	6	8	STASQUARIZ	7.50	12"—12
Inlaid Try Squares														
10	4 IN.	STEEL	POLISH.		3 IN.	ROSEWOOD	INLAID	POLISHED	SQ. IN & OUT	6	2¼	STASQUALAX	7.15	4"—10
10	6 "	"	"		3⅝ "	"	"	"	" " " "	6	3⅝	STASQUALEZ	9.35	6"—10
10	8 "	"	"		5⅜ "	"	"	"	" " " "	6	5½	STASQUALIB	12.10	8"—10
10	10 "	"	"		6½ "	"	"	"	" " " "	6	7⅞	STASQUALOC	16.50	0"—10
Winterbottom's Iron Handle Try and Mitre Squares														
1	4 IN.	STEEL	POLISH.	8THS	3 IN.	SPEC. IRON		NICKEL	SQ. IN & OUT	6	1⅝	STASQUADAR	5.00	4"—1
1	6 "	"	"	"	4 "	" "		"	" " " "	6	2⅞	STASQUADES	6.35	6"—1
1	8 "	"	"	"	5 "	" "		"	" " " "	6	4⅜	STASQUADIT	7.50	8"—1
Winterbottom's Rosewood Handle Try and Mitre Squares														
2	4½ IN.	STEEL	BLUE	8THS	3⅛ IN.	ROSEWOOD	BR. FACE PL.	POLISHED	SQ. IN & OUT	6	1⅝	STASQUADOX	5.40	4½"—2
2	6 "	"	"	"	4 "	"	" " "	"	" " " "	6	2¼	STASQUADUZ	6.00	6"—2
2	7½ "	"	"	"	5 "	"	" " "	"	" " " "	6	2⅞	STASQUAKAN	7.20	7½"—2
2	9 "	"	"	"	5¾ "	"	" " "	"	" " " "	6	3¾	STASQUAKIR	8.40	9"—2
2	12 "	"	"	"	5¾ "	"	" " "	"	" " " "	6	4	STASQUAKOS	10.80	12"—2
Improved Mitre Try Squares														
15	7½ IN.	STEEL	NICKEL	8THS	5¼ IN.	SPEC. IRON		NICKEL	SQ. IN & OUT	6	4⅛	STASQUIBON	9.90	7½"-15
17	7½ "	"	"	"	5 "	" "		"	" " " "	6	3⅜	STASQUIFAS	7.70	7½"-17

Blades are graduated Inches or Metric as desired.

Stanley Gauges

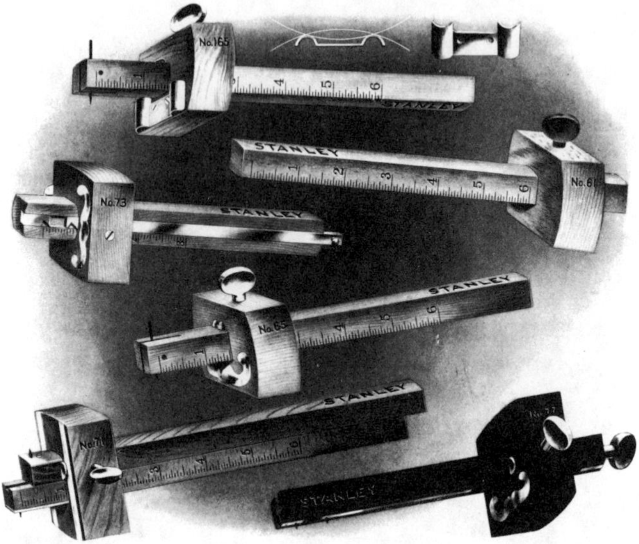

COPYRIGHT, 1909, BY THE STANLEY RULE AND LEVEL COMPANY

ILLUSTRATIONS OF NOS. 61, 65, 71,73, 77 AND 165

Stanley Gauges

STANLEY GAUGES, except No. 0 and 61, have Adjustable Steel Markers, which may be readily removed and replaced if they need sharpening. All Gauges having Brass Thumb Screws have a Brass Shoe inserted in the head under the end of the Thumb Screw to prevent the Gauge Bars from being dented by the action of the Screw.

STANLEY IMPROVED GAUGES (see cut top of opposite page) have a Metal Plate with two Convex Faces, which is attached to one side of the Gauge Head and which permits of a Gauge Line being run with perfect steadiness and accuracy around curves of any degree, either convex or concave. The Head is reversible and the flat side used for ordinary work.

Stanley Gauges														
NO.	LENGTH	TYPE	BAR		MARKING POINTS	HEAD			SPECIAL FEATURES	PACKED		CODE	PRICE DOZ. $	NO.
			MATERIAL	MARK'D		MATERIAL	TRIM	THUMB SCREW		IN BOX	WT. LBS.			
0	8½ IN	MARKING	BEECH	16THS	FIXED	BEECH		BOXWOOD		12	2⅜	STAGAGEDAR	0.75	0
61	8½ "	"	"	"	"	"		"		12	2⅞	STAGAGEDES	1.00	61
62	8½ "	"	"	"	ADJUSTABLE	"		"		12	2⅞	STAGAGEDIT	2.00	62
64	8¼ "	"	"	"	"	"	PLATE	"		12	2⅞	STAGAGEDOX	2.75	64
64½	8½ "	"	"	"	"	"	"	BRASS	OVAL HEAD	6	1⅞	STAGAGEDUZ	4.50	64½
65	8¼ "	"	BOXWOOD	"	"	BOXWOOD	"	"		6	1⅞	STAGAGEFAC	6.00	65
70	8½ "	CUTTING	BEECH	"	"	BEECH	"	BOXWOOD		12	1¼	STAGAGEFIF	4.00	70
68	8½ "	MORTISE	"	"	FIXED	"	"	BRASS	WOOD SLIDE	6	1⅞	STAGAGEFED	6.00	68
73	6½ "	MORTISE	BOXWOOD	"	"	BOXWOOD	"	"	BRASS SLIDE	6	2	STAGAGEKIR	8.00	73
76	6¼ "	"	"	"	"	"	"	"	SCREW SLIDE	6	2½	STAGAGEKUT	11.00	76
71	8½ "	MARKING MORTISE	BEECH	"	"	"	"	"	DOUBLE BAR	6	2⅛	STAGAGEFOG	8.00	71
72	8½ "	"	"	"	"	"		BOXWOOD	" "	6	1⅞	STAGAGEKAN	4.00	72
74	8¼ "	"	BOXWOOD	"	"	"	"	BRASS	" "	6	2⅜	STAGAGEKOS	14.00	74
77	6⅜ "	"	ROSEWOOD	"	"	ROSEWOOD	"	"	SCREW SLIDE	6	2½	STAGAGELAX	10.00	77
84	17 "	SLITTING	BEECH	8THS	ADJUSTABLE	BEECH		BOXWOOD	HANDLE	6	7⅝	STAGAGELIT	10.00	84
85	17½ "	PANEL	BEECH	"	"	"		"		12	5⅜	STAGAGEMAN	3.20	85
85½	20½ "	"	ROSEWOOD	"	"	ROSEWOOD	"	BRASS		6	5⅜	STAGAGEMET	18.00	85½
Stanley Improved Gauges														
161	8½ IN.	MARKING	BEECH	16THS	FIXED	BEECH		BOXWOOD		12	3½	STAGAGEREX	2.00	161
162	8½ "	"	"	"	ADJUSTABLE	"		"		12	3½	STAGAGERIZ	3.00	162
164	8¼ "	"	"	"	"	"	PLATE	"		12	3½	STAGAGEROB	3.75	164
164½	8½ "	"	"	"	"	"	"	BRASS	OVAL HEAD	6	2¼	STAGAGERUC	5.50	164½
165	8¼ "	"	BOXWOOD	"	"	BOXWOOD	"	"		6	2¼	STAGAGESOR	7.00	165
171	8½ "	MARKING MORTISE	"	"	FIXED	"	"	"	DOUBLE-BAR	6	2⅜	STAGAGETIC	9.00	171
172	8½ "	"	"	"	"	"	"	BOXWOOD	" "	6	2⅛	STAGAGETOD	5.00	172
174	8¼ "	"	"	"	"	"	"	"	" "	6	2⅞	STAGAGEVEN	15.00	174
177	6⅜ "	"	ROSEWOOD	"	"	ROSEWOOD	"	"	SCREW SLIDE	6	3	STAGAGEVOG	11.00	177

Stanley Metallic Butt, Marking, Mortise and Rabbet Gauges

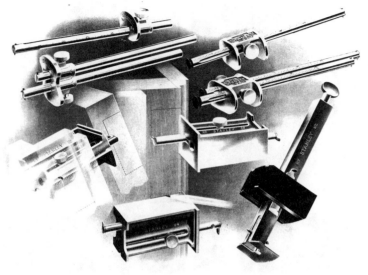

COPYRIGHT, 1909, BY THE STANLEY RULE AND LEVEL COMPANY

ILLUSTRATIONS OF NOS. 90, 91, 92, 94, 95, 97 AND 98

Stanley Metallic Butt, Marking, Mortise and Rabbet Gauges

THE STANLEY IMPROVED BUTT GAUGE. No. 95 has two Bars. One Bar has two Steel Cutters fixed upon it. When Cutter at the outer end of this Bar is set for gauging on the edge of the door, the Cutter at the inner end is set for gauging from the back of the jamb. The other Bar has a Steel Cutter to accurately gauge for the thickness of the Butt. The two ends, which are parallel, are at right angles to the Bottom and it can be used as a square from which to mark at right angles to the casing. This tool is convenient for carrying in the pocket, and is so constructed that the Bars cannot fall out.

THE STANLEY PATENT BUTT GAUGE. No. 94 has two Steel Bars. One Bar has two Steel Cutters fixed upon it for use when gauging for doors with rabbeted jambs, and in addition is of such form and has the Bar so fastened that the Bar may be reversed and the Gauge used for gauging from the casing, whether of the moulded form or flat, on doors which have a strike strip nailed on after the door is hung. It has also a second Bar with a Steel Cutter to gauge for the thickness of the Butt. The two ends which are parallel, are at right angles to the Bottom, and as one end overhangs the Bottom slightly it can be used as a square from which to mark at right angles to the casing, as shown on the opposite page.

STANLEY BUTT AND RABBET GAUGE. No. 92 has two Bars, both of Brass, one movable within the other, and graduated. The two Steel Blades or markers are at the extreme end of the inner Bar and can be adjusted to any position by means of the Thumb Screw at the opposite end of the Gauge Bar.

STANLEY IMPROVED MARKING AND MORTISE GAUGES Nos. 90 and 91 have Steel Points inserted very near the ends of the Bars to admit of being used close up in a rabbet or corner. The Head is reversible giving a broad or narrow bearing as desired.

STANLEY DUPLEX MARKING AND MORTISE GAUGES Nos. 97 and 98 have both Rollers and Steel Points, and are entirely of metal. The Heads are double faced. Roller Cutters are preferable in some work to Steel Points, being especially adapted for running over knots, across the grain or where a fine line is desired.

NO.	LENGTH	TYPE	FINISH	MARKING POINTS	BAR	HEAD OR STOCK	MARKED	SPECIAL USE	PACKED		CODE	PRICE DOZ. $	NO.
									IN BOX	WT. LBS.			
95	3 IN.	BUTT	NICKEL	END OF BAR	STEEL	SPEC. IRON	16THS	BUTT AND RABBET	1	½	STAGAGEMUN	9.00	95
94	3 "	"	"	" " "	"	" "	"	BUTT, RABBET AND MORTISE	1	⅝	STAGAGEMOL	12.00	94
92	8 "	"	POLISH	STEEL PLATE	BRASS	ROSEWOOD	"	{ BUTT, MARKING, MORTISE AND RABBET }	1	¾	STAGAGELUD	15.00	92
90	8 "	MARKING	NICKEL	ADJUSTABLE	STEEL	SPEC. IRON	"	MARKING	1	¼	STAGAGELES	4.20	90
91	8 "	MORTISE	"	"	"	" "	"	MARKING AND MORTISE	1	½	STAGAGELOC	7.80	91
97	8 "	MARKING	"	"	"	" "	"	MARKING	1	½	STAGAGENER	6.60	97
98	8 "	MORTISE	"	"	"	" "	"	MARKING AND MORTISE	1	⅝	STAGAGENIS	12.00	98

Stanley "Bailey" Adjustable Iron Plane

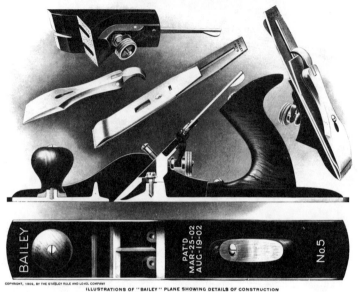

ILLUSTRATIONS OF "BAILEY" PLANE SHOWING DETAILS OF CONSTRUCTION

Stanley "Bailey" Adjustable Iron Planes

THE "BAILEY" IRON PLANE has been in use for over forty years, and during this period has maintained the leading position and has been recognized as the BEST Plane upon the market, and that there are today more "BAILEY" Iron Planes in use than all others of similar make, is a GUARANTEE of its INHERENT MERITS.

Various improvements have been introduced in its construction from time to time, coupled with which it has been the constant aim of this Company to make the "BAILEY" PLANE with such a degree of excellence that the name "BAILEY" (which is cast on every Plane) would be a guarantee of the best workmanship possible, and the increasing popularity of the "BAILEY" PLANE, we believe justifies this policy in its manufacture.

The superiority of the "BAILEY" PLANE is due to the following reasons:

IT WORKS BETTER THAN OTHER PLANES IN ANY KIND OF WOOD. IS BETTER MADE. IS MADE OF BETTER MATERIALS. IT CAN BE BETTER AND MORE EASILY ADJUSTED

The Cutter, which is thin and of uniform thickness, is a prominent feature of the "BAILEY" PLANE. The advantage of using a thin Cutter firmly held to its seat, and first recognized by the inventor of the "BAILEY" PLANE, is well known to every worker in wood, and its superiority is now generally admitted.

Briefly its advantages are:—1. Ease in grinding. 2. Less grinding, as a thin Cutter can be kept in condition by honing. 3. Less tendency to "stub off" the cutting edge when honing, hence the original bevel is kept much longer.

The Cutter is made of the best English Steel, tempered and ground by an improved process, and honed ready for use.

Experience has shown that the proper bevel for grinding the Cutter is at an angle of about 25 degrees, as this gives a stiff cutting edge.

The improved form of Cutter renders it unnecessary to detach the Cap at any time, as the Cap Screw will slide back to the extreme end of the slot in the Cutter without any danger of falling out. It may then be tightened by a turn with the thumb and finger, and the Cap will serve as a convenient handle or rest in sharpening the Cutter.

The Cutter Cap is also made of thin steel, of uniform thickness, and is fastened to the Cutter by the Cap Screw, these three parts constituting what is technically known as the Double Cutter or Double Iron.

The Adjustable Cutter Seat or "Frog" and Plane Bottom have been recently improved, and as now made, the Cutter Seat has a Front Horizontal Machined Under Surface supported on a horizontal Front Step or Seat on the Plane Bottom close up to the mouth; and a Rear Machined Under Surface, supported by an elevated Rear Step or Seat on the Plane Bottom, giving an absolutely rigid foundation for the Cutter when clamped to its Seat, as it is solidly supported clear down to the Heel of the bevel and very close to the cutting edge, and thus any possibility of the Cutter chattering on knots or hard spots is prevented.

The Cutter Seat has two slotted recesses for the Seat Screws or "Frog" Screws, by means of which the throat opening in front of the Cutter can be easily and quickly regulated to suit the various conditions of working. The Seat Screws, being located between the two supports, correctly distribute the pressure between them. The screw bosses in the Plane Bottom being very deep enable a great number of threads to engage, thus securely holding the Cutter Seat in place, and preventing any possibility of the Plane Bottom being drawn out of true when the seat is screwed hard.

The Plane Bottom has two Machined Cross Ribs, and a longitudinal Central Rib connecting them. The Rear Rib is very deep, greatly strengthening the Plane Bottom and sides at this point, while the Central Rib and Front Cross Rib prevent any tendency of the throat to sag when the Cutter Seat is screwed down hard.

The Lever Cap is held in place below its centre by the Lever Cap Screw, which acts as a fulcrum, and the Lever Cap may

Stanley "Bailey" Adjustable Iron Planes

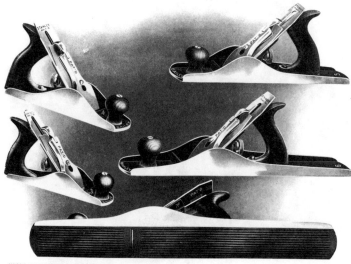

COPYRIGHT, 1909, BY THE STANLEY RULE AND LEVEL COMPANY

ILLUSTRATIONS OF NOS. 3, 4, 5, 6 AND 7C

Stanley "Bailey" Adjustable Iron Planes

be rigidly clamped down upon the Cutter Cap by means of the Lever Cam. When the Lever Cam is turned upwards and ceases to bear upon the Cutter Cap, the Lever Cap can be removed and the Cutter taken out without turning the Lever Cap Screw, the Lever Cap and Cutter being properly slotted for this purpose.

When the Cutter is clamped in place, it can be adjusted accurately lengthwise by means of the Adjusting Wheel which moves the "Y" Lever and which latter at its upper end engages in a Slot in the Cutter Cap made specially for this purpose. In effect the "BAILEY" PLANE is one solid piece from cap to bottom, while at the same time the throat opening is adjustable.

The Lateral Adjustment of the Cutter is effected by means of the Lever pivoted on the Cutter Seat and located near the top at the back side of the Cutter.

One end of this Lever engages in the slot of the Cutter and by moving it laterally, the face or cutting edge of the Cutter can be easily brought into a position exactly square with the Bottom of the Plane, if the Cutter should not be exactly true when clamped down. A revolving disc on the Lever where it engages in the Cutter prevents all friction.

The above construction is covered by recent patents.

SMOOTH BOTTOMS

NO.	LENGTH	TYPE	MATERIAL	FINISH	HANDLE AND KNOB	CUTTER						PACKED		CODE	PRICE EACH $	NO.
						MATERIAL	ADJUSTMENTS		WIDTH	SINGLE $		IN BOX	WT. LBS.			
							ENDWISE	LATERAL								
1	5½IN.	SMOOTH	SPEC. IRON	JAPAN	ROSEWOOD	TOOL STEEL	SCREW	LEVER	1¼IN.	0.18		1	1¼	STAPLAABAB	1.65	1
2	7 "	"	"	"	"	"	"	"	1⅝ "	0.21		1	2¼	STAPLAABEC	2.05	2
3	8 "	"	"	"	"	"	"	"	1¾ "	0.23		1	3⅛	STAPLAABOF	2.20	3
4	9 "	"	"	"	"	"	"	"	2 "	0.25		1	3¾	STAPLAACEL	2.40	4
4½	10 "	"	"	"	"	"	"	"	2⅜ "	0.29		1	4¾	STAPLAACON	2.75	4½
5	14 "	JACK	"	"	"	"	"	"	2 "	0.25		1	4¾	STAPLAADAR	2.75	5
5½	15 "	"	"	"	"	"	"	"	2¼ "	0.28		1	6¾	STAPLAADOX	3.15	5½
6	18 "	FORE	"	"	"	"	"	"	2⅜ "	0.29		1	7¾	STAPLAAFAC	3.50	6
7	22 "	JOINTER	"	"	"	"	"	"	2⅜ "	0.29		1	8⅛	STAPLAAFOG	4.00	7
8	24 "	"	"	"	"	"	"	"	2⅝ "	0.32		1	9¾	STAPLAAGEM	4.80	8

CORRUGATED BOTTOMS

NO.	LENGTH	TYPE	MATERIAL	FINISH	HANDLE AND KNOB	MATERIAL	ENDWISE	LATERAL	WIDTH	SINGLE $		IN BOX	WT. LBS.	CODE	PRICE EACH $	NO.
2C	7 IN.	SMOOTH	SPEC. IRON	JAPAN	ROSEWOOD	TOOL STEEL	SCREW	LEVER	1⅝IN.	0.21		1	2¼	STAPLAABID	2.05	2C
3C	8 "	"	"	"	"	"	"	"	1¾ "	0.23		1	3⅛	STAPLAABUG	2.20	3C
4C	9 "	"	"	"	"	"	"	"	2 "	0.25		1	3¾	STAPLAACIM	2.40	4C
4½C	10 "	"	"	"	"	"	"	"	2⅜ "	0.29		1	4¾	STAPLAACUP	2.75	4½C
5C	14 "	JACK	"	"	"	"	"	"	2 "	0.25		1	4¾	STAPLAADIT	2.75	5C
5½C	15 "	"	"	"	"	"	"	"	2¼ "	0.28		1	6¾	STAPLAADUZ	3.15	5½C
6C	18 "	FORE	"	"	"	"	"	"	2⅜ "	0.29		1	7¾	STAPLAAFIF	3.50	6C
7C	22 "	JOINTER	"	"	"	"	"	"	2⅜ "	0.29		1	8⅛	STAPLAAGAL	4.00	7C
8C	24 "	"	"	"	"	"	"	"	2⅝ "	0.32		1	9¾	STAPLAAGIN	4.80	8C

Stanley "Bailey" Adjustable Wood Planes

COPYRIGHT, 1909, BY THE STANLEY RULE AND LEVEL COMPANY

ILLUSTRATIONS OF NOS. 23, 24, 27, 28, 32 AND 35

Stanley "Bailey" Adjustable Wood Planes

NO.	LENGTH	TYPE	MATERIAL	FINISH TRIM'GS	HANDLE	CUTTER MATERIAL	ADJUSTMENTS ENDWISE	ADJUSTMENTS LATERAL	WIDTH	SINGLE $	PACKED IN P'K'GE	PACKED WT. LBS.	CODE	PRICE EACH $	NO.
21	7 IN.	SMOOTH	BEECH	JAPAN		TOOL STEEL	SCREW	LEVER	1¾ IN.	0.23	1	2½	STAPLAECAR	1.50	21
22	8 "	"	"	"		" "	"	"	1¾ "	0.23	1	2½	STAPLAECES	1.50	22
24	8 "	"	"	"		" "	"	"	2 "	0.25	1	2⅞	STAPLAECOX	1.50	24
23	9 "	"	"	"		" "	"	"	1¾ "	0.23	1	2½	STAPLAECIT	1.50	23
25	9½ "	BLOCK	"	"		" "	"	"	1¾ "	0.23	1	2½	STAPLAECUZ	1.50	25
35	9 "	SMOOTH	"	"	BEECH	" "	"	"	2 "	0.25	1	3¼	STAPLAESAT	1.90	35
36	10 "	"	"	"		" "	"	"	2⅜ "	0.29	1	4	STAPLAESEX	2.05	36
37	13 "	"	"	"		" "	"	"	2⅝ "	0.32	1	5	STAPLAESUC	2.20	37
26	15 "	JACK	"	"		"	"	"	2 "	0.25	1	3¾	STAPLAEDAC	1.65	26
27	15 "	"	"	"		" "	"	"	2⅛ "	0.27	1	4	STAPLAEDIF	1.90	27
27½	15 "	"	"	"		" "	"	"	2¼ "	0.28	1	4¾	STAPLAEFAL	1.90	27½
28	18 "	FORE	"	"		" "	"	"	2⅜ "	0.29	1	5½	STAPLAEFEM	2.05	28
29	20 "	"	"	"		" "	"	"	2⅜ "	0.29	1	6¼	STAPLAEFIN	2.05	29
30	22 "	JOINTER	"	"		" "	"	"	2⅜ "	0.29	1	6¼	STAPLAEFUR	2.20	30
31	24 "	"	"	"		" "	"	"	2⅜ "	0.29	1	6½	STAPLAEGAS	2.20	31
32	26 "	"	"	"		" "	"	"	2⅝ "	0.32	1	7⅝	STAPLAEGET	2.40	32
33	28 "	"	"	"		" "	"	"	2⅝ "	0.32	1	8⅜	STAPLAEGIX	2.40	33
34	30 "	"	"	"		" "	"	"	2⅝ "	0.32	1	8½	STAPLAEGOZ	2.60	34

"Bailey" "Bed Rock" and Stanley Double Cutters (Plane Irons)

WIDTH OF CUTTER	1¼ IN.	1⅝ IN.	1¾ IN.	2 IN.	2⅛ IN.	2¼ IN.	2⅜ IN.	2⅝ IN.	WIDTH OF CUTTER
PRICE SINGLE CUTTER	$0.18	$0.21	$0.23	$0.25	$0.27	$0.28	$0.29	$0.32	PRICE SINGLE CUTTER
PACKED IN BOX	6	6	6	6	6	6	6	6	PACKED IN BOX
PACKED WEIGHT	⅝ LBS.	1⅛ LBS.	1¼ LBS.	1⅝ LBS.	1¾ LBS.	2 LBS.	2¼ LBS.		PACKED WEIGHT
CODE SINGLE CUTTER	STAPLIUCEL	STAPLIUCIM	STAPLIUCON	STAPLIUCUP	STAPLIUDAR	STAPLIUDES	STAPLIUDIT	STAPLIUDOX	CODE SINGLE CUTTER
PRICE DOUBLE CUTTER	$0.32	$0.35	$0.38	$0.42	$0.45	$0.47	$0.48	$0.50	PRICE DOUBLE CUTTER
PACKED IN BOX	6	6	6	6	6	6	6	6	PACKED IN BOX
PACKED WEIGHT	1¼ LBS.	1⅞ LBS.	2⅜ LBS.	2⅞ LBS.	3 LBS.	3½ LBS.	3⅝ LBS.	4 LBS.	PACKED WEIGHT
CODE DOUBLE CUTTER	STAPLIUFAC	STAPLIUFED	STAPLIUFIF	STAPLIUFOG	STAPLIUGAL	STAPLIUGEM	STAPLIUGIN	STAPLIUGUR	CODE DOUBLE CUTTER

"Bailey" and "Bed Rock" Cutters are identical in construction and are also used on all Planes having Double Cutters except Nos. 104, 105, 122, 127, 129, 132 and 135, which latter take Stanley Cutters and differ slightly from the "Bailey." Always give number of the Plane and specify whether Single or Double Cutter is required.

Stanley "Bed Rock" Adjustable Iron Planes

COPYRIGHT, 1909, BY THE STANLEY RULE AND LEVEL COMPANY

ILLUSTRATIONS OF NOS. 603, 604, 605 IN SECTION AND DETAILS, 607 AND 606C

Stanley "Bed Rock" Adjustable Iron Planes

"BED ROCK" PLANES embody a perfection in design which combines as the name implies, a construction of the utmost solidity and with better and more adjustments than any Plane heretofore produced. Both Face and Bottom Surface of the Cutter Seat or "Frog" are machined and the Machined Bottom Surface is bedded throughout its entire surface on the Machined Surface of the Plane Bottom giving the Cutter a foundation which when the Cutter Seat is screwed down, is as solid, as if it were in ONE PIECE with the Plane Bottom.

The Cutter Seat is made with a Tongue on the Bottom side, and a corresponding Groove is formed in Seat of Plane Bottom, overcoming any possibility of a shifting or wobbling of the Cutter Seat, making it self-centering, and insuring the Cutter Seat moving at right angles with Mouth when it is adjusted. The Cutter Seat is clamped to the Plane Body by two screws, and when it is desired to open or close the Throat, it can be done by turning the Adjusting Screw at the back side of the Cutter Seat, as shown by cut on the opposite page. This combination of practically ONE-PIECE solidity and great quickness of adjustment is unique in the construction of Planes and will at once be appreciated by every intelligent workman. The Cutter rests on the Cutter Seat for its entire length down to the Heel of the Cutter, the Bevel being the only part not supported. The construction of the Cutter itself and its Adjustments are the same as in the "BAILEY" Planes described on pages 39 and 41.

SMOOTH BOTTOMS															
NO.	LENGTH	TYPE	MATERIAL	FINISH	HANDLE AND KNOB	CUTTER					PACKED		CODE	PRICE EACH $	NO.
						MATERIAL	ADJUSTMENTS		WIDTH	SINGLE $	IN BOX	WT. LBS.			
							ENDWISE	LATERAL							
602	7 IN.	SMOOTH	SPEC. IRON	JAPAN	ROSEWOOD	TOOL STEEL	SCREW	LEVER	1⅝ IN.	0.21	1	2¼	STAPLAOKAL	2.35	602
603	8 "	"	" "	"	"	" "	"	"	1¾ "	0.23	1	3¼	STAPLAOKIN	2.55	603
604	9 "	"	" "	"	"	" "	"	"	2 "	0.25	1	3⅝	STAPLAOKUR	2.75	604
604½	10 "	"	" "	"	"	" "	"	"	2⅜ "	0.29	1	4¾	STAPLAOLET	3.20	604½
605	14 "	JACK	" "	"	"	" "	"	"	2 "	0.25	1	4½	STAPLAOLOZ	3.20	605
605½	15 "	"	" "	"	"	" "	"	"	2¼ "	0.28	1	6½	STAPLAOMAD	3.60	605½
606	18 "	FORE	" "	"	"	" "	"	"	2⅜ "	0.29	1	7⅝	STAPLAOMIG	3.85	606
607	22 "	JOINTER	" "	"	"	" "	"	"	2⅜ "	0.29	1	8¾	STAPLAOMUM	4.60	607
608	24 "	"	" "	"	"	" "	"	"	2⅝ "	0.32	1	9¾	STAPLAONIR	5.50	608
CORRUGATED BOTTOMS															
602 C	7 IN.	SMOOTH	SPEC. IRON	JAPAN	ROSEWOOD	TOOL STEEL	SCREW	LEVER	1⅝ IN.	0.21	1	2¼	STAPLAOKEM	2.35	602 C
603 C	8 "	"	" "	"	"	" "	"	"	1¾ "	0.23	1	3¼	STAPLAOKOP	2.55	603 C
604 C	9 "	"	" "	"	"	" "	"	"	2 "	0.25	1	3⅝	STAPLAOLAS	2.75	604 C
604½C	10 "	"	" "	"	"	" "	"	"	2⅜ "	0.29	1	4¾	STAPLAOLIX	3.20	604½C
605 C	14 "	JACK	" "	"	"	" "	"	"	2 "	0.25	1	4½	STAPLAOLUB	3.20	605 C
605½C	15 "	"	" "	"	"	" "	"	"	2¼ "	0.28	1	6½	STAPLAOMEF	3.60	605½C
606 C	18 "	FORE	" "	"	"	" "	"	"	2⅜ "	0.29	1	7⅜	STAPLAOMOL	3.85	606 C
607 C	22 "	JOINTER	" "	"	"	" "	"	"	2⅜ "	0.29	1	8¾	STAPLAONAN	4.60	607 C
608 C	24 "	"	" "	"	"	" "	"	"	2⅝ "	0.32	1	9¾	STAPLAONOS	5.50	608 C

Stanley and "Bailey" Adjustable Iron Block and Edge Planes

COPYRIGHT, 1909, BY THE STANLEY RULE AND LEVEL COMPANY

ILLUSTRATIONS OF NOS. 9, 9½, 9¾, 18, 60, 62, 97 AND 131

Stanley and "Bailey" Adjustable Iron Block and Edge Planes

"BAILEY" BLOCK PLANES are the highest type of Block Planes manufactured and have an adjustable throat opening and Cutters with Endwise and Lateral adjustment. In addition they are made with the "HAND-Y" feature which gives the workman a more secure grip on the tool than is possible with any other design.

STANLEY KNUCKLE JOINT BLOCK PLANES are like the "Bailey" Block Planes above except they have a Knuckle Joint in the Cap which makes it a Lever too; and placing the Cap in position will also clamp the Cutter securely in its Seat.

STANLEY LOW ANGLE BLOCK PLANES have the Cutter set at a very low angle which is of great advantage when working across the grain. They have an adjustable throat opening and the Cutter is adjustable Endwise.

THE STANLEY DOUBLE END ADJUSTABLE BLOCK PLANE has a Cutter adjustable Endwise. The Plane has two Slots and a Movable Cutter Seat. When it is desired to use it as a Bull-Nose Plane the Cap and Cutter can be removed and the adjustable Cutter Seat reversed as indicated in cut on opposite page.

STANLEY CABINET MAKERS' BLOCK PLANE is used by Piano Makers, Cabinet Makers and kindred trades where an extra fine tool is required for finishing Piano-Keys, Hardwoods, etc. A metallic Handle with Slot and Set Screw is furnished with each Plane and this Handle can be attached to the Body of the Plane at either side. The Plane turned on its side will then work perfectly on a chute board for Planing Mitres, etc.

STANLEY CABINET MAKERS' EDGE PLANE is a very useful tool for Piano Makers and Cabinet Makers for trimming inside work where space prevents the use of any other Plane.

NO.	LENGTH	TYPE	FINISH	HANDLE	CUTTER					PACKED		CODE	PRICE EACH $	NO.
					MATERIAL	ADJUSTMENTS		WIDTH	PRICE $	IN BOX	WT. LBS.			
						ENDWISE	LATERAL							
9½	6 IN.	BAILEY BLOCK	JAPAN		TOOL STEEL	SCREW	LEVER	1⅝ IN.	0.17	1	1½	STAPLAAKAN	1.10	9½
9¾	6 "	" "	"	ROSEWOOD	" "	"	"	1⅝ "	0.17	1	1⅝	STAPLAAKER	1.30	9¾
16	6 "	" "	NICK.TR.		" "	"	"	1⅝ "	0.17	1	1½	STAPLAAVAM	1.25	16
15	7 "	" "	JAPAN		" "	"	"	1⅝ "	0.17	1	1⅝	STAPLAATIC	1.20	15
15½	7 "	" "	"	ROSEWOOD	" "	"	"	1⅝ "	0.17	1	1⅞	STAPLAATOD	1.40	15½
17	7 "	" "	NICK.TR.		" "	"	"	1⅝ "	0.17	1	1⅝	STAPLAAVEN	1.35	17
18	6 IN.	KNUCKLE JOINT	NICK.TR.		TOOL STEEL	SCREW	LEVER	1⅝ IN.	0.17	1	1½	STAPLAAVIA	1.30	18
19	7 "	" "	"		" "	"	"	1⅝ "	0.17	1	1⅝	STAPLAEBEL	1.40	19
60½	6 IN.	LOW ANGLE BLOCK	JAPAN		TOOL STEEL	SCREW		1½ IN.	0.17	1	1¼	STAPLAIKUR	1.10	60½
60	6 "	" " "	NICK.TR.		" "	"		1½ "	0.17	1	1¼	STAPLAIKOP	1.25	60
65½	7 "	" " "	"		" "	"		1⅝ "	0.17	1	1⅜	STAPLAILIX	1.20	65½
65	7 "	" " "	NICK.TR.		" "	"		1⅝ "	0.17	1	1⅜	STAPLAILET	1.35	65
62	14 "	" " "	JAPAN	ROSEWOOD	" "	"		2 "	0.45	1	3⅝	STAPLAILAS	2.85	62
131	8 IN.	DOUBLE END BLOCK	JAPAN		TOOL STEEL	SCREW		1⅝ IN.	0.17	1	1½	STAPLAIVEX	1.50	131
9	10 IN.	CAB. MAKERS BLOCK	NICKEL	ROSEWOOD	TOOL STEEL	SCREW		2 IN.	0.25	1	4½	STAPLAAGUR	4.10	9
97	10 "	" " EDGE	JAPAN	"	" "	"		2¼ "	0.45	1	3¾	STAPLAIPOC	2.20	97

Stanley Block, Steel and Wood Planes

COPYRIGHT, 1909, BY THE STANLEY RULE AND LEVEL COMPANY

ILLUSTRATIONS OF NOS. 100, 101, 103, 104, 110, 122, 127, 130, 135 AND 220

Stanley Block, Steel and Wood Planes

STANLEY IRON BLOCK PLANES have Non-Adjustable Cutters, except Nos. 103, 120 and 220 which are Adjustable Endwise, although the method of making these adjustments varies somewhat in detail in the different Planes.

THE STANLEY DOUBLE END IRON BLOCK PLANE No. 130 has two Slots and two Cutter Seats. It can be used as a Block Plane; or by reversing the position of the Cutter and the clamping wedge (see dotted lines in the engraving), it can be used to plane close up into corners, or places difficult to reach with any other Plane.

STANLEY ADJUSTABLE STEEL PLANES Nos. 104 and 105 have Bottoms of Pressed Steel, non-breakable. They are light weight and especially adapted for working soft woods. These Planes have Double Cutters which are Adjustable Endwise by Lever.

STANLEY ADJUSTABLE WOOD PLANES are made to meet the requirements of those users who prefer a Plane with a Wood Bottom having Double Cutters which are Adjustable Endwise by Lever rather than by a Screw.

Stanley Iron Block Planes															
NO.	LENGTH	TYPE	MATERIAL	FINISH	HANDLE	CUTTER					PACKED		CODE	PRICE EACH $	NO.
						MATERIAL	ADJUSTMENTS		WIDTH	PRICE $	IN BOX	WT. LBS.			
							ENDWISE	LATERAL							
101	3½ IN.	BLOCK	SPEC. IRON	JAPAN		TOOL STEEL			1 IN.	0.05	6	1½	STAPLAIROL	0.20	101
100	3½ "	"	"	"	IRON	" "			1 "	0.05	1	⅜	STAPLAIREG	0.25	100
102	5½ "	"	"	"		" "			1¼ "	0.10	1	⅞	STAPLAIRON	0.40	102
103	5½ "	"	"	"		" "	LEVER		1¼ "	0.10	1	⅞	STAPLAISAP	0.55	103
110	7½ "	"	"	"		" "			1⅝ "	0.13	1	1⅜	STAPLAISOT	0.55	110
120	7½ "	"	"	"		" "	LEVER		1⅝ "	0.17	1	1⅜	STAPLAITED	0.75	120
220	7½ "	"	"	"		" "	SCREW		1⅝ "	0.17	1	1½	STAPLAOJOX	0.75	220
Stanley Double End Block Plane															
130	8 IN.	BLOCK	SPEC. IRON	JAPAN		TOOL STEEL			1⅝ IN.	0.13	1	1⅝	STAPLAIVAT	0.75	130
Stanley Adjustable Steel Planes															
104	9 IN.	SMOOTH	STEEL	JAPAN	ROSEWOOD	TOOL STEEL	LEVER		2⅛ IN.	0.27	1	3⅛	STAPLAISER	2.05	104
105	14 "	JACK	"	"	"	" "	"		2⅛ "	0.27	1	3⅞	STAPLAISIS	2.60	105
Stanley Adjustable Wood Planes															
122	8 IN.	SMOOTH	BEECH	JAPAN		TOOL STEEL	LEVER		1¾ IN.	0.23	1	2⅜	STAPLAITIL	1.10	122
135	10 "	"	"	"	BEECH	" "	"		2⅛ "	0.27	1	3	STAPLAIVUC	1.50	135
127	15 "	JACK	"	"	"	" "	"		2⅛ "	0.27	1	3½	STAPLAITOM	1.50	127
129	20 "	FORE	"	"	"	" "	"		2⅜ "	0.29	1	5⅝	STAPLAITUP	1.65	129
132	26 "	JOINTER	"	"	"	" "	"		2⅝ "	0.32	1	7⅜	STAPLAIVOB	1.90	132

Stanley Belt Makers', Floor, Scrub and Furring Planes

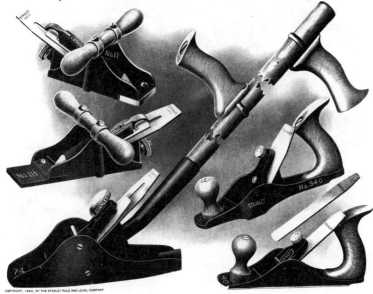

COPYRIGHT, 1909, BY THE STANLEY RULE AND LEVEL COMPANY

ILLUSTRATIONS OF NOS. 11, 11½, 40, 74 AND 340

Stanley Belt Makers', Floor, Scrub and Furring Planes

THE STANLEY BELT MAKERS' ADJUSTABLE IRON PLANE No. 11 is used by Belt Makers, for chamfering down the laps of a belt before fastening them together. It is equally well adapted for use in repairing belts in large manufacturing establishments. This Plane has Adjustable Throat and the Cutter is adjustable Endwise as described on pages 39 and 41.

STANLEY IRON FLOOR PLANES Nos. 11½ and 74 will be found useful for planing floors, Bowling Alleys, Skating Rinks, Decks of Vessels, etc.

These Planes are made in two forms, as shown by cuts of Nos. 11½ and 74 on opposite page. The former for working from a kneeling position and the latter with Handle 45 inches long for working erect. The construction of these Planes will enable the owner to do more work with less outlay of strength than can be done with any other tool. Plane No. 11½ has Adjustable Throat and the Cutter is adjustable Endwise as described on pages 39 and 41.

THE STANLEY IMPROVED SCRUB PLANES Nos. 40 and 40½ are especially adapted for roughing down work before using a Jack Plane and have Single Cutters, with the cutting edges rounded.

THE STANLEY FURRING PLANE No. 340 is a new design of tool, used for preparing lumber as it comes rough-sawed from the Mill, to remove the fur and grit before using a Smooth Plane. The construction of the Bottom is such that it will accomplish this very rapidly.

NO.	LENGTH	TYPE	MATERIAL	FINISH	HANDLE	CUTTER MATERIAL	ADJUSTMENTS ENDWISE	ADJUSTMENTS LATERAL	WIDTH	SINGLE $	PACKED IN BOX	PACKED WT. LBS.	CODE	PRICE EACH $	NO.
Belt Makers Adjustable Iron Plane															
11	5¾ IN.	BELT	SPEC.IRON	JAPAN	MAPLE	TOOL STEEL	SCREW		2⅜IN.	0.29	1	3½	STAPLAARAT	2.20	11
Iron Floor Planes															
11½	7½IN.	FLOOR	SPEC.IRON	JAPAN	MAPLE	TOOL STEEL	SCREW		2⅜IN.	0.29	1	3¾	STAPLAAREX	3.15	11½
74	10½ "	"	"	"	"	"	"		2⅝"	0.32	1	21½	STAPLAIMIG	4.95	74
Improved Scrub Plane															
40	9½IN.	SCRUB	SPEC.IRON	JAPAN	BEECH	TOOL STEEL			1¼IN.	0.20	1	2⅛	STAPLAIGAR	1.10	40
40½	10½ "	"	"	"	"	"			1½"	0.25	1	2½	STAPLAIGES	1.50	40½
Furring Plane															
340	10 IN.	FURRING	SPEC.IRON	JAPAN	BEECH	TOOL STEEL			2 IN.	0.30	1	2½	STAPLAOJUZ	1.65	340

Stanley Scraper Planes and Scrapers

COPYRIGHT, 1909, BY THE STANLEY RULE AND LEVEL COMPANY

ILLUSTRATIONS OF NOS. 0, 12, 12½, 80, 81, 82, 83, 85 AND 112

Stanley Scraper Planes and Scrapers

STANLEY "BAILEY" ADJUSTABLE VENEER SCRAPER PLANES Nos. 12, 12½ and 112 are suitable for Veneer, Cabinet and Floor scraping. The Angle of the Scraper Blades can be adjusted. No 12½ has bottom faced with Rosewood. Toothing Cutters can be furnished having 22, 28 and 32 teeth to the inch for any of these Scrapers.

STANLEY RABBET AND CABINET MAKERS' SCRAPER PLANES Nos. 85 and 87 have Adjustable Cutter Seats which permit the Mouth of the Scraper being narrowed or widened. The Handle and Knob on Scraper No. 85 can be tilted to right or left to clear the hands of the workman when scraping into corners.

STANLEY CABINET SCRAPER No. 80 is so made that the Scraper Blade may be sprung to a slight curve.

THE STANLEY SINGLE HANDED CABINET SCRAPER No. 82 is so arranged that the Blade can be tilted to any angle desired.

STANLEY SCRAPER BLADES No. 0 are made of the same high grade steel that is used in Plane Cutters.

NO.	LENGTH	TYPE	MATERIAL	FINISH	HANDLE	CUTTER					PACKED		CODE	PRICE EACH $	NO.
						MATERIAL	ADJUSTMENTS		WIDTH	PRICE $	IN BOX	WT. LBS.			
							ENDWISE	TILTING							
Stanley Iron Scraper Planes															
12	6¼IN.	VENEER	SPEC. IRON	JAPAN	ROSEWOOD	TOOL STEEL		SCREW	3 IN.	0.20	1	3¾	STAPLAAROZ	2.50	12
12½	6¼ "	"	" "	"	"	" "	" "	"	3 "	0.20	1	4	STAPLAASOR	3.30	12½
112	9 "	"	" "	"	"	" "	" "	"	3 "	0.20	1	4	STAPLAISOV	2.20	112
									TOOTH.	0.30					
85	8 "	RABBET	" "	"	"	" "			2 IN.	0.20	1	2⅝	STAPLAINAN	3.00	85
87	8 "	CABINET	" "	"	"	" "			2 "	0.20	1	2½	STAPLAINIR	2.00	87
Stanley Cabinet and Wood Scrapers															
80	11 IN.	CABINET	SPEC. IRON	JAPAN	RAISED	TOOL STEEL			2¾IN.	0.20	1	1¾	STASAPENET	1.00	80
81	10 "	"	" "	NICKEL	"	" "			2½ "	0.20	1	2¼	STASAPENIX	1.50	81
83	9½ "	WOOD	" "		MAPLE	" "			3 "	0.20	1	1¼	STASAPENUB	1.00	83
Stanley Single Handed Cabinet Scraper															
82	14½IN.	CABINET	SPEC. IRON	JAPAN	MAPLE	TOOL STEEL		SCREW	3 IN.	0.20	1	1¾	STASAPENOZ	1.05	82
Stanley Scraper Blades															
														DOZ.	
0-2½x5	5 IN.	HAND				TOOL STEEL			2½ IN.		6	1	STASAPADAR	2.50	2½x5-0
0-3" x4	4 "	"				" "			3 "		6	1	STASAPADES	2.50	3" x4-0
0-3" x5	5 "	"				" "			3 "		6	1¼	STASAPADIT	3.00	3" x5-0
0-3" x6	6 "	"				" "			3 "		6	1½	STASAPADOX	3.00	3" x6-0
0-3½x6	6 "	"				" "			3½ "		6	1⅞	STASAPADUZ	3.50	3½x6-0

Stanley and "Victor" Adjustable Circular Planes

COPYRIGHT, 1909, BY THE STANLEY RULE AND LEVEL COMPANY

ILLUSTRATIONS OF NOS. 13, 20 AND 113

Stanley Patent Adjustable Circular Plane
(WITH GRADUATED SCALE)

THE STANLEY PATENT ADJUSTABLE CIRCULAR PLANE WITH GRADUATED SCALE is a very superior tool as by means of the graduated scale on the gears, see cut on opposite page, the flexible face can be accurately set to work on an arc of the SAME CIRCLE, both concave and convex, by turning the Knob on the front of the Plane.
The Cutter is adjustable Endwise and Laterally as fully described on pages 39 and 41.

NO.	LENGTH	BOTTOM		FINISH	STOCK	CUTTER					PACKED		CODE	PRICE EACH $	NO.
		ADJUST-MENT	MATERIAL			MATERIAL	ADJUSTMENTS		WIDTH	SINGLE $	IN BOX	WT. LBS.			
							ENDWISE	LATERAL							
113	10 IN.	SCREW & LEVER	STEEL	JAPAN	SPEC. IRON	TOOL STEEL	SCREW	LEVER	1¾ IN.	0.23	1	3½	STAPLAITAZ	3.00	113

Stanley Adjustable Circular Plane

THE STANLEY ADJUSTABLE CIRCULAR PLANE has a Flexible Steel Face and by means of the Thumb Screw at each end of the Stock can be easily adapted to plane circular work, either concave or convex.
The Cutter is adjustable Endwise and Laterally as described on pages 39 and 41.

NO.	LENGTH	BOTTOM		FINISH	STOCK	CUTTER					PACKED		CODE	PRICE EACH $	NO.
		ADJUST-MENT	MATERIAL			MATERIAL	ADJUSTMENTS		WIDTH	SINGLE $	IN BOX	WT. LBS.			
							ENDWISE	LATERAL							
13	10 IN.	HAND	STEEL	JAPAN	SPEC. IRON	TOOL STEEL	SCREW	LEVER	1¾ IN.	0.23	1	3½	STAPLAASUS	3.00	13

Stanley "Victor" Adjustable Circular Planes

"VICTOR" ADJUSTABLE CIRCULAR PLANES are specially fine tools, and all parts are designed with the object of eliminating any lost motion due to wear. There are less parts subject to lost motion in this Plane than in any other Circular Plane made. The ends of the Flexible Steel Bottom being fixed, and the force applied at the centre, great accuracy of adjustment is possible and the Face is most firmly held in position.
The Cutters are adjustable Endwise and Laterally as described on pages 39 and 41.

NO.	LENGTH	BOTTOM		FINISH	STOCK	CUTTER					PACKED		CODE	PRICE EACH $	NO.
		ADJUST-MENT	MATERIAL			MATERIAL	ADJUSTMENTS		WIDTH	SINGLE $	IN BOX	WT. LBS.			
							ENDWISE	LATERAL							
20½	10 IN.	SCREW	STEEL	JAPAN	SPEC. IRON	TOOL STEEL	SCREW	LEVER	1¾ IN.	0.23	1	4	STAPLAEBON	3.50	20½
20	10 "	"	"	NICKEL	" "	" "	"	"	1¾ "	0.23	1	4	STAPLAEBIM	4.10	20

Stanley Core Box, Chute Board and Router Planes

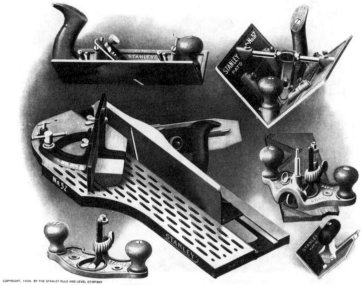

ILLUSTRATIONS OF NOS. 52, 56, 57, 71 AND 71½

Stanley Core Box Planes

STANLEY CORE BOX PLANE No. 57 includes one set of sections for working semi-circles up to 5 inches diameter. With additional intermediate sections a capacity of 10 inch diameter may be obtained.

NO.	LENGTH	TYPE	MATERIAL	FINISH	HANDLE	CUTTER					PACKED		CODE	PRICE EACH $	NO.
						MATERIAL	ADJUSTMENTS ENDWISE LATERAL		WIDTH	PRICE $	IN BOX	WT. LBS.			
56	4 IN.	CORE B'X	SPEC. IRON	NICKEL	ROSEWOOD	TOOL STEEL			⅜ IN.	0.25	1	2	STAPLAIKEM	2.25	56
57	10 "	"	"	"	BEECH	" "			⅞ "	0.30	1	6¾	STAPLAIKIN	4.40	57
						ADDITIONAL SECTIONS PER PR.				1.00					

Stanley Chute Board and Plane

THE STANLEY CHUTE BOARD AND PLANE is a very important tool especially for Pattern Makers, Cabinet Makers, Printers and Electrotypers. The Board is made of Iron, of ribbed construction, and has an Adjustable Runway for the Plane.
The Plane is especially constructed to suit this Board, the Cutter being set on a skew, making a smooth, keen cut. The Cutter being fitted with a Lateral Adjustment, a cut giving any ordinary DRAFT to a pattern can be made.
The Swivel is indexed, for cutting a Square and a Mitre (45 degrees) but by means of the Clamping Screw, can be set at any desired angle from 0 to 90 degrees. The Sliding Back will support the work close to the Plane, preventing it from splintering. The Sliding Back Clamp will hold nearly any shape of work in position to be planed.

NO.	LENGTH	TYPE	MATERIAL	FINISH	HANDLE	CUTTER					PACKED		CODE	PRICE EACH $	NO.
						MATERIAL	ADJUSTMENTS ENDWISE LATERAL		WIDTH	SINGLE $	IN BOX	WT. LBS.			
52 PLANE	22 IN.	CHUTE B'D & PLANE	SPEC. IRON	JAPAN	ROSEWOOD	TOOL STEEL	SCREW	LEVER	2⅜ IN.	0.29	1	17½	STAPLAIJUG	10.00	52
51	15 "	JOINTER	"	"	"	" "	"	"	2⅜ "	0.29	1	7⅛	STAPLAIJOF	4.50	51

Stanley Woodworkers' Router Planes

STANLEY WOODWORKERS' ROUTER PLANES should be added to the kit of every skilled Carpenter, Cabinet Maker, Stair Builder, Pattern Maker or Wheelwright. These Tools are made with both an Open or Closed Throat, and are perfectly adapted to surface the bottom of grooves, panels and all depressions below the general surface of any woodwork.

NO.	LENGTH	THROAT	MATERIAL	FINISH	HANDLE	CUTTER					PACKED		CODE	PRICE EACH $	NO.
						MATERIAL	ADJUSTMENTS ENDWISE LATERAL		WIDTH	PRICE $	IN BOX	WT. LBS.			
71	7½ IN.	OPEN	SPEC. IRON	NICKEL	BEECH	TOOL STEEL	SCREW		¼ & ½	0.30	1	2⅝	STAPLAILOZ	2.05	71
71½	7½ "	CLOSED	"	"	"	" "	"		¼ & ½	0.30	1	2⅛	STAPLAILUB	1.65	71½

Stanley Rabbet Planes

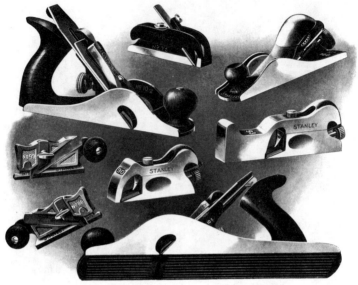

ILLUSTRATIONS OF NOS. 10C, 10½, 75, 90, 93, 98, 99 AND 140

5

Stanley Rabbet Planes

STANLEY BULL-NOSE RABBET PLANE. No. 75 is made for working close up into a corner and will be found a very convenient tool.

STANLEY SIDE RABBET PLANES Nos. 98 and 99 are very useful and convenient tools for side rabbeting and trimming dados, mouldings and grooves of all sorts. The reversible Nose-piece gives these tools a form which enable them to work close up into corners when desired.

THE STANLEY RABBET AND BLOCK PLANE. No. 140 has a detachable side which enables this tool to be changed easily and quickly from a Block Plane to Rabbet or vice versa. The Cutter is set on a skew and is adjustable by means of a Screw.

STANLEY ADJUSTABLE CABINET MAKERS' RABBET PLANES Nos. 90, 92, 93 and 94 are designed for fine Cabinet Work where extreme accuracy is required. These Planes are Nickel Plated and fitted with the "HAND-Y" feature. The Cutter is adjustable Endwise by means of a Screw and the Throat opening can be regulated to suit. The Sides and Bottom being Square with each other the Plane will lie perfectly flat on either side, and can be worked Right or Left Hand. Plane No. 90 is of the Bull-Nose pattern.

STANLEY CARRIAGE MAKERS' RABBET PLANES Nos. 10, 10½, 10C and 10½C are especially designed for heavy work and Framing and will be found to be excellent tools for a wide variety of work. The Cutter is of the Double Cutter type and is adjustable Endwise and Laterally as described on pages 39 and 41.

NO.	LENGTH	TYPE	MATERIAL	FINISH	HANDLE	CUTTER					PACKED		CODE	PRICE EACH $	NO.
						MATERIAL	ADJUSTMENTS		WIDTH	PRICE $	IN BOX	WT. LBS.			
							ENDWISE	LATERAL							
Bull-Nose, Side Rabbet and Rabbet and Block Planes															
75	4 IN.	RABBET	SPEC.IRON	JAPAN		TOOL STEEL			1 IN.	0.20	1	⅝	STAPLAIMOL	0.40	75
98	4 "	RIGHT	" "	NICKEL	ROSEWOOD	" "			½ "	0.20	1	½	STAPLAIPUD	1.00	98
99	4 "	LEFT	" "	"	"	" "			½ "	0.20	1	½	STAPLAIRAF	1.00	99
140	7 "	RABBET BLOCK	" "	NICK.TR.		" "	SCREW		1¾ "	0.20	1	1⅛	STAPLAIZAG	1.40	140
Adjustable Cabinet Makers Rabbet Planes															
90	4 IN	RABBET	SPEC.IRON	NICKEL		TOOL STEEL	SCREW		1 IN.	0.30	1	1	STAPLAINOS	2.20	90
92	5½ "	"	" "	"		" "	"		¾ "	0.30	1	1½	STAPLAINUT	2.20	92
93	6½ "	"	" "	"		" "	"		1 "	0.30	1	1¾	STAPLAIPAX	2.60	93
94	7½ "	"	" "	"		" "	"		1¼ "	0.30	1	2	STAPLAIPEZ	3.00	94
Carriage Makers Rabbet Planes—Smooth and Corrugated															
10½	9 IN.	RABBET	SPEC.IRON	JAPAN	ROSEWOOD	TOOL STEEL	SCREW	LEVER	2⅛ IN.	0.27	1	3	STAPLAAMOK	2.75	10½
10	13 "	"	" "	"	"	" "	"	"	2⅛ "	0.27	1	4¼	STAPLAAKOS	3.30	10
10½C	9 "	"	" "	"	"	" "	"	"	2⅛ "	0.27	1	3	STAPLAAMUN	2.75	10½C
10C	13 "	"	" "	"	"	" "	"	"	2⅛ "	0.27	1	4¼	STAPLAAKUT	3.30	10C

Stanley Rabbet, Dado, Match and Chamfer Planes

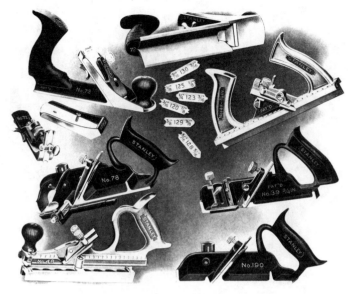

COPYRIGHT, 1909, BY THE STANLEY RULE AND LEVEL COMPANY   ILLUSTRATIONS OF NOS. 39, 48, 72, 78, 148 AND 190

Stanley Rabbet, Dado, Match and Chamfer Planes

STANLEY IMPROVED RABBET PLANES Nos. 180 to 192 will lie flat on either side and can be used Right or Left Hand while planing into corners or up against perpendicular surfaces.   All are fitted with Depth Gauge.   Nos. 190, 191, 192 have Spurs.

THE STANLEY DUPLEX RABBET AND FILLETSTER PLANE No. 78 becomes a Rabbet Plane by removing the Arm to which the Fence is secured.   Having two Seats for the Cutter it can be used as a Bull-Nose Rabbet or an ordinary Rabbet Plane. The Arm to which the Fence is secured can be screwed to either side of the Stock, thus making a Right or Left Hand Filletster. This Plane is fitted with a Spur for working across the grain and also has a Depth Gauge.

STANLEY IMPROVED DADO PLANES No. 39 have Skew Cutters, Adjustable Depth Gauge, and two Adjustable Spurs.

STANLEY TONGUING AND GROOVING PLANES Nos. 48 and 49 have two separate Cutters a suitable distance apart, and when the Guide or Fence is set, as shown opposite, both Cutters work forming the Tongue.   The Fence is hung on a pivot and can be swung around, end for end.   This movement covers one Cutter and furnishes a guide for making a Groove to match.

STANLEY DOUBLE END MATCH PLANES, cut the Tongue with one side, and by reversing ends, cut Grooves to match.

THE STANLEY CHAMFER PLANE No. 72 finishes work without other tools.   No. 72½ has extra Section for Beading, etc.

NO.	LENGTH	TYPE	MATERIAL	FINISH	HANDLE	SPECIAL FEATURES	CUTTER		PACKED		CODE	PRICE EACH $	NO.
							WIDTH	PRICE $	IN. BOX	WT. LBS.			
180	8 IN.	RABBET	SPEC.IRON	JAPAN	SPEC. IRON		1½IN.	0.20	1	2½	STAPLAOGIM	1.10	180
181	8 "	"	" "	"	" "		1¼ "	0.20	1	2¼	STAPLAOGON	1.10	181
182	8 "	"	" "	"	" "		1 "	0.20	1	2	STAPLAOGUP	1.10	182
190	8 "	"	" "	"	" "	HAS SPUR	1½ "	0.20	1	2½	STAPLAOJAR	1.25	190
191	8 "	"	" "	"	" "	" "	1¼ "	0.20	1	2¼	STAPLAOJES	1.25	191
192	8 "	"	" "	"	" "	" "	1 "	0.20	1	2	STAPLAOJIT	1.25	192
78	8½ "	DUPLEX RABBET	" "	" "	" "	HAS SPUR AND FENCE	1½ "	0.20	1	3	STAPLAIMUM	1.65	78
39-¼"	8 "	DADO	" "	" "	" "	" SPURS SKEW CUTTER	¼ "	0.20	1	1¾	STAPLAIDAB	1.65	¼"-39
39-⅜"	8 "	"	" "	" "	" "	" " " "	⅜ "	0.20	1	1¾	STAPLAIDEC	1.65	⅜"-39
39-½"	8 "	"	" "	" "	" "	" " " "	½ "	0.20	1	1¾	STAPLAIDID	1.65	½"-39
39-⅝"	8 "	"	" "	" "	" "	" " " "	⅝ "	0.20	1	1¾	STAPLAIDOF	1.65	⅝"-39
39-¾"	8 "	"	" "	" "	" "	" " " "	¾ "	0.20	1	1¾	STAPLAIDUG	1.65	¾"-39
39-⅞"	8 "	"	" "	" "	" "	" " " "	⅞ "	0.20	1	1¾	STAPLAIFEL	1.65	⅞"-39
39-1"	8 "	"	" "	" "	" "	" " " "	1 "	0.20	1	1¾	STAPLAIFON	1.65	1"-39
48	10½"	TONGUE GROOVE	" "	NICKEL	NICKEL	FOR BOARDS ¾ TO 1¼IN.	5/16"	0.17	1	2¾	STAPLAIJAC	2.75	48
49	10 "	"	" "	"	"	" " ⅜" ¾"	3/16"	0.17	1	2⅜	STAPLAIJED	2.75	49
146	9 "	DOUBLE MATCH	" "	"	"	" " ⅜ IN. ⅛"GROOVE	⅛ "	0.65	1	1½	STAPLAIZOR	2.20	146
147	9 "	" "	"	"	"	" " ⅝IN. 3/16" "	3/16 "	0.65	1	1⅞	STAPLAIZUS	2.20	147
148	9 "	" "	"	"	"	" " ⅞ IN. ¼" "	¼ "	0.65	1	2⅜	STAPLAOGEL	2.20	148
72	9 "	CHAMFER	" "	JAPAN	ROSEWOOD	CHAMFERS UP TO 1½IN.	1⅝ "	0.20	1	3⅜	STAPLAIMAD	2.20	72
72½	9 "	"	" "	"	"	EX. BEAD'G. SECT'N. & 6 TOOLS			1	4⅛	STAPLAIMEF	3.30	72½

Stanley Beading, Plow, Dado and Matching Planes

COPYRIGHT, 1909, BY THE STANLEY RULE AND LEVEL COMPANY

ILLUSTRATIONS OF NOS. 46, 50, AND 141 WITH CUTTER EQUIPMENTS

Stanley Beading, Plow, Dado and Matching Planes

THE STANLEY COMBINED BEADING AND MATCHING PLANE. No. 50 for Beading cannot be surpassed, and by adjustment of the Fence, Centre Beading can be done up to 5 inches from the edge of the boards.

STANLEY ADJUSTABLE DADO AND PLOW PLANES Nos. 46 and 47 have skew Cutters.

STANLEY BULL-NOSE PLOW AND MATCHING PLANES Nos. 141 and 143 have interchangeable Fronts and with the Short Front on, it takes the form of a Bull-Nose Plow, and will easily work up to and into a ½-inch hole as in sash fitting, stair work, etc.

NO.	LENGTH	TYPE	MATERIAL	FINISH	HANDLE	CUTTER					PACKED		CODE	PRICE EACH $	NO.
						MATERIAL	ADJUSTMENTS ENDWISE	LATERAL	WIDTH	PRICE $	IN BOX	WT. LBS.			
50	9¼ IN.	BEADING	SPEC. IRON	NICKEL	NICKEL	TOOL STEEL			BELOW	BELOW	1	3	STAPLAIJIF	4.50	50
46	10½ "	PLOW	" "	"	ROSEWOOD	" "			"	"	1	5¾	STAPLAIGOX	8.00	46
47	10½ "	DADO	" "	"	"	" "			"	"	1	3¾	STAPLAIGUZ	4.50	47
143	9¼ "	MATCH	" "	"	"	" "			"	"	1	4⅜	STAPLAIZIP	6.00	143
141	9¼ "	"	" "	"	"	" "			"	"	1	5½	STAPLAIZEH	8.00	141

8 CUTTERS SUPPLIED WITH PLANE NO. 50

NAME	BEADING							MATCHING	NAME
NO. OF CUTTER	21A	22A	23A	24A	25A	26A	27A	5A AND 12A	NO. OF CUTTER
WIDTH " "	⅛ IN.	³⁄₁₆ IN.	¼ IN.	⁵⁄₁₆ IN.	⅜ IN.	⁷⁄₁₆ IN.	½ IN.	PAIR ¼ IN.	WIDTH " "
PRICE " "	$0.15	0.15	0.15	0.20	0.20	0.25	0.25	0.65	PRICE " "

11 CUTTERS SUPPLIED WITH PLANE NO. 46

NAME	PLOW AND DADO							FIL'ST'R	TONGU'G	SLITT'G	NAME
NO. OF CUTTER	11B	12B	13B	14B	16B	17B	19B	20B	9B	5B	8	NO. OF CUTTER
WIDTH " "	³⁄₁₆ IN.	¼ IN.	⁵⁄₁₆ IN.	⅜ IN.	½ IN.	⅝ IN.	⅞ IN.	1¼ IN.	1½ IN.	¼ IN.		WIDTH " "
PRICE " "	0.15	0.15	0.15	0.20	0.20	0.20	0.25	0.25	0.50	0.50	0.30	PRICE " "

6 CUTTERS SUPPLIED WITH PLANE NO. 47

NAME	DADO					SLITTING	NAME
NO. OF CUTTER	14B	16B	17B	19B	20B	8	NO. OF CUTTER
WIDTH " "	⅜ IN.	½ IN.	⅝ IN.	⅞ IN.	1¼ IN.		WIDTH " "
PRICE " "	0.20	0.20	0.20	0.25	0.25	0.30	PRICE " "

10 CUTTERS SUPPLIED WITH PLANES NOS. 143 AND 141, FILLETSTER FOR NO. 141 ONLY

NAME	PLOWS								FIL'ST'R	TONGU'G	SLITT'G	NAME
NO. OF CUTTER	10C	11C	12C	13C	14C	15C	16C	17C	9C	5C	8	NO. OF CUTTER
WIDTH " "	⅛ IN.	³⁄₁₆ IN.	¼ IN.	⁵⁄₁₆ IN.	⅜ IN.	⁷⁄₁₆ IN.	½ IN.	⅝ IN.	1½ IN.	¼ IN.		WIDTH " "
PRICE " "	0.15	0.15	0.15	0.15	0.20	0.20	0.20	0.20	0.50	0.50	0.30	PRICE " "

Stanley "45" Plow, Beading, Rabbet and Matching Plane

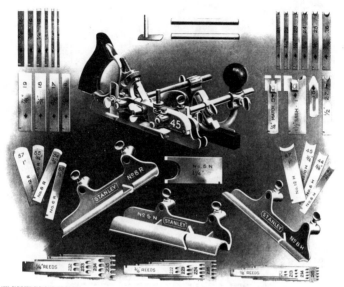

COPYRIGHT, 1909, BY THE STANLEY RULE AND LEVEL COMPANY

ILLUSTRATION OF NO 45 WITH ATTACHMENTS AND CUTTER EQUIPMENT

Stanley "45" Plow, Beading, Rabbet and Matching Plane

THE STANLEY "45" PLOW, BEADING, RABBET AND MATCHING PLANE combines a Main Stock and Sliding Section so arranged that Cutters of different widths can be used. It is fitted with an adjustable Fence or Guide and a Depth Gauge, also with Spurs for use in working across the grain and can be used Right or Left Hand.

This Plane combines seven tools in one: 1. Beading and Centre Beading Plane. 2. Rabbet and Filletster Plane. 3. Dado Plane. 4. Plow Plane. 5. Matching Plane. 6. Sash Plane. 7. A Superior Slitting Plane.

EXTRA BOTTOMS AND CUTTERS shown on the opposite page may be used to advantage by substituting the specially formed detachable Bottoms for the Sliding Section mentioned above. A special Bottom is required for each Cutter and these are known as HOLLOW, ROUND, and NOSING Bottoms.

EXTRA REEDING CUTTERS as illustrated on the opposite page can be supplied at the prices given in the table below.

NO.	LENGTH	TYPE	MATERIAL	FINISH	HANDLE	CUTTER						PACKED		CODE	PRICE EACH $	NO.
						MATERIAL	ADJUSTMENTS		WIDTH	PRICE $	IN BOX	WT. LBS.			
							ENDWISE	LATERAL							
45	10 IN.	PLOW	SPEC. IRON	NICKEL	ROSEWOOD	TOOL STEEL	SCREW		BELOW	BELOW	1	9½	STAPLAIGIT	9.00	45

20 ◆ CUTTERS SUPPLIED WITH PLANE NO. 45.

NAME	PLOW AND DADO										NAME
NO. OF CUTTER	◆10	◆11	◆12	◆13	◆14	◆15	◆16	◆17	◆18	◆19	NO. OF CUTTER
WIDTH '' ''	⅛ IN.	³⁄₁₆IN.	¼IN.	⁵⁄₁₆IN.	⅜IN.	⁷⁄₁₆IN.	½IN.	⅝IN.	¾IN.	⅞IN.	WIDTH '' ''
PRICE '' ''	$0.15	0.15	0.15	0.15	0.20	0.20	0.20	0.20	0.20	0.25	PRICE '' ''

NAME	BEADING							SASH	TONGUE	SLITT'G	NAME
NO. OF CUTTER	◆21	◆22	◆23	◆24	◆25	◆26	◆27	◆1	◆5	◆8	NO. OF CUTTER
WIDTH '' ''	⅛ IN.	³⁄₁₆IN.	¼IN.	⁵⁄₁₆IN.	⅜IN.	⁷⁄₁₆IN.	½IN.	1½IN.	¼IN.		WIDTH '' ''
PRICE '' ''	$0.15	0.15	0.15	0.20	0.20	0.25	0.25	0.50	0.50	0.30	PRICE '' ''

EXTRA BOTTOMS AND CUTTERS FOR PLANE NO. 45.

NAME	HOLLOWS				ROUNDS				NOSING	NAME
NO. OF BOTTOM	6H	8H	10H	12H	6R	8R	10R	12R	5N	NO. OF BOTTOM
WORKS SEGMENT OF CIRCLE	¾ IN.	1 IN.	1¼ IN.	1½ IN.	¾ IN.	1 IN.	1¼ IN.	1½ IN.	1¼ IN.	WORKS SEGMENT OF CIRCLE
PRICE OF BOTTOM	$0.75	0.75	0.75	0.75	0.75	0.75	0.75	0.75	1.10	PRICE OF BOTTOM
NO. OF CUTTER	53	54	55	57	43	44	45	47	5N	NO. OF CUTTER
WIDTH '' ''	½ IN.	⅝ IN.	¾ IN.	1 IN.	½ IN.	⅝ IN.	¾ IN.	1 IN.	1¼ IN.	WIDTH '' ''
PRICE '' ''	$0.20	0.20	0.20	0.20	0.20	0.20	0.20	0.20	0.25	PRICE '' ''

EXTRA REEDING CUTTERS FOR PLANE NO. 45.

NAME	⅛ IN. REEDS				³⁄₁₆ IN. REEDS				¼ IN. REEDS				NAME
NO. OF CUTTER	212	213	214	215	222	223	224	225	232	233	234	235	NO. OF CUTTER
'' '' BEADS	2	3	4	5	2	3	4	5	2	3	4	5	'' '' BEADS
PRICE '' CUTTER	$0.20	0.30	0.40	0.50	0.20	0.30	0.40	0.50	0.20	0.30	0.40	0.50	PRICE '' CUTTER

Stanley Patent Universal "55" Plane

COPYRIGHT, 1909, BY THE STANLEY RULE AND LEVEL COMPANY

ILLUSTRATION OF NO. 55 WITH SPECIMENS OF WORK DONE BY PLANE

Stanley Patent Universal "55" Plane

The STANLEY PATENT UNIVERSAL "55" PLANE will do a greater variety of work than can be done with a full line of so called Fancy Planes.

The REGULAR EQUIPMENT sent with this Plane comprises the 52 CUTTERS marked ◆, arranged in 4 separate wooden cases, and packed with the Plane. A further line of 41 SPECIAL CUTTERS are regularly made. With the complete line of Cutters there is practically no end to the variety of work which can be done with this Plane and a few samples are shown opposite.

NO. "55" PLANE is 10 INCHES long and weighs only 7¾ lbs. (with 93 Cutters 11 lbs.) and replaces a full line of 93 Fancy Planes weighing probably 90 lbs., thus justifying the name UNIVERSAL given it. It consists of the following leading parts:

THE MAIN STOCK, which carries the various Cutters firmly clamped to it by the Cutter Bolt, the Cutters being adjustable Endwise by means of the Adjusting Wheel.

THE SLIDING SECTION has a Patent Adjustable Bottom, vertically adjustable by means of a Differential Screw.

THE SLIDING SECTION REQUIRES CAREFUL ADJUSTMENT LATERALLY with each different Cutter used as it acts as a support for the left edge of the Cutter, and should be brought into position so that the Left Edge of the Cutter just overlaps it, so as to insure giving the Cutter a good support at the outer edge. If the Sliding Section OVERLAPS the Edge of the Cutter it binds in working and causes the Plane to drag or work hard. The small upper right hand cut on the opposite page shows the proper setting but with the overlap somewhat EXAGGERATED in order to show this feature clearly.

THE ADJUSTABLE BOTTOM of the Sliding Section should also be set slightly above the left cutting edge of the Cutter and NOT IN THE SAME LEVEL with the Main Stock unless a Cutter has its extreme Cutting Edges on the SAME LEVEL.

THE AUXILIARY CENTRE BOTTOM is used as an extra Support when needed, and it is necessary to use it in all forms of Hollows, Rounds and Ogees, as it prevents the Cutter from gouging into the work; and it should be brought into a position slightly above the lowest point of the Cutter. Its position is adjusted Vertically by means of the Screw and Adjusting Nut and it is regulated laterally by means of the Thumb Screw. It can also be used with advantage in cutting many forms of mouldings, as it acts to steady the Plane, as is shown by the illustration on page 68, where Plane is shown having cut a moulding. Although both Fences are there shown, ordinarily the Left Fence only would be used.

With the SLIDING SECTION and AUXILIARY CENTRE BOTTOM it is possible to use Cutters of PRACTICALLY ANY SHAPE and having their EXTREME CUTTING EDGES in DIFFERENT LEVELS which is not possible with any other Plane.

THE RIGHT AND LEFT FENCES are intended to be attached to the Arms on the Right and Left Hand sides of the Plane, although they may be used on either side, or for working wide work the position of the Right Hand Fence can be reversed. Both Fences are provided with handles for steadying the plane in working.

IN SETTING THE FENCE care should be taken to see that the Face of the Tilting Guide Plate is exactly parallel with the side of the Cutter, as otherwise the Plane will have a tendency to RUN TO or FROM the Edge of the Work and as the Cutter goes down into the wood, causes the Plane to Bind or Run Away from the side of the Work. The two small cuts on the left side of the Plane opposite, show this feature.

THE LEFT FENCE has a LATERAL ADJUSTMENT by means of a SCREW for extra fine work. The Rosewood Guide of either Fence can be Tilted to any desired angle up to 45 degrees for working Chamfers by simply loosening the Screws.

THE PATENTED CAM REST as shown separately at the top of page 68 is now supplied with "55" Plane and also "45" Plane can be fastened to either Arm outside or between the Plane and the Fence and helps to keep the Plane Level. The Cam Rest being eccentric the depth is regulated by merely turning the Cam in the proper adjustment. When used on the Back Arm in combination with the Auxiliary Centre Bottom, it forms an extra rest and tends to keep the Plane from rocking.

Stanley Patent Universal "55" Plane

Special Tools for No 55

Regular Tools with No. 55

Special Tools for No 55

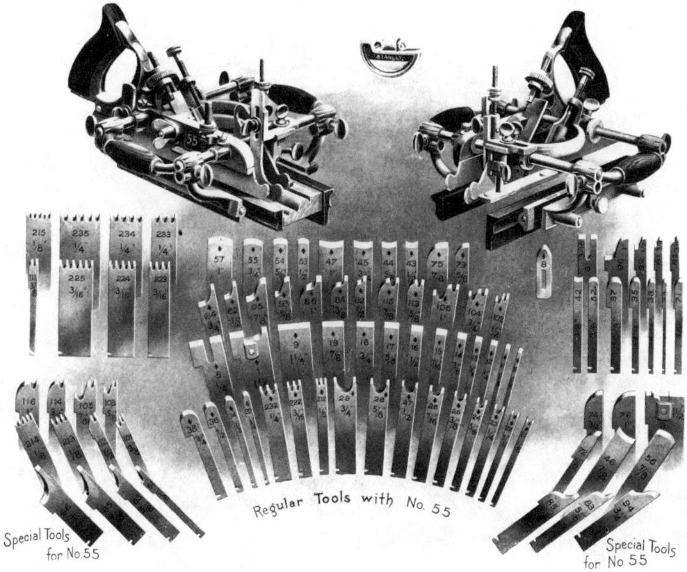

COPYRIGHT, 1909, BY THE STANLEY RULE AND LEVEL COMPANY

ILLUSTRATIONS OF NO. 55 WITH 52♦ CUTTERS REGULARLY SUPPLIED AND 41 SPECIAL CUTTERS

Stanley Patent Universal "55" Plane

THE ADJUSTABLE DEPTH GAUGE attached to the Main Stock has an Adjusting Screw and Nut for regulating depth.

THE BEADING GAUGE attached to the Sliding Section acts as an extra support or steadier for the Plane in Beading.

THE SPURS or Side Cutters fitted in the Main Stock and Sliding Section are used in working across the grain and should be set in line with the edges of the Cutter and far enough BELOW the cutting edge to cut the grain in advance of the Cutter proper and fully the thickness of the shaving the Cutter is taking out.

NO.	LENGTH	TYPE	MATERIAL	FINISH	HANDLE	CUTTER						PACKED		CODE	PRICE EACH $	NO.
						MATERIAL	ADJUSTMENTS		WIDTH	PRICE $	IN BOX	WT. LBS.			
							ENDWISE	LATERAL								
55	10 IN.	UNIVER'L	SPEC. IRON	NICKEL	ROSEWOOD	TOOL STEEL	SCREW		BELOW	BELOW	1	15¼	STAPLAIKAL	18.00	55

52 CUTTERS MARKED♦SUPPLIED WITH PLANE. OTHERS EXTRA

NAME	SASH		MATCH		SLITT'G	FIL'STR	PLOW AND DADO										NAME
NO	♦1	2	♦5	6	♦8	♦9	♦10	♦11	♦12	♦13	♦14	♦15	♦16	♦17	♦18	♦19	NO.
WIDTH	1½"	1½"	¼"	³⁄₁₆"		1¼"	⅛"	³⁄₁₆"	¼"	⁵⁄₁₆"	⅜"	⁷⁄₁₆"	½"	⅝"	¾"	⅞"	WIDTH
PRICE	$0.50	0.50	0.50	0.50	0.30	0.25	0.15	0.15	0.15	0.15	0.20	0.20	0.20	0.20	0.20	0.25	PRICE

NAME	BEADING										FLUTING						NAME
NO.	♦21	♦22	♦23	♦24	♦25	♦26	♦27	♦28	♦29	31	♦32	33	♦34	35	♦36	37	NO.
WIDTH	⅛"	³⁄₁₆"	¼"	⁵⁄₁₆"	⅜"	⁷⁄₁₆"	½"	⅝"	¾"	³⁄₁₆"	¼"	⁵⁄₁₆"	⅜"	⁷⁄₁₆"	½"	⅝"	WIDTH
PRICE	$0.15	0.15	0.15	0.20	0.20	0.25	0.25	0.30	0.30	0.30	0.30	0.30	0.30	0.30	0.30	0.30	PRICE

NAME	FLUT'G	HOLLOWS						ROUNDS					QUARTER HOLLOWS			NAME
NO	♦38	42	♦43	♦44	♦45	46	♦47	52	♦53	♦54	♦55	56	♦57	61	♦62	63	NO.
WIDTH	¾"	⅜"	½"	⅝"	¾"	⅞"	1"	⅜"	½"	⅝"	¾"	⅞"	1"	⅜"	½"	⅝"	WIDTH
PRICE	0.30	0.20	0.20	0.20	0.20	0.20	0.20	0.20	0.20	0.20	0.20	0.20	0.20	0.45	0.45	0.45	PRICE

NAME	QUARTER HOLLOWS			QUARTER ROUNDS							REVERSE OGEES						NAME
NO	♦64	65	66		71	72	73	74	♦75	76	81	♦82	83	♦84	85	♦86	NO.
WIDTH	¾"	⅞"	1"		⅜"	½"	⅝"	¾"	⅞"	1"	⅜"	½"	⅝"	¾"	⅞"	1"	WIDTH
PRICE	$0.50	0.50	0.50		0.45	0.45	0.45	0.50	0.50	0.50	0.45	0.45	0.45	0.50	0.50	0.50	PRICE

NAME	ROMAN OGEES						GRECIAN OGEES						QUAR. ROUNDS WITH BEAD			NAME
NO.	91	92	♦93	94	♦95	96	101	♦102	103	♦104	105	♦106		111	112	♦113	NO.
WIDTH	⅜"	½"	⅝"	¾"	⅞"	1"	⅜"	½"	⅝"	¾"	⅞"	1"		⅜"	½"	⅝"	WIDTH
PRICE	$0.45	0.45	0.45	0.50	0.50	0.50	0.45	0.45	0.45	0.50	0.50	0.50		0.45	0.45	0.45	PRICE

NAME	QR. R'D'S WITH BEAD				³⁄₁₆" REEDS					¼" REEDS					NAME
NO.	114	♦115	116	NO. BEADS	♦212	213	214	215	♦222	223	224	225	♦232	233	234	235	NO. BEADS
WIDTH	¾"	⅞"	1"		2	3	4	5	2	3	4	5	2	3	4	5	
PRICE	$0.50	0.50	0.50	PRICE	0.20	0.30	0.40	0.50	0.20	0.30	0.40	0.50	0.20	0.30	0.40	0.50	PRICE

Parts of "Bailey" "Bed Rock" and Miscellaneous Planes

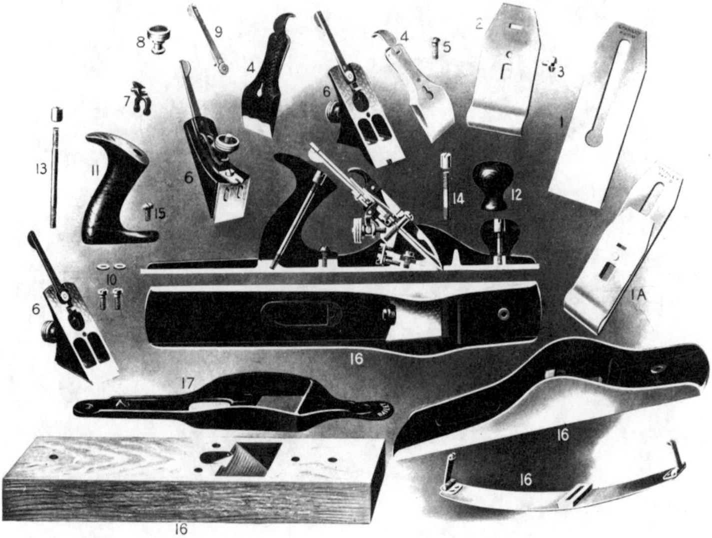

COPYRIGHT, 1909, BY THE STANLEY RULE AND LEVEL COMPANY

ILLUSTRATIONS OF PARTS OF PLANES HAVING DOUBLE CUTTERS AND WITH "BAILEY" TYPE OF CUTTER ADJUSTMENTS

Parts of "Bailey" "Bed Rock" and Miscellaneous Planes

NO.	1	2 2c	3 3c	4 4c	4½ 4½c	5 5c	5½ 5½c	6 6c	7 7c	8 8c	9	10 10c	10½ " c	11 11½	13	20	20½	21	22	23	24	25	26	NO.
	$	$	$	$	$	$	$	$	$	$	$	$	$	$	$	$	$	$	$	$	$	$	$	
1A	0.32	0.35	0.38	0.42	0.48	0.42	0.47	0.48	0.48	0.50	0.42	0.45	0.45	0.48	0.38	0.38	0.38	0.38	0.38	0.38	0.42	0.36	0.42	1A
1	.18	.21	.23	.25	.29	.25	.28	.29	.29	.32	.25	.27	.27	.29	.23	.23	.23	.23	.23	.23	.25	.23	.25	1
2	.14	.14	.15	.17	.19	.17	.19	.19	.19	.18	.13	.18	.18	.13	.15	.15	.15	.15	.15	.15	.17	.13	.17	2
3	.05	.05	.05	.05	.05	.05	.05	.05	.05	.05	.05	.05	.05	.05	.05	.05	.05	.05	.05	.05	.05	.05	.05	3
4	.25	.25	.25	.25	.25	.25	.25	.25	.25	.25	.25	.25	.25	.25	.25	.25	.25	.20	.20	.20	.20	.20	.20	4
5	.05	.05	.05	.05	.05	.05	.05	.05	.05	.05	.05	.05	.05	.05	.05	.05	.05	.05	.05	.05	.05	.05	.05	5
6	.35	.35	.35	.35	.35	.35	.35	.35	.35	.35	.35	.35	.35	.35	.35	.35	.35	.30	.30	.30	.30	.30	.30	6
7	.05	.05	.05	.05	.05	.05	.05	.05	.05	.05	.05	.05	.05	.05	.05	.05	.05	.05	.05	.05	.05	.05	.05	7
8	.10	.10	.10	.10	.10	.10	.10	.10	.10	.10	.10	.10	.10	.10	.10	.10	.10	.10	.10	.10	.10	.10	.10	8
9	.10	.10	.10	.10	.10	.10	.10	.10	.10	.10	.10	.10	.10		.10	.10	.10	.10	.10	.10	.10	.10	.10	9
10	.05	.05	.05	.05	.05	.05	.05	.05	.05	.05	.05	.05	.05	.05	.05	.05	.05	.05	.05	.05	.05	.05	.05	10
11	.20	.20	.20	.20	.20	.20	.20	.20	.20	.20	.20	.20	.20	.30									.10	11
12	.15	.15	.15	.15	.15	.15	.15	.15	.15	.15	.15	.15	.15					.10	.10	.10	.10	.10	.10	12
13	.10	.10	.10	.10	.10	.10	.10	.10	.10	.10		10	.10					.10	.10	.10	.10	.10	.10	13
14	.10	.10	.10	.10	.10	.10	.10	.10	.10	.10		.10	.10					.10	.10	.10	.10	.10	.10	14
15					.05	.05	.05	.05	.05	.05														15
16	.65	.85	1.00	1.00	1.20	1.20	1.20	1.65	2.35	2.85	3.00	1.65	1.50	1.30	.60	.60	.60	.40	.40	.40	.40	.40	.50	16
17															1.00	1.50	1.50	.20	.20	.20	.20	.20	.20	17

NO.	27	27½	28	29	30	31	32	33	34	35	36	37	51	113	602 " c	603 " c	604 " c	604½ " c	605 " c	605½ " c	606 " c	607 " c	608 " c	NO.
	$	$	$	$	$	$	$	$	$	$	$	$	$	$	$	$	$	$	$	$	$	$	$	
1A	0.45	0.47	0.48	0.48	0.48	0.48	0.50	0.50	0.50	0.42	0.48	0.50	0.48	0.38	0.35	0.38	0.42	0.48	0.42	0.47	0.48	0.48	0.50	1A
1	.27	.28	.29	.29	.29	.29	.32	.32	.32	.25	.29	.32	.29	.23	.21	.23	.25	.29	.25	.28	.29	.29	.32	1
2	18	.19	.19	.19	.19	.19	.18	.18	.18	.17	.19	.18	.19	.15	.14	.15	.17	.19	.17	.19	.19	.19	.18	2
3	.05	.05	.05	.05	.05	.05	.05	.05	.05	.05	.05	.05	.05	.05	.05	.05	.05	.05	.05	.05	.05	.05	.05	3
4	.20	.20	.20	.20	.20	.20	.20	.20	.20	.20	.20	.20	.25	.25	.30	.30	.30	.30	.30	.30	.30	.30	.30	4
5	.05	.05	.05	.05	.05	.05	.05	.05	.05	.05	.05	.05	.05	.05	.05	.05	.05	.05	.05	.05	.05	.05	.05	5
6	.30	.30	.30	.30	.30	.30	.30	.30	.30	.30	.30	.30	.35	.35	.50	.50	.50	.50	.50	.50	.50	.50	.50	6
7	.05	.05	.05	.05	.05	.05	.05	.05	.05	.05	.05	.05	.05	.05	.05	.05	.05	.05	.05	.05	.05	.05	.05	7
8	.10	.10	.10	.10	.10	.10	.10	.10	.10	.10	.10	.10	.10	.10	.10	.10	.10	.10	.10	.10	.10	.10	.10	8
9	.10	.10	.10	.10	.10	.10	.10	.10	.10	.10	10	10	.10	.10	.10	.10	.10	.10	.10	.10	.10	.10	.10	9
10	.05	.05	.05	.05	.05	.05	.05	.05	.05	.05	.05	.05	.05	.05	.05	.05	.05	.05	.05	.05	.05	.05	.05	10
11	.10	.10	10	.10	.10	.10	.10	.10	.10	.10	.10	.10	.20	.15	.20	.20	.20	.20	.20	.20	.20	.20	.20	11
12	.10	.10	.10	.10	.10	.10	.10	.10	.10	.10	.10	.10	.15		.15	.15	.15	.15	.15	.15	.15	.15	.15	12
13	.10	.10	.10	.10	.10	.10	.10	.10	.10	.10	.10	.10	10		.10	.10	.10	.10	.10	.10	.10	.10	.10	13
14	.10	.10	.10	.10	.10	.10	.10	.10	.10	.10	.10	.10	.10		.10	.10	.10	.10	.10	.10	.10	.10	.10	14
15													.05					.05	.05	.05	.05	.05	.05	15
16	.50	.50	.70	.70	.80	.80	.85	.85	.85	.40	.50	.70	3.00	.60	1.10	1.25	1.25	1.50	1.50	1.60	2.20	3.10	3.50	16
17	.20	.20	.20	.20	.20	.20	.20	.20	.20	.20	.20	.20		1.00										17

NO.	NAME OF PART	CODE	NO.	NAME OF PART	CODE	NO.	NAME OF PART	CODE
1A	DOUBLE CUTTER (DOUBLE IRON)	STAPARABAB	7	ENDWISE ADJUSTING LEVER	STAPARAFAC	15	PLANE HANDLE SCREW	STAPARAKAN
1	CUTTER (PLANE IRON)	STAPARABEC	8	" " " WHEEL	STAPARAFED	16	" BOTTOM	STAPARAKOS
2	" CAP (PLANE IRON CAP)	STAPARABID	9	LATERAL ADJUSTING LEVER	STAPARAFIF	17	" " TOP CASTINGS	STAPARAKUT
3	" " SCREW	STAPARABOF	10	SEAT SCREWS ("FROG") (EACH)	STAPARAFOG	18	DETACHABLE SIDE	STAPARALAX
3½	" BOLT AND NUT	STAPARABUG	11	PLANE HANDLE	STAPARAGAL	19	" " SCREWS (EACH)	STAPARALEZ
4	" LEVER CAP	STAPARACEL	12	" KNOB	STAPARAGEM	21	ECCENTRIC PLATE AND PIN	STAPARALOC
5	" " " SCREW	STAPARACIM	13	" HANDLE BOLT & HEAD	STAPARAGIN	22	" " KNOB	STAPARAMOL
6	" SEAT COMPLETE ("FROG")	STAPARACON	14	" KNOB " " "	STAPARAGUR			

ALWAYS GIVE PLANE NUMBER AND PART NUMBER, OR CODE FOR EACH, IN ORDERING PARTS

Parts of Stanley and "Bailey" Block and Miscellaneous Planes

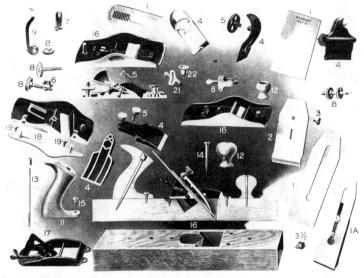

ILLUSTRATIONS OF PARTS OF BLOCK PLANES AND PLANES HAVING DOUBLE CUTTERS WITHOUT "BAILEY" STYLE OF CUTTER ADJUSTMENTS

Parts of Stanley and "Bailey" Block and Miscellaneous Planes

NO.	9½	9¾	12	12½	15	15½	16	17	18	19	40	40½	56	57	60	60½	62	65	65½	71	71½	72	72½	NO.
	$	$	$	$	$	$	$	$	$	$	$	$	$	$	$	$	$	$	$	$	$	$	$	
1	0.17	0.17	0.20	0.20	0.17	0.17	0.17	0.17	0.17	0.17	0.20	0.25	0.25	0.30	0.17	0.17	0.30	0.17	0.17	0.30	0.30	0.20	0.20	1
4	.10	.10	.25	.25	.10	.10	.15	.15	.20	.20	.10	.10	.15	.15	.15	.10	.15	.15	.10			.10	.10	4
5	.05	.05			.05	.05	.05	.05	.05	.05	.05	.05	.05	.05	.05	.05	.05	.05	.05			.05	.05	5
6			.60	.60																				6
7	.05	.05			.05	.05	.05	.05	.05	.05														7
8	.10	.10	.10	.10			.10	.10	.10	.10					.10	.10	.15	.10	.10					8
9	.10	.10					.10	.10	.10	.10														9
10																								10
11		.25	.35	.35		.25					.10	.10	.20	.10			.30			.15	.15	.30	.30	11
12											.10	.10	.10	.10			.15			.15	.15	.15	.15	12
13											.10	.10	.10	.10			.10					.10	.10	13
14			.05	.05							.10	.10	.10	.10			.10			.10	.10	.10	.10	14
15																								15
16	.70	.70	1.20	1.20	.75	.75	.70	.75	.70	.75	.70	1.00	1.00	2.50	.60	.60	1.75	.75	.75	1.00	1.00	1.50	1.50	16
21	.10	.10					.10	.10	.10	.10					.10	.10	.15	.10	.10					21
22	.10	.10					.10	.10	.10	.10					.10	.10	.25	.10	.10					22

NO.	74	85	97	100	101	102	103	104	105	110	112	120	122	127	129	130	131	132	135	140	220	340	NO.
	$	$	$	$	$	$	$	$	$	$	$	$	$	$	$	$	$	$	$	$	$	$	
1A	0.50							0.45	0.45				0.38	0.45	0.48				0.50	0.45			1A
1	.32	0.20	0.20	0.45	0.05	0.05	0.10	.10	.27	.27	0.13	0.20	.17	.23	.27	.29	0.13	0.17	.32	.27	0.20	0.17	0.30	1
2	.05							.18	.18				.15	.18	.19				.18	.18			2
3	.05							.05	.05				.05	.05	.05				.05	.05			3
3½								.05	.05				.05	.05	.05				.05	.05			3½
4	.30	.20	.20	.15	.05	.05	.10	.10	.10	.10	.20	.10	.10	.10	.10	.10	.10	.10	.10	.15	.10	.10	4
5				.05																.05	.05	.05	5
6		.30	.30					.10					.35	.15	.20	.20			.15	.20	.10	.10	6
7								.20	.20				.20	.20	.20								7
8														.10					.10	.10			8
10	1.00	.05	.05																				10
11		.25	.20	.15				.20	.20		.20			.10	.10			.10	.10	.15		.10	11
12		.20	.20					.15	.15	.10	.15	.10	.10	.10	.10		.10	.15	.10	.15	1.0	.10	12
13		.10	.10					.10	.10		.10			.10	.10							.10	13
14		.10	.10	.10				.10	.10													.10	14
15														.05	.05				.05	.03			15
16	2.20	1.00	.80	1.00	.10	.10	.15	.20	.85	1.35	.25	1.20	.30	.40	.45	.70	.35	.70	.85	.40	.75	.30	.80	16
17														.30	.30				.30	.30			17
18																			.25				18
19																			.10				19

NO.	NAME OF PART	NO.	NAME OF PART	NO.	NAME OF PART	NO.	NAME OF PART
1A	DOUBLE CUTTER (DOUBLE IRON)	5	CUTTER LEVER CAP SCREW	11	PLANE HANDLE	17	PLANE HANDLE TOP CASTINGS
1	CUTTER (PLANE IRON)	6	" SEAT COMPLETE ("FROG")	12	" KNOB	18	DETACHABLE SIDE
2	" CAP (PLANE IRON CAP)	7	ENDWISE ADJUSTING LEVER	13	" HANDLE BOLT & HEAD	19	" " SCREWS EACH
3	" " SCREW	8	" " WHEEL	14	" KNOB	21	ECCENTRIC PLATE AND PIN
3½	" BOLT AND NUT	9	LATERAL ADJUSTING LEVER	15	PLANE HANDLE SCREW	22	" " KNOB
4	" LEVER CAP	10	SEAT SCREWS ("FROG") (EACH)	16	" BOTTOM		

ALWAYS GIVE PLANE NUMBER AND PART NUMBER, OR CODE FOR EACH, IN ORDERING PARTS

Parts of Stanley Universal "55", Rabbet, Dado, Plow, Match Planes

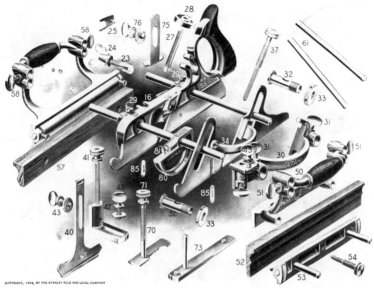

ILLUSTRATION OF PARTS OF STANLEY "UNIVERSAL" PLANE NO. 55 AND REPRESENTING ALL RABBET, DADO, PLOW AND SIMILAR PLANES

Parts of Stanley Universal "55", Rabbet, Dado, Plow, Match Planes

NO.	39	45	46	47	48	49	50	55	75	78	90	92	93	94	98	99	141	143	146	147	148	180 to 182	190 to 192	NO.
	$	$	$	$	$	$	$	$	$	$	$	$	$	$	$	$	$	$	$	$	$	$	$	
1	0.20	3.50	2.00	1.00	0.20	0.20	1.75	6.00			0.20	0.20	0.30	0.30	0.30	0.20	0.20	2.00	2.00	0.65	0.65	0.20	0.20	1
4	.10				.10	.10														.15	.15	.10	.10	4
16	1.20	2.50	2.50	2.50	2.00	2.00	1.25	3.00		.30	1.00	1.75	1.75	2.10	2.50		.60	.60	3.00	3.00	1.50	.75	.90	16
23		.15	.15	.15			.15	.15																23
24		.15	.15	.15			.15	.15																24
25		.05	.05	.05			.25	.25																25
27		.10						.10			.20	.20	.20	.20										27
28		.10						.10																28
29		.10	.10	.10				.10																29
30		1.50	1.50	1.50			.30	.75																30
32								.15																32
33								.15																33
34								1.25																34
37								.20																37
40								.30																40
41								.10																41
42								.30																42
50		.75	.75		.50	.50	.75	1.35		.25								1.00	1.00					50
52								.20																52
53								.40																53
54								.20																54
56								1.00																56
57								.20																57
60		.50	.50	.50			.50	.50									.50	.50						60
61		.25	.25	.25			.25	.25		.15														61
70	.20	.20	.20	.20			.20	.20		.20							.20	.20				.20	.20	70
71		.10						.10																71
73		.20						.30																73
75		.10	.10	.10				.10																75
76		.10	.10	.10				.10											.10	.10				76
80		.40						.40																80
81		.10						.10																81
85	.10	.05	.05	.05			.05	.05		.05													.05	85

THUMB SCREWS NOS. 3), 43, 51, AND 58, $0.10 EACH

NO.	NAME OF PART	CODE	NO.	NAME OF PART	CODE	NO.	NAME OF PART	CODE
1	CUTTER (* PER SET)	STAPARABAB	34	ADJUSTABLE BOTTOM	STAPAREBON	58	RIGHT FENCE THUMB SCREWS	STAPAREFIN
4	" CAP	STAPARACEL	37	" " SCREW	STAPAREBUR	60	LONG ARMS (PAIR)	STAPAREFUR
16	MAIN STOCK OR BOTTOM	STAPARAKOS	40	CENTRE BOTTOM	STAPARECAR	61	SHORT ARMS (PAIR)	STAPAREGAD
23	CUTTER BOLT	STAPARANIS	41	" " ADJUST. NUT	STAPARECES	70	ADJUST. DEPTH GAUGE	STAPAREGIG
24	" " WING NUT	STAPARANOT	42	ANGLE IRON & " SCREW	STAPARECIT	71	" " NUT	STAPAREGOL
25	" " CLIP AND SCREW	STAPARARAT	43	" " THUMB SCREW	STAPARECOX	73	" BEADING STOP	STAPAREGUM
27	" " ADJUST. SCREW	STAPARAREX	50	LEFT FENCE	STAPARECUZ	75	SLITTING CUTTER STOP	STAPARELAT
28	" " WHEEL	STAPARARIZ	51	" " THUMB SCREW	STAPAREDAC	76	THUMB SCREW	STAPARELEX
29	ARM SET SCREWS (EACH)	STAPARARUC	52	TILTING GUARD PLATE (WOOD)	STAPAREDED	80	CAM STOP	STAPARELIZ
30	SLIDING SECTION	STAPARASOR	53	" IRON WITH SWIVEL	STAPAREDIF	81	" " SET SCREW	STAPARELOB
31	THUMB SCREW	STAPARASUS	54	LEFT FENCE ADJUST. SCREW	STAPAREDOG	85	SPURS WITH SCREWS (EACH)	STAPARELUC
32	THIMBLE	STAPAREBEL	56	RIGHT FENCE	STAPAREFAL			
33	" CHECK NUT	STAPAREBIM	57	" " TILTING PLATE	STAPAREFEM			

ALWAYS GIVE PLANE NUMBER AND PART NUMBER, OR CODE FOR EACH, IN ORDERING PARTS

Stanley Mitre Boxes

COPYRIGHT, 1909, BY THE STANLEY RULE AND LEVEL COMPANY

ILLUSTRATION OF NO. 244 WITH BACK SAW AND SHOWING SEGMENT OF CIRCLE FIRMLY SUPPORTED BY STOCK GUIDE

Stanley Mitre Boxes

STANLEY MITRE BOXES are constructed on entirely novel lines and embody EXCLUSIVE and IMPORTANT FEATURES not to be found in any other Mitre Box. They are thoroughly mechanical in design, have all parts made by jig and template, and are INTERCHANGEABLE.

They are compact, strong and durable, are quickly and easily put together for ease in carrying, have the greatest strength with the least weight, and will do the WIDEST RANGE OF WORK of any Mitre Box made.

THE BACK AND FRAME, GRADUATED QUADRANT AND SWIVEL ARM BEARING are in one piece and accurately machined.

THE QUADRANT is accurately graduated in Degrees as well as being marked for cutting multi-sided pieces and will remain mathematically correct. Experience has shown this to be a more accurate and far superior form of construction to a built up or riveted frame.

THE LEGS which are detachable are so designed as to give great stability to the Box and being of Malleable Iron are UNBREAKABLE.

THE SWIVEL ARM is pivoted in the Frame and has a Bushing so fitted as to prevent any play of the parts. It is provided with a Taper Index Pin which engages in holes on the under side of the Quadrant at the commonly used Angles permitting the cutting of 4, 5, 6, 8, 12, and 24 Sided Pieces or by setting the Saw at 0 a Square Cut can be made. By merely releasing the Clamping Lever the Taper Index Pin enters the hole of the Quadrant.

THE INDEX PIN being TAPER is always tight in the hole and the position of the Swivel Arm is always held rigidly and correctly without any LOST MOTION, and remains true and tight, as any wear in the hole is compensated for by the Taper Pin. This form of construction is far superior and more accurate than the ordinary slotted form of Quadrant subject to wear.

THE INDEX SIGHT PLATE with fine hair line graduation at bottom of Front Saw Guide Upright enables the workman to swing the Swivel Arm accurately up to one of the Index Holes or to any Degree of Graduation on the Quadrant that is desired.

THE SWIVEL ARM can be set at any point between the Index Holes on the Graduated Quadrant merely by releasing the Clamping Lever, which AUTOMATICALLY locks it in the desired position. This feature is shown by the small sectional cut at the bottom of page 80.

THE CLAMPING LEVER under the front of the Swivel Arm may be held up by means of a swinging Thumb Lever, the workman can then swing the Saw or Swivel Arm to any line of the Quadrant, and by a slight movement of the Thumb Lever, the Clamping Lever is released and the Swivel Arm AUTOMATICALLY locked in any desired position.

A SECOND SOCKET in the Swivel Arm is provided in which the Front Saw Guide Upright can be placed, permitting the use of a short Saw or allowing a much longer stroke with the standard or regular Saw. By placing the Saw Guide Upright in the outer hole an extra wide range of work can be done with these boxes and they will then saw at an angle of 30 DEGREES and without using the Stock Guide.

By placing straight work against one of the Guides, instead of against the back of the Box, the MOST ACUTE ANGLES can be cut.

Stanley Mitre Boxes

COPYRIGHT, 1909, BY THE STANLEY RULE AND LEVEL COMPANY

ILLUSTRATION OF NO. 358 WITH SAW HELD ABOVE WORK AND IN THE ACT OF BEING TRIPPED. STOCK GUIDE USED AS LENGTH GAUGE

Stanley Mitre Boxes

THE SAW GUIDE UPRIGHTS are Steel Rods and carry the Saw Guide Cylinders in which the Saw Works. These Uprights, which are instantly removable, are adjustably set in the Swivel Arm, and are clamped by turning the Expanding Screw at the Base, and may be adjusted to hold the Saw WITHOUT SIDE PLAY, thus securing great accuracy in the working.

AUTOMATIC CATCHES at the top of the Saw Guides hold the Saw locked and CLEAR OF THE WORK when not in use, allowing the workman to use both hands in placing the work. By simply moving the Stop on the Saw against the Lever Trip, the FRONT CATCH is released and the Saw falls slightly pitched forward, automatically releasing the REAR CATCH without any NECESSITY for the workman TAKING HIS HAND FROM THE SAW or TOUCHING THE TRIP LEVER.

MOVABLE STOPS are attached to the Saw Uprights, which can be set so as to permit the Saw to cut only to the desired depth or to prevent cutting through the Base Board or on to the Metal Frame. A Spring, put on one Upright, cushions the Saw should it fall and also slightly lifts the Saw off the work when not pressed down.

A TIE BAR is provided at the top of the Uprights giving great rigidity. When it is necessary to place long work in the Box this Bar can be quickly removed by turning the thumb screws which secure it to the uprights.

STOCK GUIDES are fitted on the back of the Frame and are held by a Clamping Device, and may be used for holding the work or as a Length Gauge by Clamping the Guides on the Plate in the Board as shown by cut on opposite page. By using the Stock Guides, segments of circles or irregular forms may be held securely in the Box as shown by the cut on page 76. Mouldings the shape of which gives no support can be held firmly and always in the same position.

THE TWO ADJUSTABLE SPURS in the back of the Frame hold the work from slipping.

The NARROW OPENING in the Back of the Frame is specially adapted for sawing narrow work.

NO.	LENGTH	WIDTH BOARD	CAPACITY AT			SIZE SAW	PACKED		MITRE BOX ONLY		PACKED		MITRE BOX AND SAW		NO.
			RIGHT ANGLE	MITRE 45°	30 WITHOUT GUIDE		IN BOX	WT. LBS.	CODE	PRICE $	IN BOX	WT. LBS.	CODE	PRICE $	
240	18 IN.	4⅛ IN.	8¼ IN.	5½ IN.	3½ IN.	20x4 IN.	1	23	STAM ITASAL	9.50	1	28	STAM ITEGAL	10.50	240
242	18 "	4⅛ "	" "	" "	" "	22x4 "	1	23	STAMITASEM	9.50	1	28¼	STAMITEGEM	10.75	242
244	18 "	4⅛ "	" "	" "	" "	24x4 "	1	23	STAM ITASIN	9.50	1	28½	STAM ITEGIN	11.00	244
246	18 "	4⅛ "	" "	" "	" "	26x4 "	1	23	STAMITASOP	9.50	1	30	STAMITEGUR	11.25	246
346	20½ "	4½ "	9½ "	6½ "	4⅛ "	26x4 "	1	29	STAMITASUR	10.50	1	34	STAMITERAT	12.25	346
358	20½ "	4½ "	" "	" "	" "	28x5 "	1	29	STAMITATAR	10.75	1	36	STAMITEREX	13.00	358
460	24 "	5¾ "	11 "	7½ "	5⅛ "	30x6 "	1	42	STAMITATES	13.50	1	51	STAM ITERIZ	16.00	460

The Back Saws for the above Mitre Boxes are especially made by Henry Disston & Sons, Ltd.

Stanley Mitre Boxes

ILLUSTRATION OF NO. 50½ USING ORDINARY PANEL SAW

Stanley Mitre Boxes

STANLEY MITRE BOXES Nos. 50 and 50½ while not having all the refinements of the Mitre Boxes described on pages 77 and 79 are thoroughly strong and accurate tools at a moderate price.

The No. 50, designated as No. 60 when furnished with Back Saw, has long been favorably known and is now made with several improvements. The Roller Saw Guides always a feature in this Box are still retained.

The No. 50½, designated as No. 60½ when furnished with Back Saw, has a different form of Saw Guide.

THE BACK AND FRAME, INDEXED QUADRANT AND SWIVEL ARM BEARING are in one piece and accurately machined.

THE QUADRANT is accurately Indexed for cutting multi-sided pieces and will remain mathematically correct. Experience has shown this to be a more accurate and superior form of construction than a built up or riveted frame.

THE SWIVEL ARM is pivoted in the frame and has a Bushing so fitted as to prevent any play of the parts. It is provided with a Taper Index Pin which engages in the Indexed Holes on under side of Quadrant at the commonly used angles, permitting of the cutting of—4, 5, 6, 8, 12 and 24 sided pieces or by setting the Saw at 0 a square cut can be made. By merely releasing the Index Pin Lever the Taper Index Pin enters the desired Hole in the Quadrant.

THE SWIVEL ARM can be set at any point between the Index holes on the Quadrant by means of the Clamping Set Screw on the Swivel just back of the Front Saw Guide Upright.

THE SAW GUIDE UPRIGHTS are Steel Rods and carry the Saw Guides in which the Saw works. These Uprights which are instantly removable are adjustably set in the Swivel Arm, and are clamped by turning the Swivel Arm Set Screw and may be adjusted to hold the Saw without SIDE PLAY, thus securing great accuracy in working.

The special feature of these Boxes is that any ordinary PANEL SAW may be used in place of Back Saw if desired. To use the Panel Saw in the No. 50 it is only necessary to change the inserted plate which connects the Back Roller Saw Guides into the lower groove and then the blade of the Saw will be stiffly supported by both sets of Rollers and do the work of a Back Saw.

The No. 50½ is made with two small holes near the top of the Back Saw Guide and by putting a pin or nail through these a PANEL SAW can be used.

MOVABLE STOPS are attached to the Saw Guide Uprights which can be set so as to permit the Saw to cut only to the desired depth or to prevent cutting through the Base Board or on to the Metal Frame.

NO.	LENGTH	WIDTH BOARD	CAPACITY AT		SIZE SAW	PACKED		MITRE BOX ONLY		PACKED		MITRE BOX AND SAW		NO.
			RIGHT ANGLE	MITRE 45		IN BOX	WT. LBS.	CODE	PRICE $	IN BOX	WT. LBS.	CODE	PRICE $	
50	18 IN.	4 IN.	7¼ IN.	4¾ IN.		1	20	STAMITABOX	7.00					50
50½	18 "	" "	" "	" "		1	20	STAMITABUZ	6.50					50½
60	18 "	" "	" "	" "	20 x 4 IN.					1	25	STAMITECEL	10.00	60
60½	18 "	" "	" "	" "	20 x 4 IN.					1	25	STAMITECON	9.50	60½

Parts of Stanley Mitre Boxes

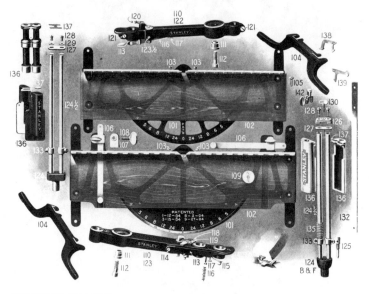

ILLUSTRATIONS **OF PARTS OF MITRE BOXES**

Parts of Stanley Mitre Boxes

NO.	NAME OF PART	NUMBER OF MITRE BOX									CODE	NO.
		50	50½	240	242	244	246	346	358	460		
		$	$	$	$	$	$	$	$	$		
101	FRAME	3.00	3.00	3.50	3.50	3.50	3.50	4.20	4.20	5.60	STAMOTICEL	101
102	,, BOARD	.30	.30	.30	.30	.30	.30		.30	.50	STAMOTICIM	102
103	,, BACK SPUR	.05	.05	.05	.05	.05	.05	.05	.05	.05	STAMOTICON	103
104	,, LEG	.30	.30	.30	.30	.30	.30	.35	.35	.40	STAMOTICUP	104
105	,, ,, SCREW	.05	.05	.05	.05	.05	.05	.05	.05	.05	STAMOTIDAR	105
106	STOCK GUIDE			.25	.25	.25	.25	.25	.25	.25	STAMOTIDES	106
107	,, ,, CLAMP			.05	.05	.05	.05	.05	.05	.05	STAMOTIDIT	107
108	,, ,, ,, THUMB SCREW			.10	.10	.10	.10	.10	.10	.10	STAMOTIDOX	108
109	,, ,, PLATE			.05	.05	.05	.05	.05	.05	.05	STAMOTIDUZ	109
110	SWIVEL ARM	.75	.75	1.25	1.25	1.25	1.25	1.40	1.40	1.65	STAMOTIFAC	110
111	,, ,, BUSHING	.15	.15	.15	.15	.15	.15	.15	.15	.15	STAMOTIFED	111
112	,, ,, ,, SCREW	.15	.15	.15	.15	.15	.15	.15	.15	.15	STAMOTIFIF	112
113	INDEX CLAMPING LEVER	.10	.10	.20	.20	.20	.20	.20	.20	.25	STAMOTIFOG	113
114	,, ,, ,, FULCRUM SCREW			.05	.05	.05	.05	.05	.05	.05	STAMOTIKAN	114
115	,, ,, ,, CATCH OR LOCK			.05	.05	.05	.05	.05	.05	.05	STAMOTIKOS	115
116	,, ,, ,, SPRING			.05	.05	.05	.05	.05	.05	.05	STAMOTIKUT	116
117	,, ,, ,, SCREW			.05	.05	.05	.05	.05	.05	.05	STAMOTILAX	117
118	SWIVEL ARM SIGHT PLATE			.10	.10	.10	.10	.10	.10	.10	STAMOTILEZ	118
119	,, ,, ,, SCREW			.05	.05	.05	.05	.05	.05	.05	STAMOTILOC	119
120	,, ,, POSITION SCREW	.05	.05								STAMOTIMOL	120
121	,, ,, CLAMP ,,	.05	.05								STAMOTIMUN	121
122	,, ,, COMPLETE FOR NOS. 50 AND 50½	1.00	1.00								STAMOTINER	122
123	,, ,, ,, ,, 240 TO 460			2.50	2.50	2.50	2.50	2.75	2.75	3.00	STAMOTINIS	123
123½	,, ,, INDEX BUSHING SET SCREW	.05	.05								STAMOTINOT	123½
124	SAW GUIDE "T" BASE	.25	.25								STAMOTIPIL	124
124B	,, ,, ,, (BACK)			.50	.50	.50	.50	.50	.50	.50	STAMOTIPOM	124B
124F	,, ,, ,, (FRONT)			.50	.50	.50	.50	.50	.50	.50	STAMOTISAG	124F
124½	,, ,, UPRIGHTS (EACH)	.15	.15	.20	.20	.20	.20			.25	STAMOTISOR	124½
125	,, ,, "T" BASE EXPANDING SCREW			.10	.10	.10	.10	.10	.10	.10	STAMOTISUS	125
126	,, ,, UPRIGHT CAP			.05	.05	.05	.05	.05	.05	.05	STAMOTOCAR	126
127	,, ,, ,, PLATE	.05	.05	.05	.05	.05	.05	.05	.05	.05	STAMOTOCES	127
128	,, ,, ,, ,, SCREW	.05	.05	.05	.05	.05	.05	.05	.05	.05	STAMOTOCIT	128
129	,, ,, ,, ,, WASHER	.05	.05	.05	.05	.05	.05	.05	.05	.05	STAMOTOCOX	129
130	,, ,, ,, ,, THUMB			.05	.05	.05	.05	.05	.05		STAMOTOCUS	130
132	,, ,, TIE BAR			.10	.10	.10	.10	.10	.15	.15	STAMOTODAC	132
133	,, ,, STOP AND SCREW	.15	.15	.15	.15	.15	.15	.15	.15	.15	STAMOTODED	133
135	,, ,, LIFTING SPRING			.05	.05	.05	.05	.05	.05	.05	STAMOTODIF	135
136	,, ,, CYLINDER (EACH)	.75	.25	.35	.35	.35	.35	.35	.35		STAMOTODOG	136
137	,, ,, ,, INSERTED PLATE	.05	.05	.05	.05	.05	.05	.05	.05	.05	STAMOTOFAL	137
138	,, ,, ,, TRIP LEVER BACK			.15	.15	.15	.15	.15	.15	.15	STAMOTOFEM	138
139	,, ,, ,, ,, FRONT			.15	.15	.15	.15	.15	.15	.15	STAMOTOFIN	139
142	,, TRIP CLAMP AND THUMB SCREW			.15	.15	.15	.15	.15	.15	.15	STAMOTOFUR	142

ALWAYS GIVE MITRE BOX NUMBER AND PART NUMBER, OR CODE FOR EACH, IN ORDERING PARTS

Stanley Concealed Ratchet Bit Braces

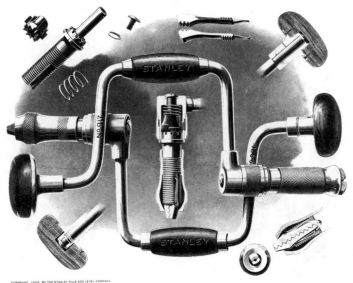

COPYRIGHT, 1909, BY THE STANLEY RULE AND LEVEL COMPANY

ILLUSTRATIONS OF NOS. 917 AND 921 WITH VARIOUS DETAILS

Stanley Concealed Ratchet Bit Braces

STANLEY CONCEALED RATCHET BIT BRACES are of the highest quality as regards workmanship, material and finish and embody improvements and refinements in mechanical construction not previously contained in any Bit Brace.

The Ratchet Gear and the Cam Sleeve, which actuates the Clutch, are in line with the Bit, which makes it more convenient in handling than where the Cam Sleeve is at right angles, have no projections to hurt the hand and present a neat appearance. There is a complete protection for the working mechanism and it is always free from dirt, grit, and moisture, and retains oil for a long time. Further this construction permits of a larger and longer Spindle Bearing than any other form of Ratchet Bit Brace on the market, and consequently better wearing qualities.

The Ratchet Gear is made of steel one inch in diameter, hardened, driven on, and securely pinned to the Spindle, forming the Main Spindle Bearing.

The two-piece Clutch is made of steel forgings, machined and hardened. FIVE teeth are in engagement when working as a Ratchet, as against ONE tooth in other forms of Ratchet. The Clutch being backed up by a large spiral spring makes a very strong lock.

The Chuck Body Screw is of steel, and by removing this, the whole Ratchet mechanism may be taken apart. The parts are interchangeable, and may be replaced or reassembled with little trouble.

The Jaws are drop forgings, machined and hardened and the recesses in the Chuck Body for the Jaws are also machined.

Nos. 911 and 921 have the Alligator pattern of Jaws and the No. 917 Braces have the Interlocking pattern of Jaws which are interlocked in machined recesses in the Chuck Body which hold them laterally.

All these Braces have Cocobolo Heads and Handles and Ball Bearings in the Heads.

NO.	SWEEP	TYPE OF RATCHET	FINISH OF BRACE	JAWS FORGED STEEL	SPINDLE AND CHUCK BODY	HANDLE AND HEAD	HEAD		PACKED		CODE	PRICE DOZ. $	NO.
							TRIM	BEARING	IN BOX	WT. LBS.			
911	6 IN.	CONCEALED	NICKEL	ALLIGATOR	ONE PIECE	COCOBOLO	METAL CLAD	BALL	2	5½	STABITABAB	24.00	6–911
"	8 "	"	"	"	"	"	"	"	2	5¾	STABITABEC	26.00	8– "
"	10 "	"	"	"	"	"	"	"	2	6½	STABITABID	28.00	10– "
"	12 "	"	"	"	"	"	"	"	2	6¾	STABITABOF	30.00	12– "
"	14 "	"	"	"	"	"	"	"	2	7	STABITABUG	32.00	14– "
917	6 IN.	"	"	INTERLOCKING	"	"	"	"	2	5	STABITAHAS	26.40	6–917
"	8 "	"	"	"	"	"	"	"	2	5½	STABITAHET	28.80	8– "
"	10 "	"	"	"	"	"	"	"	2	6	STABITAHIX	31.20	10– "
"	12 "	"	"	"	"	"	"	"	2	6½	STABITAHOZ	33.60	12– "
"	14 "	"	"	"	"	"	"	"	2	7	STABITAHUB	36.00	14– "
921	6 IN.	"	"	ALLIGATOR	"	"	METAL QUILL	"	2	5¼	STABITARAT	22.00	6–921
"	8 "	"	"	"	"	"	"	"	2	5½	STABITAREX	24.00	8– "
"	10 "	"	"	"	"	"	"	"	2	6¼	STABITARIZ	26.00	10– "
"	12 "	"	"	"	"	"	"	"	2	6½	STABITAROB	28.00	12– "
"	14 "	"	"	"	"	"	"	"	2	7	STABITARUC	30.00	14– "

Stanley Box Ratchet Bit Braces

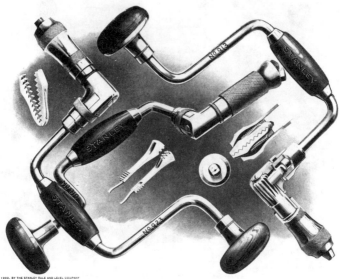

COPYRIGHT, 1909, BY THE STANLEY RULE AND LEVEL COMPANY

ILLUSTRATIONS OF NOS. 913, 919, AND 923 WITH VARIOUS DETAILS

Stanley Box Ratchet Bit Braces

STANLEY BOX RATCHET BIT BRACES are of the highest quality as regards workmanship, material and finish. They are what might be termed the most improved form of manufacture of that style of Ratchet Brace, where the Ratchet Gear is on the Spindle and the Ratchet Pawls are set at Right Angles to the Gear, and really forming a part of the Sweep.

The Ratchet Gear teeth are cut on the Spindle which is made extra large and specially strong.

The Gear Teeth are encased, although the Pawls are necessarily exposed in this form of construction, as shown by the cuts opposite. This feature guards the user's hands from the teeth and prevents dust or dirt from clogging the Gear.

The Chuck Body and Spindle are made of one piece turned out of solid steel which is far superior to a malleable Iron Chuck Body with a wire Spindle fastened to it.

The Chuck Body Screw is of steel and by removing this the whole Ratchet mechanism may be taken apart. The parts are interchangeable and may be replaced or reassembled with little trouble.

The Jaws are drop forgings, machined and hardened and the recesses in the Chuck Body for the Jaws are also machined.

Nos. 913 and 923 have the Alligator pattern of Jaws and the No. 919 Braces have the Interlocking pattern of Jaws which are interlocked in machined recesses in the Chuck Body which hold them laterally.

All these Braces have Cocobolo Heads and Handles and Ball Bearings in the Heads.

NO.	SWEEP	RATCHET	FINISH OF BRACE	JAWS FORGED STEEL	SPINDLE AND CHUCK BODY	HANDLE AND HEAD	HEAD		PACKED		CODE	PRICE DOZ. $	NO.
							TRIM	BEARING	IN BOX	WT. LBS.			
913	6 IN.	ENCASED	NICKEL	ALLIGATOR	ONE PIECE	COCOBOLO	METAL CLAD	BALL	2	5¼	STABITACAH	22.00	6–913
"	8 "	"	"	"	"	"	"	"	2	5½	STABITACEL	24.00	8– "
"	10 "	"	"	"	"	"	"	"	2	6½	STABITACIM	26.00	10– "
"	12 "	"	"	"	"	"	"	"	2	6¾	STABITACON	28.00	12– "
"	14 "	"	"	"	"	"	"	"	2	7	STABITACUP	30.00	14– "
919	6 IN.	"	"	INTERLOCKING	"	"	"	"	6	16	STABITALAX	22.80	6–919
"	8 "	"	"	"	"	"	"	"	6	17	STABITALEZ	24.00	8– "
"	10 "	"	"	"	"	"	"	"	6	18	STABITALIB	27.00	10– "
"	12 "	"	"	"	"	"	"	"	6	20	STABITALOC	30.00	12– "
"	14 "	"	"	"	"	"	"	"	6	21	STABITALUD	33.00	14– "
923	6 IN.	"	"	ALLIGATOR	"	"	METAL QUILL	"	2	5¼	STABITATAV	20.00	6–923
"	8 "	"	"	"	"	"	"	"	2	5½	STABITATEW	22.00	8– "
"	10 "	"	"	"	"	"	"	"	2	6	STABITATIC	24.00	10– "
"	12 "	"	"	"	"	"	"	"	2	6½	STABITATOD	26.00	12– "
"	14 "	"	"	"	"	"	"	"	2	6¾	STABITATUF	28.00	14– "

Stanley Non-Ratchet or Sleeve Bit Braces

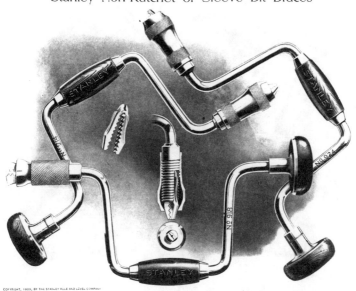

COPYRIGHT, 1909, BY THE STANLEY RULE AND LEVEL COMPANY

ILLUSTRATIONS OF NOS. 914, 918, AND 924 WITH VARIOUS DETAILS

Stanley Non-Ratchet or Sleeve Bit Braces

STANLEY NON-RATCHET OR SLEEVE BIT BRACES are Nickel Plated throughout and are of the best quality as regards workmanship, material and finish.

There is one important feature of all Stanley Bit Braces to which we call particular attention; namely, that the Chuck Body is turned out of Solid Steel, which is far superior to a Malleable Chuck Body.

It can readily be appreciated that making this part of steel adds greatly to the strength of the Brace. Furthermore making the Chuck Body of Steel allows the cutting of a much better thread with which the thread of the Shell is to engage.

Two styles of Shells or Sleeves and Jaws are used in this line of Bit Braces. No. 914 and No. 924 have the Alligator pattern of Jaws drop forged, machined and hardened.

Braces No. 918 have the Interlocking pattern of Jaws of hardened Steel which are interlocked in the recesses of the Sleeves and hold them laterally.

The recesses in the Chuck Body for receiving the Jaws are accurately machined, as are the Jaws themselves.

The Heads are made of polished Cocobolo, and are Metal Clad in Braces No. 918 and 914 and with Metal Quill in Braces No. 924.

All these Braces have Cocobolo Heads and Handles and Ball Bearings in the Head.

NO.	SWEEP	TYPE OF BRACE	FINISH OF BRACE	JAWS FORGED STEEL	CHUCK BODY	HANDLE AND HEAD	HEAD		PACKED		CODE	PRICE DOZ. $	NO.
							TRIM	BEARING	IN BOX	WT. LBS.			
914	6 IN.	NON-RATCHET	NICKEL	ALLIGATOR	STEEL	COCOBOLO	METAL CLAD	BALL	2	4¼	STABITADAR	17.00	6"914
"	8 "	"	"	"	"	"	" "	"	2	4½	STABITADES	18.00	8"—"
"	10 "	"	"	"	"	"	" "	"	2	5¼	STABITADIT	20.00	10"—"
"	12 "	"	"	"	"	"	" "	"	2	5¾	STABITADOX	22.00	12"—"
"	14 "	"	"	"	"	"	" "	"	2	6	STABITADUZ	24.00	14"—"
918	6 IN.	"	"	INTERLOCKING	"	"	" "	"	6	13	STABITAJAD	17.40	6"918
"	8 "	"	"	"	"	"	" "	"	6	14	STABITAJEF	18.00	8"—"
"	10 "	"	"	"	"	"	" "	"	6	16	STABITAJIG	21.00	10"—"
"	12 "	"	"	"	"	"	" "	"	6	17	STABITAJOL	24.00	12"—"
"	14 "	"	"	"	"	"	" "	"	6	18	STABITAJUM	27.00	14"—"
924	6 IN.	"	"	ALLIGATOR	"	"	METAL QUILL	"	2	4	STABITAZAL	15.00	6"924
"	8 "	"	"	"	"	"	" "	"	2	4½	STABITAZEM	16.00	8"—"
"	10 "	"	"	"	"	"	" "	"	2	5¼	STABITAZIN	18.00	10"—"
"	12 "	"	"	"	"	"	" "	"	2	5¾	STABITAZOP	20.00	12"—"
"	14 "	"	"	"	"	"	" "	"	2	6	STABITAZUR	22.00	14"—"

Stanley "Victor" Ratchet Bit Braces

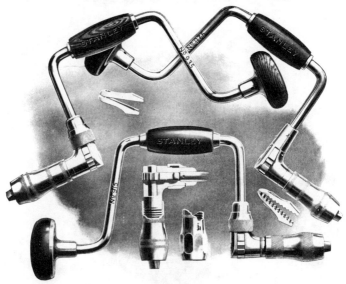

COPYRIGHT, 1909, BY THE STANLEY RULE AND LEVEL COMPANY   ILLUSTRATIONS OF NOS. 915, 935 AND 975 WITH VARIOUS DETAILS

Stanley "Victor" Ratchet Bit Braces

"VICTOR" RATCHET BIT BRACES are Nickel Plated throughout in Braces Nos. 915, 935, and 945, and polished in Nos. 955, and 965 and all are of high quality as regards workmanship, materials and finish.

The Ratchet Gear is on the Spindle and is the style of Ratchet most commonly used, that is, with the Ratchet Gear fastened to the Spindle by a pin and with both Pawl and Gear exposed, and while a good and serviceable Brace, has not the advantages of the Ratchet Gears shown on pages 84 and 86.

The Chuck Body and Spindle are one piece turned out of Solid Steel, which is far superior to a Malleable Chuck Body with a wire Spindle fastened to it and the recesses for receiving the Jaws are accurately machined.

The Jaws are of hardened Steel of the Alligator pattern on the No. 915 Line and of the Plain pattern on the other lines.

The Shells are made of the Round or Octagonal pattern as shown on the cuts opposite.

For a moderate price Brace, the "Victor" is strongly recommended as regards working qualities, strength, design and general finish, and will be found superior to Braces of other manufacture sold at a like price.

NO.	SWEEP	TYPE OF BRACE	FINISH OF BRACE	JAWS STEEL	SPINDLE AND CHUCK BODY	HANDLE AND HEAD	HEAD		PACKED		CODE	PRICE DOZ. $	NO.
							TRIM	BEARING	IN BOX	WT. LBS.			
915	8 IN.	RATCHET	NICKEL	ALLIGATOR	ONE PIECE	EBONITE	METAL CLAD	PLAIN	6	15	STABITAFAC	16.80	8-915
"	10 "	"	"	"	" "	"	" "	"	6	16	STABITAFED	17.40	10" "
"	12 "	"	"	"	" "	"	" "	"	6	18	STABITAFOG	18.00	12" "
"	14 "	"	"	"	" "	"	" "	"	6	20	STABITAFUZ	18.60	14" "
935	8 IN.	"	"	PLAIN	" "	COCOBOLO	METAL QUILL	"	6	13½	STABITEKAN	15.25	8-935
"	10 "	"	"	"	" "	"	" "	"	6	14½	STABITEKOS	16.00	10" "
"	12 "	"	"	"	" "	"	" "	"	6	16½	STABITEKUT	16.75	12" "
945	8 IN.	"	"	"	" "	HARDWOOD	" "	"	6	13	STABITENIS	13.00	8-945
"	10 "	"	"	"	" "	"	" "	"	6	14½	STABITENOT	13.75	10" "
"	12 "	"	"	"	" "	"	" "	"	6	16	STABITENUV	14.50	12" "
955	8 IN.	"	POLISHED	"	" "	"	" "	"	6	13	STABITESAG	11.75	8-955
"	10 "	"	"	"	" "	"	" "	"	6	14	STABITESOR	12.50	10" "
"	12 "	"	"	"	" "	"	" "	"	6	15½	STABITESUS	13.25	12" "
965	8 IN.	"	"	"	" "	"	WOODEN QUILL	"	6	12	STABITEWAL	10.25	8-965
"	10 "	"	"	"	" "	"	" "	"	6	13½	STABITEWIN	11.00	10" "
"	12 "	"	"	"	" "	"	" "	"	6	15	STABITEWUR	11.75	12" "
975	8 IN.	"	"	"	" "	"	METAL QUILL	"	6	13	STABITOGAC	8.40	8-975
"	10 "	"	"	"	" "	"	" "	"	6	15	STABITOGED	9.60	10" "
"	12 "	"	"	"	" "	"	" "	"	6	16	STABITOGOG	11.40	12" "

Round Shells are supplied regularly but the Octagonal form is furnished when so ordered.

Stanley "Victor" Non-Ratchet or Sleeve Bit Braces

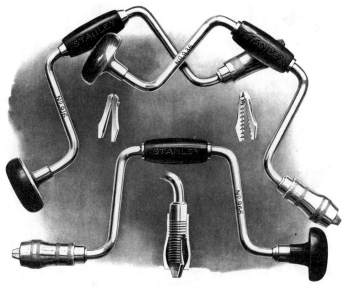

COPYRIGHT, 1909, BY THE STANLEY RULE AND LEVEL COMPANY

ILLUSTRATIONS OF NOS. 916, 936 AND 966 WITH VARIOUS DETAILS

Stanley "Victor" Non-Ratchet or Sleeve Bit Braces

"VICTOR" NON-RATCHET or SLEEVE BRACES are of high quality as regards workmanship, materials and finish.

The Chuck Body is turned out of Solid Steel which is far superior to a Malleable Chuck Body and the recesses for receiving the Jaws are accurately machined.

The Jaws are of hardened Steel of the Alligator pattern on the No. 916 line and the Plain pattern on the other lines.

The Shells are made of the Round or Octagonal pattern as shown on the cuts opposite.

The Heads are made of Cocobolo, highly polished on the No. 936 line of Braces, and of Hardwood, stained, on the other numbers. The No. 966 line of Braces which have a Head with Wooden Quill. The other numbers have the regular form of Head with Metal Quill.

For a cheap Brace, this line of "Victor" Braces is strongly recommended as regards working qualities, strength, design and general finish and will be found superior to Braces of other manufacture sold at a like price.

NO.	SWEEP	TYPE OF BRACE	FINISH OF BRACE	JAWS STEEL	CHUCK BODY	HANDLE AND HEAD	HEAD TRIM	HEAD BEARING	PACKED IN BOX	PACKED WT. LBS.	CODE	PRICE DOZ. $	NO.
916	8 IN.	NON-RATCHET	NICKEL	ALLIGATOR	STEEL	EBONITE	METAL CLAD	PLAIN	6	12	STABITAGAL	10.80	8″-916
″	10 ″	″	″	″	″	″	″ ″	″	6	14	STABITAGEM	11.40	10″ ″
″	12 ″	″	″	″	″	″	″ ″	″	6	16	STABITAGIN	12.00	12″ ″
″	14 ″	″	″	″	″	″	″ ″	″	6	18	STABITAGOT	12.60	14″ ″
936	8 IN.	″	″	PLAIN	″	COCOBOLO	METAL QUILL	″	6	11	STABITEMEG	9.50	8″-936
″	10 ″	″	″	″	″	″	″ ″	″	6	12½	STABITEMOL	10.25	10″ ″
″	12 ″	″	″	″	″	″	″ ″	″	6	14½	STABITEMUN	11.00	12″ ″
946	8 IN.	″	″	″	″	HARDWOOD	″ ″	″	6	10½	STABITEPAZ	7.25	8″-946
″	10 ″	″	″	″	″	″	″ ″	″	6	12	STABITEPIL	8.00	10″ ″
″	12 ″	″	″	″	″	″	″ ″	″	6	14	STABITEPOM	8.75	12″ ″
956	8 IN.	″	POLISHED	″	″	″	″ ″	″	6	10	STABITEVAM	6.00	8″-956
″	10 ″	″	″	″	″	″	″ ″	″	6	12	STABITEVEN	6.75	10″ ″
″	12 ″	″	″	″	″	″	″ ″	″	6	14	STABITEVIA	7.50	12″ ″
966	8 IN.	″	″	″	″	″	WOODEN QUILL	″	6	10	STABITODAR	4.75	8″-966
″	10 ″	″	″	″	″	″	″ ″	″	6	11	STABITODES	5.25	10″ ″
″	12 ″	″	″	″	″	″	″ ″	″	6	12½	STABITODOX	6.00	12″ ″
976	8 IN.	″	″	″	″	″	METAL QUILL	″	6	10	STABITOLAL	6.00	8″-976
″	10 ″	″	″	″	″	″	″ ″	″	6	12	STABITOLIN	6.60	10″ ″
″	12 ″	″	″	″	″	″	″ ″	″	6	14	STABITOLUR	7.20	12″ ″

Round Shells are supplied regularly but the Octagonal form is furnished when so ordered.

Parts of Stanley and "Victor" Bit Braces

ILLUSTRATIONS OF PARTS OF BIT BRACES

Parts of Stanley and "Victor" Bit Braces

NO	STANLEY BIT BRACES									"VICTOR" BIT BRACES												NO.
	911	913	914	917	918	919	921	923	924	915	916	935	936	945	946	955	956	965	966	975	976	
	$	$	$	$	$	$	$	$	$	$	$	$	$	$	$	$	$	$	$	$	$	
401	0.35	0.40	0.25	*	*	*	0.35	0.40	0.35	0.25	0.25	0.20	0.25	0.20	0.25	0.20	0.25	0.20	0.25	0.20	0.20	401
402	.10	.10		.10			.10	.10	.10													402
403	.05	.05				.05	.05	.05														403
404	.40	.40	.40				.40	.40	.40	.35	.35	.30	.30	.30	.30	.25	.25	.25	.25	.25	.25	404
405				*	*	*						.35	.35	.35	.30	.30	.30	.30	.30	.30	.30	405
406				*	*	*																406
407	.25			.25			.25					.35	.35	.35	.30	.30	.30	.30	.30	.30	.30	407
408		.15						.15		.15	.15	.15		.15		.15		.15				408
409	.40		.40				.40															409
410		.20				.20	.20	.20		.15	.15	.15		.15		.15		.15				410
411	.10	.05		.10		.05	.10	.05		.05	.05	.05		.05		.05		.05				411
413	.25		.25				.25															413
414		*				*		*					*		*		*		*		*	414
415½		.05						.05		.05												415½
416	.30	.30	.30			.30	.30	.30	.30	.30	.30											416
417				.30	.30	.30																417
418												.20	.20	.20	.20	.20		.20		.20	.20	418
419	*	*		*		*	*	*		*	*		*		*		*		*			419
420— 6"	*	*	*	*	*	*	*	*	*	*	*		*		*		*		*			420— 6"
420— 8"	*	*	*	*	*	*	*	*	*	*	*		*		*		*		*			420— 8"
420—10"	*	*	*	*	*	*	*	*	*	*	*	*	*	*	*	*	*	*	*	*	*	420—10"
420—12"	*	*	*	*	*	*	*	*	*	*	*	*	*	*	*	*	*	*	*	*	*	420—12"
420—14"	*	*	*	*	*	*	*	*	*	*	*	*	*	*	*	*	*	*	*	*	*	420—14"
425	.05	.05	.05	.05	.05	.05	.05	.05	.05	.05	.05	.05	.05	.05	.05	.05	.05			.05	.05	425
427	.05	.05	.05	.05	.05	.05	.05	.05	.05													427
428	.10	.10	.10	.10	.10	.10	.10	.10	.10													428
430	.35	.35	.35	.35	.35	.35	.35	.35	.35	.15	.15	.35	.35	.15	.15	.15	.15			.15	.15	430
431																		.20	.20			431
432	.45	.45	.45	.45	.45	.45				.40	.40											432
433							.30	.30	.30			.20	.20	.20	.20	.15	.15			.15	.15	433

+ SPECIAL PRICES QUOTED ONLY ON APPLICATION

NO.	NAME OF PART	CODE	NO.	NAME OF PART	CODE	NO.	NAME OF PART	CODE
401	CHUCK BODY	STABORACEL	413	CAM AND SLEEVE	STABORAKAN	420	14" SWEEP	STABORANER
402	" " SCREW	STABORACIM	414	" RING	STABORAKIR	425	QUILL WASHER	STABORANIS
403	" " "D" WASHER	STABORACON	415	CHUCK BODY COLLAR	STABORAKOS	426	BALL BEARING BALL CUP	STABORANOT
404	SHELL ROUND	STABORACUP	415½	" " WASHER	STABORAKUT	427	" " PLATE	STABORARAT
405	" CYLINDRICAL	STABORAFAC	416	ALLIGATOR JAWS	STABORALAX	428	BALLS PER SET	STABORAREX
406	" OCTAGONAL	STABORAFED	417	INTERLOCKING JAWS	STABORALEZ	430	HEAD	STABORAROB
407	CLUTCH GEAR WITH PIN	STABORAFIT	418	PLAIN JAWS	STABORALIB	431	" WITH WOODEN QUILL	STABORARUC
408	RATCHET " " "	STABORAFOG	419	RATCHET END	STABORALUD	432	METAL CLAD QUILL	STABORASAG
409	CLUTCH	STABORAGAL	420	6" SWEEP	STABORAMAF	433	" QUILL	STABORASUS
410	PAWL WITH PIN	STABORAGEM	420	8" "	STABORAMEG			
411	" OR CLUTCH SPRING	STABORAGIN	420	10" "	STABORAMOL			
412	" PIN	STABORAGUR	420	12" "	STABORAMUN			

ALWAYS GIVE BIT BRACE NUMBER AND PART NUMBER, OR CODE FOR EACH, IN ORDERING PARTS

Stanley Bit Gauge, Center Punches, Nail Sets, Bit Brace Tools

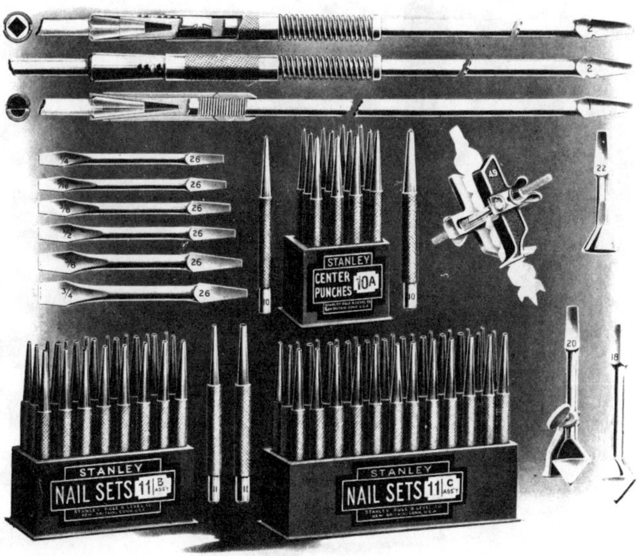

COPYRIGHT, 1909, BY THE STANLEY RULE AND LEVEL COMPANY

ILLUSTRATIONS OF NOS. 1, 2, 10, 10A, 11, 11B, 11C, 18, 20, 22, 26 AND 49

Stanley Bit Gauge, Center Punches, Nail Sets, Bit Brace Tools

The STANLEY ADJUSTABLE BIT GAUGE No. 49 will bore any number of holes to a given depth and can be attached to any size of Bit up to 1 inch. The stop being on both sides does not break the Bit or bend the Worm.

STANLEY EXTENSION BIT HOLDERS enable the user to bore through Walls, Floors, etc., where an ordinary Bit will not reach, and any length or combination will follow up a 5/8-inch Bit. The Holder is lipped to hold the Bit in withdrawing.

THE NO. 1 (Foss Patent) has the Jaw and Shank in one piece of steel and the Bit is clamped by screwing up the Nut.

THE NO. 2, A GREAT TIME SAVER, has a Square Socket which receives the Square Shank of the Bit and by compressing the Spring the Jaws open, instantly closing when the Spring is released. The Jaws are adjustable and will fit any ordinary Bit.

STANLEY CENTER PUNCHES, NAIL SETS and SCREW DRIVER BITS are oil tempered and fully guaranteed.

"WHEELER" WOOD COUNTERSINKS are suitable for every variety of wood screws. No. 20 is fitted with a Gauge.

NO.	LENGTH	MATERIAL	FINISH	USED ON BITS	SPECIAL USE	PACKED IN BOX	PACKED WT. LBS.	CODE	PRICE DOZ. $	NO.
49	2 1/2 IN.	SPEC. IRON	NICKEL	UP TO 1 IN.	TO BORE HOLES OF UNIFORM DEPTH	6	3/8	STABOTAGAG	7.20	49

NO	LENGTH	TIP	PACKED IN BOX	PACKED WT. LBS.	CODE	PRICE DOZ. $	NO.	NO.	LENGTH	TIP	PACKED IN BOX	PACKED WT. LBS.	CODE	PRICE DOZ. $	NO.
No.1 Extension Bit Holders								No.2 Extension Bit Holders							
1	12 IN.	9/16 IN.	6	2 7/8	STABOTABEL	13.75	12"—1	2	12 IN.	9/16 IN.	6	2 7/8	STABOTAKAN	13.75	12"—2
1	16 "	"	6	3 1/2	STABOTABIM	13.75	16"—1	2	16 "	"	6	3 1/2	STABOTAKER	13.75	16"—2
1	18 "	"	6	4	STABOTABON	15.25	18"—1	2	18 "	"	6	4	STABOTAKIS	15.25	18"—2
1	20 "	"	6	4 3/8	STABOTABUR	15.25	20"—1	2	20 "	"	6	4 3/8	STABOTAKOT	15.25	20"—2
1	24 "	"	6	5 1/4	STABOTACAC	17.50	24"—1	2	24 "	"	6	5 1/4	STABOTASEX	17.50	24"—2
1	30 "	"	6	6 3/8	STABOTACOG	20.50	30"—1	2	30 "	"	6	6 3/8	STABOTASIZ	20.50	30"—2
Center Punches								Nail Sets							
10	4 IN.	5/64 IN.	12	3/4	STACENAPED	1.40	5/64"—10	11	4 IN.	2/32 IN.	12	3/4	STANALAPED	1.40	2/32"—11
"	4 "	1/8 "	12	7/8	STACENAPIL	1.40	1/8"—10	11	4 "	3/32 "	12	7/8	STANALAPIL	1.40	3/32"—11
"	4 "	5/32 "	12	7/8	STACENAPOM	1.40	5/32"—10	11	4 "	4/32 "	12	7/8	STANALAPOM	1.40	4/32"—11
10 ASS'T'D	4 "	ASS'T'D	12	7/8	STACENARAT	1.40	ASS'T'D 10	11 ASS'T'D	4 "	ASS'T'D	12	7/8	STANALARAT	1.40	ASS'T'D-11
10 A	4 "	"	12	7/8	STACENAREX	1.40	" 10A	11 A	4 "	"	12	7/8	STANALAREX	1.40	" 11A
10 B	4 "	"	24	1 3/4	STACENARIZ	1.40	" 10B	11 B	4 "	"	24	1 3/4	STANALARIZ	1.40	" 11B
10 C	4 "	"	36	2 5/8	STACENASAL	1.40	" 10C	11 C	4 "	"	36	2 5/8	STANALASAL	1.40	" 11C
Screw Driver Bits															
26—1/4"	4 1/2 IN.	1/4 IN.	12	1	STABOTELAX	1.40	1/4"—26	26—5/8"	5 IN.	5/8 IN.	12	2 1/4	STABOTERIX	1.40	5/8"—26
26—5/16"	4 3/4 "	5/16 "	12	1 1/4	STABOTELEZ	1.40	5/16"—26	26—3/4"	5 "	3/4 "	12	2 1/4	STABOTERUC	1.40	3/4"—26
26—3/8"	5 "	3/8 "	12	1 1/2	STABOTELOC	1.40	3/8"—26	26-ASS'T'D	ASS'T'D	ASS'T'D	12	1 1/2	STABOTESAC	1.40	ASS'T'D-26
26—1/2"	5 "	1/2 "	12	1 3/4	STABOTERAT	1.40	1/2"—26								
"Wheeler" Wood Countersinks								Wood Dowel Sharpener							
18	4 IN.	1 IN.	6	3/4	STABOTEKAR	3.00	18	22	4 IN.	1 IN.	6	3/4	STABOTEKUZ	3.00	22
20	4 "	1 "	6	1	STABOTEKET	4.50	20								

Stanley "Hurwood" Screw Drivers

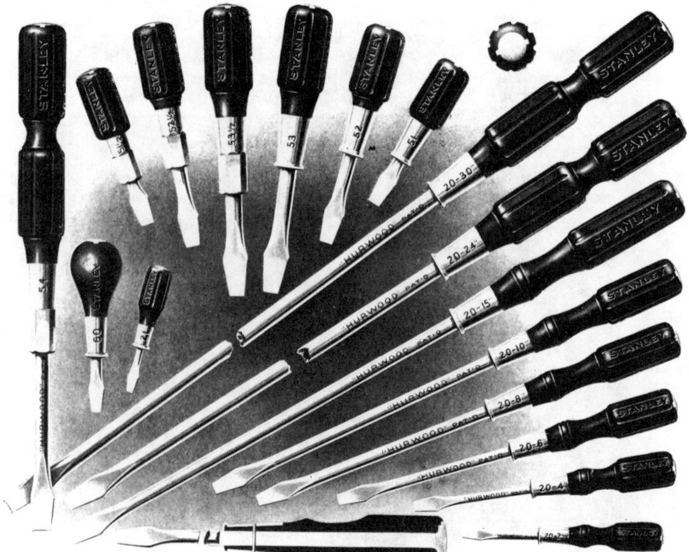

COPYRIGHT, 1909, BY THE STANLEY RULE AND LEVEL COMPANY

ILLUSTRATIONS OF NOS. 20 OR 25 OF VARIOUS SIZES AND NOS. 21, 51, 51½, 52, 52½, 53, 53½, 54 AND 60

Stanley "Hurwood" Screw Drivers

"HURWOOD" SCREW DRIVERS are mechanically the best Screw Driver ever offered and will stand more hard usage than any Driver made. They are made with the Blade, Shank and Head formed of ONE piece of steel, as shown by the cut at the bottom of the opposite page.

A Rivet through the Ferrule, Handle and Shank, as well as the form of the Head, which is made with two projecting Wings as shown by the cuts on the opposite page, securely fastens the Handle.

"HURWOOD" MACHINISTS' SCREW DRIVERS are especially adapted for heavy work where a long Driver cannot be conveniently used. Nos. 51½, 52½, 53½ and 54 are made with a Hexagon on Shank for use with a wrench. No. 54 has a long Double Grip Handle.

The Blades are finely tempered and the whole tool is well finished and fully warranted.

"HURWOOD" ELECTRICIAN SCREW DRIVERS No. 25 have Insulated Heads but otherwise are same as No. 20.

NO.	BLADE				LENGTH OVER ALL	TYPE	BLADE SHANK AND HEAD	HANDLE FINISH	PACKED		CODE NO. 25	CODE NO. 20	PRICE DOZ. $	NO.
	LENGTH	MATERIAL	DIAM.	TIP					IN BOX	WT. LBS.				
20 AND 25	2½ IN.	STEEL	7/32 IN.	5/32 IN.	6½ IN.	STANDARD	ONE PIECE	EBONITE	6	¾	STASCRAGEM	STASCRABAB	3.00	2½" — 20
"	3 "	"	" "	3/16 "	7 "	"	" "	"	6	⅞	STASCRAGIN	STASCRABEC	3.50	3" — 25
"	4 "	"	¼ "	7/32 "	8 "	"	" "	"	6	1⅜	STASCRAGOP	STASCRABID	4.25	4" — "
"	5 "	"	5/16 "	" "	10 "	"	" "	"	6	2⅛	STASCRAGUR	STASCRABOF	5.00	5" — "
"	6 "	"	" "	¼ "	11½ "	"	" "	"	6	3	STASCRAKAN	STASCRABUG	6.00	6" — "
"	7 "	"	11/32 "	9/32 "	13½ "	"	" "	"	6	3¼	STASCRAKIR	STASCRADAR	7.00	7" — "
"	8 "	"	⅜ "	5/16 "	14½ "	"	" "	"	6	3¾	STASCRAKOS	STASCRADES	8.00	8" — "
"	9 "	"	" "	11/32 "	15½ "	"	" "	"	6	4	STASCRAKUT	STASCRADIT	9.00	9" — "
"	10 "	"	" "	⅜ "	16½ "	"	" "	"	6	4¼	STASCRALAX	STASCRADOX	10.00	10" — "
"	12 "	"	" "	" "	18½ "	"	" "	"	6	4¾	STASCRALEZ	STASCRADUZ	12.00	12" — "
"	15 "	"	7/16 "	7/16 "	23 "	"	" "	"	6	9¼	STASCRALIB	STASCRAFAC	15.00	15" — "
"	18 "	"	½ "	15/32 "	27 "	"	" "	"	6	10½	STASCRALOC	STASCRAFED	18.00	18" — "
"	24 "	"	" "	½ "	33½ "	"	" "	"	6	13½	STASCRALUD	STASCRAFIF	24.00	24" — "
"	30 "	"	" "	9/16 "	39½ "	"	" "	"	6	16½	STASCRAMOL	STASCRAFOG	30.00	30" — "
21	1½ "	"	7/32 "	5/32 "	4 "	BABY	" "	"	6	½		STASCRAGAL	3.00	21
60	1⅝ "	"	5/16 "	9/32 "	5½ "	HANDY	" "	"	6	1½		STASCRIMAL	5.00	60
51	1¾ "	"	⅜ "	9/32 "	5¼ "	MACHINIST	" "	"	6	1¾		STASCRENAX	5.00	51
52	3 "	"	7/16 "	15/32 "	7¼ "	"	" "	"	6	2¾		STASCRENOC	9.00	52
53	4 "	"	½ "	½ "	9½ "	"	" "	"	6	4¼		STASCREPAF	12.00	53
51½	1½ "	"	⅜ "	9/32 "	5½ "	HEXAGON	" "	"	6	2		STASCRENEZ	8.00	51½
52½	2⅝ "	"	7/16 "	15/32 "	7½ "	"	" "	"	6	3		STASCRENUD	12.00	52½
53½	3¼ "	"	½ "	½ "	9 9/16 "	"	" "	"	6	4½		STASCREPEG	15.00	53½
54	10 "	"	½ "	" "	18 "	"	" "	"	6	8⅜		STASCREPOL	30.00	54

Stanley "Hurwood" Screw Drivers

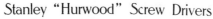

COPYRIGHT, 1909, BY THE STANLEY RULE AND LEVEL COMPANY
ILLUSTRATIONS OF NOS. 40 OR 45, AND NOS. 50 OR 55 OF VARIOUS SIZES

Stanley "Hurwood" Screw Drivers

"HURWOOD" SCREW DRIVERS are mechanically the best Driver ever offered and will stand more hard usage than any Driver made. They are made with the Blade, Shank and Head formed of ONE piece of steel, as shown by the cut at the bottom of page 98. A Rivet through the Ferrule, Handle and Shank, as well as the form of the Head, which is made with two projecting Wings, as shown by cuts opposite, securely fastens the Handle.

Particular attention is called to the shape of the Tip on the Cabinet Makers' type of Screw Driver. The sides are parallel, instead of tapered as in the Standard type of driver and will follow up a screw even if deeply countersunk, without injuring or marring the woodwork.

The Blades are finely tempered, and the whole tool is well finished and fully warranted.

"HURWOOD" ELECTRICIAN SCREW DRIVERS Nos. 55 & 45 have Insulated Heads but are otherwise like Nos. 50 & 40.

NO.	BLADE				LENGTH OVER ALL	TYPE	BLADE SHANK AND HEAD	HANDLE FINISH	PACKED		CODE NO. 55	CODE NO. 50	PRICE DOZ. $	NO.
	LENGTH	MATERIAL	DIAM.	TIP					IN BOX	WT. LBS.				
50 AND 55	1½ IN.	STEEL	5/32 IN.	1/8 IN.	4 IN.	SPECIAL	ONE PIECE	EBONITE	6	½	STASCREPUM	STASCREHIT	3.00	1½" 50 55
"	2½ "	"	" "	" "	6 "	"	"	"	6	½	STASCRIFAR	STASCREJAL	3.00	2½"— "
"	3 "	"	" "	" "	6½"	"	"	"	6	⅝	STASCRIFES	STASCREJEM	3.50	3"— "
"	4 "	"	" "	" "	7½"	"	"	"	6	⅝	STASCRIFIT	STASCREJIN	4.25	4"— "
"	5 "	"	" "	" "	8½"	"	"	"	6	¾	STASCRIFOX	STASCREJOP	5.00	5"— "
"	6 "	"	" "	" "	9½"	"	"	"	6	¾	STASCRIFUZ	STASCREJUR	6.00	6"— "
"	7 "	"	" "	" "	10½"	"	"	"	6	¾	STASCRILAC	STASCRELAS	7.00	7"— "
"	8 "	"	" "	" "	11½"	"	"	"	6	¾	STASCRILED	STASCRELET	8.00	8"— "
"	9 "	"	" "	" "	12½"	"	"	"	6	⅞	STASCRILIF	STASCRELIX	9.00	9"— "
"	10 "	"	" "	" "	13½"	"	"	"	6	⅞	STASCRILOG	STASCREMAN	10.00	10"— "
"	12 "	"	" "	" "	15½"	"	"	"	6	1	STASCRILUH	STASCREMIR	12.00	12"— "
											NO. 45	NO. 40		
40 AND 45	2½ IN.	STEEL	7/32 IN.	7/32 IN.	6½"	CABINET MAKERS'	ONE PIECE	EBONITE	6	¾	STASCREDAB	STASCRANER	3.00	2½" 40 45
"	3½"	"	" "	" "	7½"	"	"	"	6	1	STASCREDEC	STASCRANIS	3.50	3½"— "
"	4½"	"	" "	¼ "	9 "	"	"	"	6	1⅜	STASCREDID	STASCRANOT	4.25	4½"— "
"	5½"	"	" "	" "	10½"	"	"	"	6	1½	STASCREDOF	STASCRANUV	5.00	5½"— "
"	6½"	"	¼ "	" "	11½"	"	"	"	6	1⅝	STASCREDUG	STASCRAPAZ	6.00	6½"— "
"	7½"	"	" "	" "	12½"	"	"	"	6	1¾	STASCREFEL	STASCRAPIL	7.00	7½"— "
"	8½"	"	" "	" "	13½"	"	"	"	6	1⅞	STASCREFIM	STASCRAPOM	8.00	8½"— "
"	9½"	"	" "	" "	14½"	"	"	"	6	2	STASCREFON	STASCRARAT	9.00	9½"— "
"	10½"	"	" "	" "	16½"	"	"	"	6	2⅛	STASCREFUP	STASCRAREX	10.00	10½"— "
"	12½"	"	" "	" "	17½"	"	"	"	6	2¼	STASCREGAR	STASCRARIZ	12.00	12½"— "
"	15½"	"	" "	1" "	20½"	"	"	"	6	2⅝	STASCREGES	STASCRAROB	15.00	15½"— "
"	18½"	"	" "	" "	23½"	"	"	"	6	2⅞	STASCREGIT	STASCRARUC	18.00	18½"— "
"	24½"	"	" "	" "	29½"	"	"	"	6	3¼	STASCREGOX	STASCRATIC	24.00	24½"— "
"	30½"	"	" "	" "	35½"	"	"	"	6	3½	STASCREGUZ	STASCRATOD	30.00	30½"— "

Stanley "Defiance," "Leader" and Cast Steel Screw Drivers

ILLUSTRATIONS OF NOS. 64, 70, 75, 80 AND 86 OF VARIOUS SIZES

Stanley "Defiance," "Leader" and Cast Steel Screw Drivers

STANLEY "DEFIANCE." SCREW DRIVERS are made of the best quality of steel, tempered and polished, and the Blade securely fastened in the Handle by a Pin which passes through the Ferrule.

NO.	В	ADE	LENGTH	TRADE		HANI	DLE	PAC	KED		Domini	PRICE	
	LENGTH	MATERIAL	ALL	NAME	TYPE	MATERIAL	FINISH	IN BOX	WT	CODE	CODE	DOZ	NO.
75	21/21N.	STEEL	61/2IN	"DEFIANCE"	CABINET	HARDWOOD	STAINED	6	7/8	-		-	
**	31/2 11	4.4	71/2"	61	MAKERS	11	STATIVED	6			STASCROLAN	3.00	21/2-7
4.4	41/211	44	9 "	- 11	11				1 2		STASCROLIR	3.50	31/2"-
4.6	51/2 11	- 11	101/2:1	- 11	1 6			6	13/8	1	STASCROLOS	4.25	41/2"-
416	61/211	1155	111/2"	- 11	- 11	- "	44	6	11/2	1	STASC ROLUT	5.00	51/2-
6.6	71/2"	6.6	121/2"	64		64	44	6	15/8	1	STASCRONAX	6.00	61/2"—
6.6	81/2 11	- 11			- (4	- 64	44	6	13/4	1	STASRCONEZ	7.00	71/2"
	91/211		131/2"	11	- 11	314	44	6	17/8	1	STASCRONIB	8.00	
		1.	141/2"	**	- 11	4.6	44	6	2	1	STASCRONOC		
44	101/211	**	151/2"	66	11	- 11	- 61	6	21/8	1		9.00	91/2,-
44	12/211	11	17/2"	4.6	- 11	- 11	- 11	6	21/4	1	STASCRONUD	10.00	101/2-
70	21/2IN.	STEEL	61/211	"DEFIANCE"	STANDARD	- 11			274	1	STASCROPID	12.00	121/2-
4.4	3 "	44	7 "	44	11			6	5/8 3/4	1	STASCRITAX	3.00	21/2-7
4.4	4 "	317	8 "	- 11	"	- 11	**	6	74		STASCRITEZ	3.50	3" -
44	5 "		10 "	- 11		41	6.6	6	11/4	1	STASCRITIB	4.25	4"
11	6 "	- 11			- 11	44	66	6	13/4	1	STASCRITOC	5.00	5" —
11			11/2"	6.6	- 11	44	44	6	2	1	STASCRIVAL	6.00	6" —
			131/2"	4.4	14	4.1	66	6	23/8	1	STASCRIVEM		
4.4	8 11	- 11	14/2"	2.0	11	66	66	6	3	1		7.00	7" -
44	9 "	6.4	15/20	6.6	- 11	- (1	44	6	31/4	1	STASCRIVIN	8.00	8" -
6.6	10 "	11	16/20	4.6	- 11				3%	1	STASCRIVOP	9.00	9"
4.4	12 "	11	181/211	11	11	"	"	6	3%		STASCRIVUR	10.00	10 -
44	15 "		23 "	44	11			6	37/8	1	STASCRIZAN	12.00	12" - "
44	18 "		27 "	- 11		11	66	6	61/4	1	STASCRIZIR	15.00	15" - "
					**	44	66	6	8		STASCRIZOS	18.00	18" - "
80	21/2IN.	STEEL	6 "	"LEADER"	STANDARD			6	1/2		STASCRUBAR		
	3 "	44	7 "	6.6	66	6.6	- 65	6	5/8			0.80	21/2-8
44	4 "	110	8 "	6.6	- 66	44	66	6	, 70		STASCRUBES	0.90	3," - "
4.4	5 "	11	9 "	4.4	- 61	- 11		6	111		STASCRUBIT	1.00	4" - "
4.6	6 "	4.4	11 0	4.6	- 61	10			13/4		STASCRUBOX	1,10	5" - "
1.6	7 11	11	121/211	11	- 11		44	6	174		STASCRUBUZ	1.20	6" - "
44	8 "		14 "	66	1 1	44	**	6	21/4	1	STASCRUDAC	1.30	7" - "
44	9 "	- 66				4.6	61	6	23/4	1	STASCRUDED	1.40	8 - "
44	10 "		15 "	4.4	- 11	66	61	6	3	1	STASCRUDIE	1.50	9" - "
			16, "	4.6	6.6	44	41	6	31/4	1	STASCRUDOG		
"	12 "	"	181/2	44	4.	44	66	6	35/8		STASCRUDUH	1.60	10" - "
4 AND 8 6	11/21N.		.1/							NO.64	NO.86		
- ANDOO		CASTSTEEL	41/2 11	CAST STEEL	STANDARD.		64 VARN.	12	1/2	STASCRINAS	STASCRUFAL		6
100	2 "	11 11	51/211	41	14	61	86 POL.	6	1/2	STASCRINET	STASCRUFEM	1.00	1 1/2 8
	3 "	44 41	61/2"	6.6	16	- 66	44	6	1/2 5/8			1.50	2" —
4.5	4 "	11 11	9 "	- 4	11				11/4	STASCRINIX	STASCRUFIN	2.00	3" - "
11	5 "		11 "	66	11	"			6	1 /4	STASCRINOZ	STASCRUFOP	2.50	4" - "
11	6 "	11	121/211		11		**	6	11/2	STASCRINUB	STASCRUFUR	3.00	5" - "
11	7 11		31/2 "			11	44	6	21/8	STASCRIPAN	STASCRULAS	3.50	6" - "
11	8 "			11	**	4.6	44	6	21/2	STASCRIPEP	STASCRULET	4.00	7" - "
	10 "			44	14	4.6	66	6	31/8	STASCRIPIR	STASCRULIX	4.75	8" - "
			17, "	- (1)	14	6.	44	6	31/8	STASCRIPOS	STASCRULOZ	4.75	
	12 "	64 66	19/211	6.6	44	- 11		6	51/2			6.00	10" "
									U/2	DIMOURIPUT	STASCRULUD	8.00	12" - "

Stanley and "Hurwood" Awls and Ice Picks

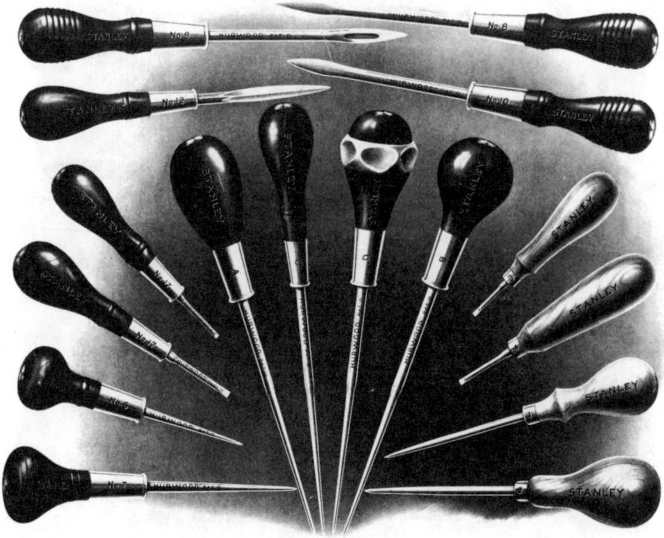

COPYRIGHT, 1909, BY THE STANLEY RULE AND LEVEL COMPANY

ILLUSTRATIONS OF AWLS NOS. 1, 2, 3, 4, 6, 7, 8, 9, 10, 12, 17 AND ICE PICKS A, B, C, AND D

Stanley and "Hurwood" Awls and Ice Picks

"HURWOOD" AWLS AND ICE PICKS are made with the Blade, Shank and Head formed of ONE piece of steel the same as "Hurwood" Screw Drivers illustrated on pages 98 and 100.

A Rivet passing through the Ferrule, Handle and Shank as well as the form of the Head which is made with two projecting Wings, shown by the cuts on pages 98 and 100, securely fastens the Handle.

The Points are finely tempered and are guaranteed to meet the requirements for which these are made.

STANLEY SCRATCH AND BRAD AWLS are made of the best quality Steel and the Points are finely tempered.

NO.	BLADE				LENGTH OVER ALL	TYPE	BLADE SHANK AND HEAD	HANDLE FINISH	PACKED		CODE	PRICE DOZ. $	NO.
	LENGTH	MATERIAL	DIAMETER	POINT					IN BOX	WT. LBS.			
Stanley "Hurwood" Brad and Scratch Awls													
17	1¼ IN.	STEEL	3/32 IN.	FLAT	5 IN.	BRAD	ONE PIECE	EBONITE	12	1⅜	STAAWLEFOZ	3.50	1¼ IN.–17
17	1½ "	"	5/32 "	"	5½ "	"	" "	"	12	1⅝	STAAWLEFUB	3.50	1½ " –17
17	ASS'T'D	"	ASS'T'D	"	ASS'T'D	"	" "	"	12	1½	STAAWLEGAN	3.50	ASS'T'D–17
6	2¾ IN.	"	¼ IN.	NEEDLE	5¼ IN.	SCRATCH	" "	"	6	¾	STAAWLEDIN	3.50	6
7	3½ "	"	¼ "	"	6½ "	"	" "	"	6	1⅛	STAAWLEDOP	3.75	7
Stanley "Hurwood" Tinners Belt and Thong Awls													
8	3¾ IN.	STEEL	¼ IN.	NEEDLE	7½ IN.	TINNERS	ONE PIECE	EBONITE	6	1¾	STAAWLEDUR	4.00	8
9	4½ "	"	¼ "	EYE	8½ "	BELT	" "	"	6	1⅜	STAAWLEFAS	4.00	9
10	4½ "	"	¼ "	NO EYE	8½ "	"	" "	"	6	1⅜	STAAWLEFET	4.00	10
12	3 "	"	7/32 "	SQ. POINT	7 "	THONG	" "	"	6	1	STAAWLEFIX	4.00	12
Stanley "Hurwood" Ice Picks													
A	5½ IN.	STEEL	7/32 IN.	NEEDLE	9½ IN.	ICE PICK	ONE PIECE	EBONITE	6	1⅝	STAICEARAT	4.00	A
B	5½ "	"	7/32 "	"	9½ "	" "	" "	"	6	1⅝	STAICEAREX	4.00	B
C	5½ "	"	5/32 "	"	9½ "	" "	" "	"	6	1	STAICEARIZ	3.00	C
D	5½ "	"	7/32 "	"	9½ "	" "	" "	"	6	2	STAICEARUC	5.25	D
Stanley Scratch and Brad Awls													
												GROSS	
1	3 IN.	STEEL	5/32 IN.	NEEDLE	6½ IN.	SCRATCH		POLISHED	12	⅞	STAAWLECAR	7.00	1
2	3½ "	"	3/16 "	"	6½ "	"		"	12	1½	STAAWLECES	8.50	2
3–ASS'T'D	SMALL	"	ASS'T'D	FLAT	ASS'T'D	BRAD		"	12	⅞	STAAWLECOX	6.50	ASS'T'D–3
4– "	LARGE	"	"	"	"	"		"	12	1⅛	STAAWLEDAL	7.00	" –4

The Lengths and Diameters in above table are approximately correct

Stanley and "Bailey" Spoke Shaves

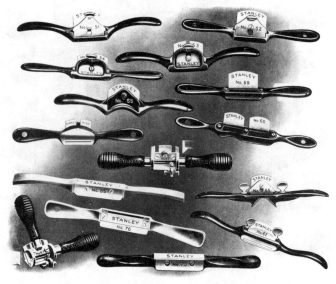

COPYRIGHT, 1909, BY THE STANLEY RULE AND LEVEL COMPANY

ILLUSTRATIONS OF NOS. 51, 52, 53, 54, 55, 59, 60, 62, 63, 65, 67, 73, 76 AND 85

Stanley and "Bailey" Spoke Shaves

"BAILEY" IRON SPOKE SHAVES Nos. 51 to 64 are superior in style and finish to any on the market.

The STANLEY PATENT CHAMFER SPOKE SHAVE No. 65 will chamfer an edge any desired width up to 1½ inches and can be easily adjusted by means of the Thumb Screws attached to the guides.

STANLEY RAZOR EDGE SPOKE SHAVES Nos. 72 to 85 are so called from the shape of the Cutter, which is Hollow Ground, giving a keen cutting edge. The Adjustable Front can be moved up or down and a coarse or fine shaving can be cut.

The STANLEY UNIVERSAL SPOKE SHAVE. No. 67 has both Handles detachable so that either of them can be screwed into the socket on the top of the stock, thus allowing the Spoke Shave to be worked into the corners, or panels, as no other Spoke Shave can do. They are supplied with both a straight and curved bottom.

NO.	HANDLE				TYPE	CUTTER			DOZEN $	PACKED		CODE	PRICE DOZ. $	NO.
	LENGTH	STYLE	MATERIAL	FINISH		MATERIAL	FACE	WIDTH		IN BOX	WT. LBS.			
51	10 IN.	RAISED	SPEC. IRON	JAPAN		TOOL STEEL	STRAIGHT	2⅛ IN.	1.00	6	3⅞	STASPOADAR	3.50	51
52	10 "	STRAIGHT	" "	"		" "	"	2⅛ "	1.00	6	3⅞	STASPOADES	3.50	52
53	10 "	RAISED	" "	"	ADJUSTABLE	" "	"	2⅛ "	1.00	6	4⅜	STASPOADIT	4.50	53
54	10 "	STRAIGHT	" "	"	"	" "	"	2⅛ "	1.00	6	4⅜	STASPOADOX	4.50	54
55	10 "	RAISED	" "	"		" "	HOLLOW	2⅛ "	1.00	6	3⅞	STASPOADUZ	3.00	55
56	18 "	STRAIGHT	" "	"	COOPERS	" "	STRAIGHT	2⅝ "	1.50	6	12½	STASPOAKAN	7.00	56
56½	19 "	"	" "	" -		" "	"	4 "	2.00	6	15¼	STASPOAKEP	9.00	56½
57	18 "	"	" "	"	"	" "	"	2⅛ "	1.00	6	7½	STASPOAKIR	4.50	57
58	10 "	"	" "	"		" "	"	2⅛ "	1.00	6	3½	STASPOAKOS	3.00	58
59	10 "	"	" "	"		" "	"	2⅛ "	1.00	6	4	STASPOAKUT	3.50	59
60	10 "	"	" "	"	DOUBLE	" "	HOL. & STR.	1½ "	1.50	6	4⅜	STASPOALAX	4.50	60
62	10 "	RAISED	" "	"	REVERSIBLE	" "	STRAIGHT	2⅛ "	1.00	6	5	STASPOALEZ	6.00	62
63	9 "	STRAIGHT	" "	"	CONVEX BOTTOM	" "	"	1¾ "	0.75	6	2¾	STASPOALIB	2.00	63
64	9 "	"	" "	"		" "	"	1¾ "	0.75	6	2¾	STASPOALOC	2.00	64
65	9½"	RAISED	" "	"	CHAMFER	" "	"	1½ "	0.75	6	4⅜	STASPOALUD	6.00	65

Stanley Razor Edge Spoke Shaves

NO.	LENGTH	STYLE	MATERIAL	FINISH	TYPE	MATERIAL	FACE	WIDTH	DOZEN $	IN BOX	WT. LBS.	CODE	PRICE DOZ. $	NO.
72	11 IN.	STRAIGHT	SPEC. IRON	JAPAN	RAZOR EDGE	TOOL STEEL	STRAIGHT	2 IN.	6.00	3	2¼	STASPOANOT	12.00	72
73	11 "	"	" "	"	"	" "	"	2½ "	6.00	3	2½	STASPOARAT	13.20	73
75	11 "	"	" "	NICKEL	"	" "	"	2 "	6.00	3	2¼	STASPOAREX	13.80	75
76	11 "	"	" "	"	"	" "	"	2½ "	6.00	3	2½	STASPOARIZ	15.00	76
81	11 "	"	ROSEWOOD	POLISHED	"	" "	"	2 "	6.00	3	¾	STASPOAROB	16.80	81
82	12 "	"	"	"	"	" "	"	2½ "	6.00	3	1	STASPOARUC	18.00	82
84	11 "	"	BOXWOOD	"	"	" "	"	2 "	6.00	3	¾	STASPOATIC	16.80	84
85	12 "	"	"	"	"	" "	"	2½ "	6.00	3	1	STASPOATOD	18.00	85

Stanley Universal Spoke Shaves

NO.	LENGTH	STYLE	MATERIAL	FINISH	TYPE	MATERIAL	FACE	WIDTH	DOZEN $	IN BOX	WT. LBS.	CODE	PRICE DOZ. $	NO.
67	9¼ IN.	DETACHABLE	ROSEWOOD	POLISHED	UNIVERSAL	TOOL STEEL	STRAIGHT	1⅞ IN.	2.40	1	¾	STASPOANER	18.00	67

Stanley Hand Beaders, Box Scraper, Cornering Tools, Chisel Gauge

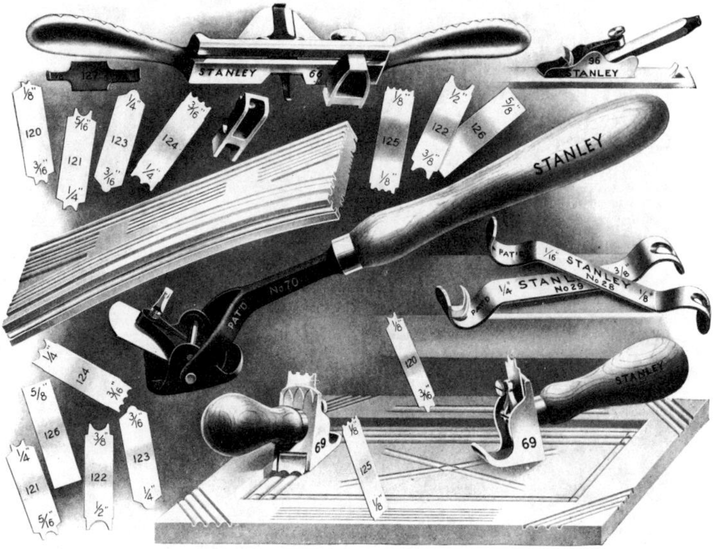

COPYRIGHT, 1909, BY THE STANLEY RULE AND LEVEL COMPANY

ILLUSTRATIONS OF NOS. 28, 29, 66, 69, 70 AND 96

Stanley Hand Beaders

The STANLEY UNIVERSAL HAND BEADER No. 66 is designed for Beading, Reeding, or Fluting straight or irregular surfaces, and for all kinds of Routing. A Square Gauge for straight work and an Oval Gauge for curved work is supplied.

The STANLEY SINGLE HANDED BEADER No. 69 is supplied with six Cutters and one Blank for Beading, Reeding, Fluting, etc.

NO.	HANDLE				TYPE	CUTTER				PACKED		CODE	PRICE DOZ. $	NO.
	LENGTH	STYLE	MATERIAL	FINISH		MATERIAL	FACE	WIDTH	PRICE $	IN BOX	WT. LBS.			
66	11½ IN.	RAISED	SPEC. IRON	NICKEL	UNIVERSAL	TOOL STEEL	BELOW	⅝ IN.	BELOW	1	1⅜	STABEDALAX	12.00	66
69	5 "	"	BEECH	POLISHED	SINGLE HAND	" "	"	⅝ "	"	1	⅜	STABEDALOC	9.00	69

7 CUTTERS SUPPLIED WITH BEADERS NOS. 66 AND 69. EXTRA ROUTER WITH NO. 66 ONLY

NAME	SINGLE BEADS			FLUTER	2 & 3 BEADS	3 & 4 BEADS	BLANK	ROUTER	NAME
NO. OF CUTTER	120	121	122	123	124	125	126	127	NO. OF CUTTER
SIZE	⅛ & 3/16 IN.	¼ & 5/16 IN.	⅜ & ½ IN.	3/16 & ¼ IN.	3/16 & ¼ IN.	⅛ IN.	⅝ IN.	⅛ & ¼ IN.	SIZE
PRICE OF CUTTER	0.05	0.05	0.05	0.05	0.05	0.05	0.05	0.05	PRICE OF CUTTER

Stanley Box Scraper, Cornering Tools and Chisel Gauge

The STANLEY BOX SCRAPER No. 70 is an excellent tool well adapted for scraping Boxes, Floors, etc.

STANLEY CORNERING TOOLS Nos. 28 and 29 are so sharpened that they can always cut with the grain without changing the position of the work.

The STANLEY ADJUSTABLE CHISEL GAUGE No. 96 is for use in connection with any ordinary ¼-inch Chisel. A shaving of any desired thickness can be raised, for Blind Nailing or for inlaying wood strips in ornamental surface work.

NO.	HANDLE				TYPE	CUTTER				PACKED		CODE	PRICE DOZ. $	NO.
	LENGTH	STYLE	MATERIAL	FINISH		MATERIAL	FACE	WIDTH	PRICE $	IN BOX	WT. LBS.			
70	13 IN.	ROUND	MAPLE	POLISHED	BOX SCRAPER	TOOL STEEL	CURVED	2 IN.	DOZ. 1.50	6	6	STASAPENAS	6.00	70

Stanley Cornering Tools

NO.	LENGTH	MATERIAL	FINISH	CUTTER	USE	PACKED		CODE	PRICE DOZ. $	NO.
						IN BOX	WT. LBS.			
28	5½ IN.	STEEL	NICKEL	1/16 & ⅛ IN.	FOR ROUNDING SHARP CORNERS	6	¾	STACORATOR	4.80	28
29	5½ "	"	"	3/16 & ¼ "	" " " "	6	¾	STACORATUS	4.80	29

Stanley Chisel Gauge

NO.	LENGTH	MATERIAL	FINISH	CUTTER	USE	IN BOX	WT. LBS.	CODE	PRICE DOZ. $	NO.
96	2¼ IN.	SPEC. IRON	NICKEL	USE ¼" CHISEL	BLIND NAILING-ATTACH TO CHISEL-BEV. EDGE UP	6	½	STACHIAGAL	2.40	96

Stanley Trammel Points, Plumb Bobs and Pencil Clasp

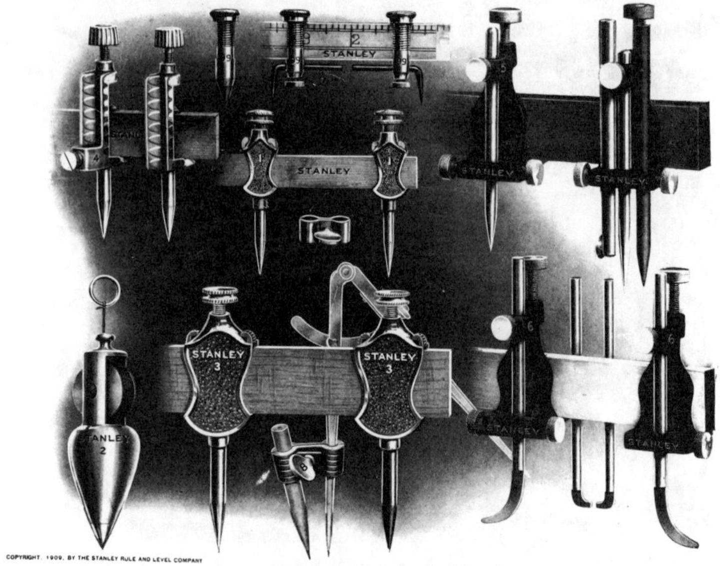

COPYRIGHT 1909, BY THE STANLEY RULE AND LEVEL COMPANY

ILLUSTRATIONS OF NOS. 1, 2, 3, 4, 5, 6, 8 AND 99

1

Stanley Trammel Points

STANLEY RULE TRAMMEL POINTS No. 99 are a practical form of Trammel Point adapted for use on an ordinary Carpenter's Rule, and on many kinds of work will take the place of more expensive Trammel Points, Calipers or Dividers.

STANLEY BRONZE TRAMMEL POINTS Nos. 1 to 3 have Steel Points on either of which a Pencil Socket, which accompanies each pair, can be firmly clamped close up to the main stock.

The STANLEY IMPROVED TRAMMEL POINTS No. 4 can be attached to one side of any straight stick. The special form of the Socket on one of these heads makes it possible to use an ordinary sized lead pencil or a full sized oval carpenter's pencil.

STANLEY MACHINISTS' ADJUSTABLE TRAMMEL POINTS Nos. 5 and 6 are made with long and short points, roller marker and four special curved points for use as outside or inside Calipers. One Point is adjustable so that the points can be adjusted by the Set Screws and the article accurately Calipered or any desired circle scribed accurately.

NO.	LENGTH	TYPE	MATERIAL	FINISH	FOR STRAIGHT EDGE	POINTS	SET COMPR'S	ACCESSORIES	PACKED		CODE	PRICE DOZ. $	NO.
									IN BOX	WT. LBS.			
99	2 IN.	RULE	BRASS	POLISHED	¾ IN.	STEEL	3 PIECES	PENCIL SOCKET	1 SET	⅜	STATRAINOT	6.00	99
1	3½ "	BRONZE	BRONZE	"	⅝ "	"	3 "	" CLASP	"	¼	STATRAIMAL	14.40	1
2	4½ "	"	"	"	1 "	"	3 "	" "	"	⅜	STATRAIMEM	18.00	2
3	5½ "	"	"	"	1¼ "	"	3 "	" "	"	⅝	STATRAIMIN	25.00	3
4	4½ "	IMPROVED	SPEC. IRON	NICKEL	1⅜ "	"	2 "		"	¼	STATRAIMUR	9.00	4
5	4½ "	ADJUSTABLE	" "	JAPAN	1½ "	"	4 "	2 PAIR POINTS	"	1	STATRAINER	EACH 2.00	5
6	4½ "	"	" "	"	1½ "	"	9 "	COMPLETE-9 PIECES	"	2	STATRAINIS	3.00	6

Stanley Adjustable Plumb Bobs and Pencil Clasp

The STANLEY ADJUSTABLE PLUMB BOBS Nos. 1, 2 and 5 are constructed with a Reel at the upper end upon which the line may be kept. By dropping the Bob with a slight jerk, any desired length of line may be reeled off. A Spring which has its bearing on the Reel, will check and hold the Bob firmly at any point on the line. The pressure of the Spring may be decreased by means of the Screw which passes through the Reel. A suitable length of line is supplied reeled on each Plumb Bob.

The STANLEY PATENT PENCIL CLASP No. 8 is a very useful little article for attaching to a pair of ordinary Dividers.

NO.	LENGTH	MATERIAL	FINISH	SPECIAL	PACKED		CODE	PRICE DOZ. $	NO.
					IN BOX	WT. LBS.			
1	3½ IN.	BRONZE	POLISHED	REEL WITH SPRING CHECK AND LINE	1	⅝	STAPLUABAL	21.60	1
2	4 "	"	"	" " " " " "	1	¾	STAPLUABEM	25.20	2
5	4½ "	SPEC. IRON	NICKEL	" " " " " "	1	⅞	STAPLUABIN	12.00	5
Stanley Patent Pencil Clasp									
8	1¼ IN.	STEEL	NICKEL	PACKED 12 ON ORNAMENTAL CARD	24	1	STAPENACIL	1.25	8

Stanley Chalk Line Reels, Clapboard Tools and Roofing Brackets

COPYRIGHT, 1909, BY THE STANLEY RULE AND LEVEL COMPANY

ILLUSTRATIONS OF NOS. 1, 11, 14, 88 AND 89

Stanley Chalk Line Reels

STANLEY CHALK LINE REELS are of Hardwood polished, and supplied either with or without Line and Scratch Awls.

NO.	LENGTH	DIAMETER	MATERIAL	FINISH	CENTER DRILLED FOR	ACCESSORIES		PACKED		CODE	PRICE GROSS $	NO.
						BEST CHALK LINE	SCRATCH AWL	IN BOX	WT. LBS.			
11	4 IN.	2¼ IN.	MAPLE	POLISHED	SCRATCH AWL			12	2	STARELABAR	10.80	11
12	3 "	2 "	"	"	" "			36	2⅞	STARELALAX	4.30	12
13	3 "	2 "	"	"	" "	60 FEET		12	1½	STARELALEZ	21.00	13
14	3 "	2 "	"	"	" "		STANLEY NO.1	12	2½	STARELALIB	11.40	14
15	3 "	2 "	"	"	" "	" "	" "	12	3⅞	STARELALOC	27.00	15

Stanley Clapboard Siding Marker and Gauge

The STANLEY CLAPBOARD SIDING MARKER No. 88 can be used with one hand while the other is employed in holding the clapboard. A one half inch movement marks a full line across the clapboard over and conforming to the edge of the Corner Board.

The STANLEY CLAPBOARD SIDING GAUGE No. 89 is a simple and practical Clapboard Gauge or Holder. The two thin steel blades, which form part of the base of the tool, will slide under the last Clapboard already laid. The clapboard to be laid can be held any width to the weather by means of the graduated scale.

NO.	LENGTH	WIDTH	MATERIAL	FINISH	HANDLE	SPECIAL	PACKED		CODE	PRICE DOZ. $	NO.
							IN BOX	WT. LBS.			
88	8¾ IN.	4 IN.	SPEC. IRON	NICKEL	HARDWOOD	MARKER BLADE TOOL STEEL BLUED	1	⅞	STACLAIRAT	6.00	88
89	8¾ "	2½ "	" "	"	"	GAUGE GRADUATED 8 THS	3	1¾	STACLAIREX	6.00	89

Stanley Patent Roofing Brackets

STANLEY ROOFING BRACKETS are so constructed that any increase of pressure or weight from above increases its security by pressing the spurs into the shingles. Two steel spurs also project above the horizontal surface of the Bracket to secure the Staging Boards. There are no loose parts to get lost and no nail holes are made in the roof.

NO.	LENGTH	WIDTH	MATERIAL	FINISH	FIXED TO ROOF BY	STAGING BOARD HELD BY	PACKED		CODE	PRICE DOZ. $	NO.
							IN BOX	WT. LBS.			
1	8 IN.	1 IN.	SPRING STEEL	JAPAN	9 PURS	SPURS	6	6¾	STAROFABAR	3.50	1

Stanley Mallets, Hammers, Awl Hafts and Screw Driver Handles

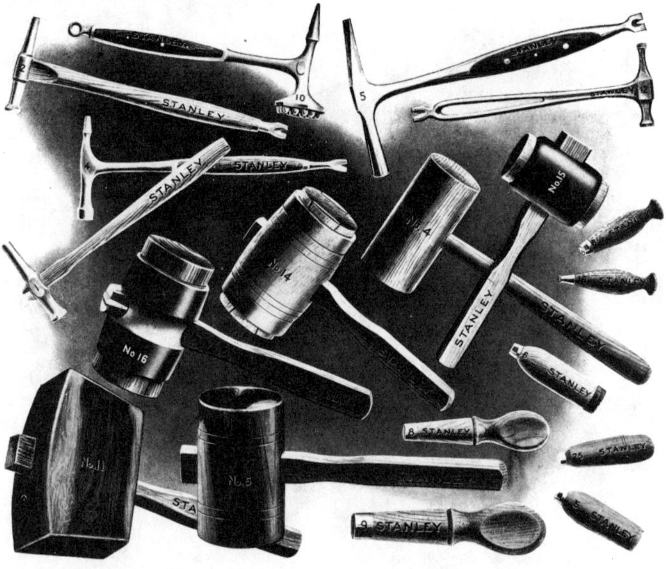

COPYRIGHT 1909, BY THE STANLEY RULE AND LEVEL COMPANY

ILLUSTRATIONS OF NOS. 1, 2, 4, 4, 5, 5, 6, 6½, 8, 9, 10, 10, 11, 12, 14, 15, 16 AND 25

Stanley Mallets, Hammers, Awl Hafts and Screw Driver Handles

Mallets

NO.	HEAD LENGTH	HEAD TYPE AND MATERIAL	HEAD SIZE	HEAD FINISH	HANDLE LENGTH	HANDLE MATERIAL	HANDLE FINISH	PACKED IN BOX	PACKED WT. LBS. DOZ.	CODE	PRICE DOZ. $	NO.
1	5 IN.	ROUND HICKORY	3 IN. DIAM.	POLISH	10½ IN.	HARDWOOD	MORTISED	NOT BOXED	15½	STAMALEBAR	1.50	1
2	5½ "	" "	3½ " "	"	13 "	"	"		22	STAMALEBES	2.00	2
3	6 "	" "	4 " "	"	13 "	"	"		28½	STAMALEBIT	2.50	3
5	5 "	" LIGNUMVITAE	3 " "	"	10½ "	"	"		19	STAMALECAC	3.00	5
6	5½ "	" "	3½ " "	"	13 "	"	"		29¼	STAMALEGAL	4.00	6
7	6 "	" "	4 " "	"	13 "	"	"		44	STAMALEGEM	5.00	7
8	6 "	SQUARE HICKORY	2½ x 3½ IN.	"	10½ "	"	"		16	STAMALEGIN	2.00	8
9	6½ "	" "	2¾ x 3¾ "	"	13 "	"	"		21½	STAMALEGOP	2.50	9
10	7 "	" "	3 x 4 "	"	13 "	"	"		24	STAMALEGUR	3.00	10
11	6 "	" LIGNUMVITAE	2½ x 3½ "	"	10½ "	"	"		22	STAMALEKAN	3.75	11
12	6½ "	" "	2¾ x 3¾ "	"	13 "	"	"		31	STAMALEKIR	4.75	12
13	7 "	" "	3 x 4 "	"	13 "	"	"		36¼	STAMALEKOS	5.75	13
14	6 "	ROUND HICKORY IRON RINGS	4 IN. DIAM.	"	13 "	"	"		34½	STAMALERAT	5.50	14
14½	5½ "	" " " "	3½ " "	"	10½ "	"	"		23	STAMALEREX	4.00	14½
15	4 "	" IRON HICKORY ENDS	2½ " "	"	10½ "	"	"		34	STAMALESOR	4.00	15
16	5½ "	MALL. IRON SOCKET HICK. ENDS	3 " "	"	12 "	"	"		43½	STAMALESUS	7.50	16
4	5½ "	TINNERS ROUND HICKORY	2¼ " "	"	10½ "	"	"		10½	STAMALEBOX	1.00	4

Tack and Upholsterers Hammers

NO.	HEAD LENGTH	HEAD TYPE AND MATERIAL	HEAD SIZE	HEAD FINISH	HANDLE LENGTH	HANDLE MATERIAL	HANDLE FINISH	PACKED IN BOX	PACKED WT. LBS.	CODE	PRICE DOZ. $	NO.
1	3¾ IN.	MAGNETIC TACK CLAW HEAD S. I.		X PLATE	10 IN.	HARDWOOD	POLISHED	12	3½	STAHAMERAC	1.25	1
2	4 "	" " " HANDLE "		" "	10½ "	"	"	12	4¼	STAHAMERED	1.50	2
3	4⅜ "	" " " " "		" "	11½ "	"	"	12	5	STAHAMERIF	1.75	3
12	3⅜ "	" " " " "		" "	10 "	CAST IRON	X PLATE	12	5¾	STAHAMORUR	1.25	12
4	4 "	" " " M. I.		POLISH	10¾ "	MALLEABLE IRON WOOD PLATES	POLISHED	12	5¼	STAHAMEROG	2.50	4
5	6 "	UPHOLSTERERS " " "		"	12 "	" "	"	12	9½	STAHAMERUX	5.00	5

Steak Hammers and Ice Picks

NO.	HEAD LENGTH	HEAD TYPE AND MATERIAL	HEAD SIZE	HEAD FINISH	HANDLE LENGTH	HANDLE MATERIAL	HANDLE FINISH	PACKED IN BOX	PACKED WT. LBS.	CODE	PRICE DOZ. $	NO.
7	4 IN.	STEAK HAMMER AND ICE PICK		JAPAN	10 IN.	HARDWOOD	POLISHED	6	4½	STAHAMORAL	2.25	7
8	4 "	" " " " "		X PLATE	10 "	"	"	6	4½	STAHAMOREM	3.00	8
9	4½ "	" " " " "		JAPAN	10 "	MALLEABLE IRON WOOD PLATES	"	6	5½	STAHAMORIN	4.00	9
10	4½ "	" " " " "		X PLATE	10 "	" "	"	6	5½	STAHAMOROP	4.50	10

Awl Hafts and Handles and Screw Driver Handles

NO.	LENGTH	TYPE AND MATERIAL	TRIM	FINISH	NAME OF HANDLE	SPECIAL FEATURE	PACKED IN BOX	PACKED WT. LBS.	CODE	PRICE GROSS $	NO.
5	4 IN.	AWL HAFT HICKORY		POLISH	PEG.	STEEL SCREW AND NUT	12	2	STAAWLABAB	10.00	5
6	4 "	" " "	LEATH'R TOP	"	"	" " " "	12	2	STAAWLABEC	12.00	6
7	4½ "	" " "	" "	"	"	" " " "	12	2⅞	STAAWLABOF	14.00	7
6½	3¾ "	" " APPLETREE		"	SEWING	" " " "	12	2	STAAWLABID	12.00	6½
10	4 "	" " BEECH	BR. FERRULE	"	"		36	1½	STAAWLABUG	3.50	10
11	3½ "	" " "	" "	"	PEG.		36	3¼	STAAWLACEL	3.50	11
25	ASSORTED	" HANDLE "	" "	"	BRAD		36	2	STAAWLACON	3.50	25
7	SMALL	DRIVER HANDLE BEECH	" "	"	DRIVER	ASSORTED SIZES	12	1½	STASCRUNER	12.00	7
8	LARGE	" " "	" "	"	"	" "	12	2⅛	STASCRUNIS	15.00	8
9	EXTRA LARGE	" " "	" "	"	"	" "	12	3	STASCRUNOT	18.00	9

The following pages are
the beginning of the
1926 catalog which is
the second section of
this book.

To the Users of

STANLEY TOOLS

IN publishing this catalogue, it has been our purpose to present to the users of STANLEY TOOLS a hand-book containing a comprehensive description and complete specifications, prices, etc., of the tools we manufacture.

The prices shown are merely a guide as to the comparative value of the different tools. You should be able to purchase same from your hardware dealer to better advantage than were you to order direct.

Stanley Tools are sold in every civilized country, and stocks are carried by all leading jobbers and dealers in hardware.

SPECIAL BOOKLETS AND CIRCULARS

In a book of this kind it is impracticable to go into all the details necessary to fully explain how to use many of our special tools, but we gladly furnish information and instructions for any tool which is not completely explained in this catalogue.

STANLEY PLANES

There is no tool in the Stanley line better known and respected than the Stanley Plane.

The Stanley Plane has been for many years and is today the last word in fine tool design and manufacture.

GUARANTEE

Every article is carefully inspected before shipment and guaranteed; any article showing a defect in workmanship or material will be replaced free of charge if returned to us.

MANUFACTURING EXPERIENCE

This Company has been engaged in designing and manufacturing Carpenter Tools since 1857 under the name Stanley. For several years prior to that time the same business was carried on under other names. We are thus enabled to manufacture and offer tools which are

STANLEY
S.W.

the product of more than 75 years of study and experience. Their design, strength and convenience in use, make them a standard of value for carpenters and all users of tools.

Coupled with the making of tools is the experience of the hardware end of the business. Here again careful attention to detail in the manufacturing processes has made the name Stanley, a name meaning quality when builders hardware is discussed.

TRADE MARKS

A trade-mark is really a trade name or device to designate or indicate the manufacturer of specific articles; that is, "Bed Rock," "Bailey," "Stanley," "Victor," "Zig Zag," "Forty-five," "Fifty-five," "Gage Self Setting," "Hurwood," "Everlasting," "Odd Jobs," etc., as used are names and numbers identifying certain tools made only by this Company.

BOXING AND LABELING

Stanley Tools are also identified by the Boxes in which they are packed, the boxes are of a distinctive yellow color and have dark green labels of a special copyrighted design.

IN GENERAL

Suggestions from Stanley Tool users will always be appreciated and will be given careful consideration by our engineering department.

The tables given in the last pages of this book will prove very valuable.

We wish to express our great appreciation for the preference which has been shown our tools in the past, and trust we may be favored with your continued and valued patronage.

STANLEY WROUGHT HARDWARE

This organization also manufactures a full line of Wrought Steel Hardware, Butts and Hinges, Garage Hardware, Storm Sash and Screen Hardware, Box Strapping, Shelf Brackets. Cold Rolled Steel, and Wrought Steel Specialties.

Catalogues illustrating the various lines will be sent to those interested.

THE STANLEY RULE & LEVEL PLANT
THE STANLEY WORKS

INDEX

STANLEY BOXWOOD RULES

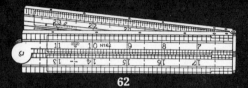

62

66½ A

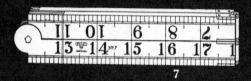

7

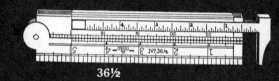

36½

68 A

32

65

STANLEY
S.W.

STANLEY BOXWOOD RULES

STANLEY BOXWOOD RULES have a superiority due to the quality and season-ing of the Wood, the weight of the Metal used in the Joints and Trimmings, the accuracy of the Graduations and the care given to the finish.

As will be noted in the following pages, they are made in a wide range of numbers, varying in length, width, form of Joints and Plates, style of trim, and graduations.

All joints, plates, bindings, tips, etc., are made of brass which prevents rusting.

The principal distinguishing feature of all Boxwood Rules is the main or central joint which is designated as Round, Square, Arch, or Double Arch Joint.

In the ROUND JOINT type there is one flange or wing inserted in each leg of the rule, the leg and the wing being pinned together as shown by the cut opposite.

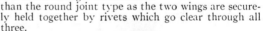

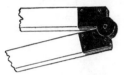

The SQUARE JOINT type has two wings to each leg, one on each outside face of the wood. This is a much stronger construction than the round joint type as the two wings are secure-ly held together by rivets which go clear through all three.

The ARCH JOINT follows practically the same form of construction as the Square Joint. However, the wings are larger, more graceful in form, and cover more of the surface of the wood.

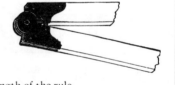

The DOUBLE ARCH JOINT is the same construction as the Single Arch Joint, but this Arch Joint is repeated at the folding joint as well as at the central joint, which again adds to the strength of the rule.

The PLATES of the folding joint are made in two styles: MIDDLE PLATES in which the plates are set in the center of the wood and pinned.

EDGE PLATES in which the plates are fastened to the outer edge of the wood by rivets which go through both wood and plate, holding all three firmly together. This latter form insures a much stronger joint.

A Full Bound Rule is one having a brass binding extending along both inside and outside edges of each leg.

A Half Bound Rule is one having a brass binding extending only along the out-side edges of the legs.

Drafting Scales are used for laying out work or reading drawings where a scale of ¼ and ½ inch, etc., to the foot is found convenient.

Rules No. 7 and all rules bearing letter A have figures nearly twice as large as those on the regular rules and both figures and graduations are extra wide and black.

Rules with metric graduations on both sides or with metric on one side and inches on the other, also those with "English Marking"—that is, with the numbers reading from left to right, can be furnished if so ordered. When rules with English marking are wanted add E to the number, when English and Metric are wanted add E & M.

STANLEY BOXWOOD RULES

TWO FOOT   FOUR FOLD   1 INCH WIDE

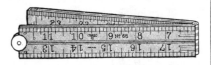

No.	Each
68 Round Joint, Middle Plates Graduated 8ths and 16ths Inches	**.25**

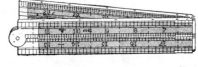

No.	Each
62 Square Joint, Full Bound, Drafting Scales. Graduated 8ths, 10ths, 12ths, 16ths Inches	**.90**

68A Round Joint, Middle Plates, Extra
large Figures. Graduated 8ths and
16ths Inches   **.25**

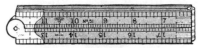

51 Arch Joint, Middle Plates, Drafting
Scales. Graduated 8ths, 10ths, 12ths,
16ths Inches   **.45**

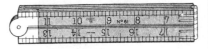

61 Square Joint, Middle Plates, Graduated 8ths to 16ths Inches   **.35**
61A Graduated 8ths to 16ths Inches, Extra
Large Figures (See **68A**)   **.35**

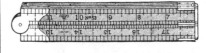

53 Arch Joint, Edge Plates, Drafting Scales
Graduated 8ths, 10ths, 12ths and 16ths
Inches   **.55**

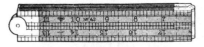

63 Square Joint, Edge Plates, Drafting
Scales. Graduated 8ths, 10ths, 12ths
and 16ths Inches   **.45**

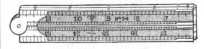

54 Arch Joint, Full Bound, Drafting Scales
Graduated 8ths, 10ths, 12ths and 16ths
Inches   **1.10**

*ARCHITECTS RULE

84 Square Joint, Half Bound, Drafting
Scales. Graduated 8ths, 10ths, 12ths,
16ths Inches   **.75**

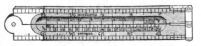

53½ Arch Joint, Edge Plates, Drafting
Scales. 8ths, 10ths, 12ths and 16ths
Inches   **.90**

*The inside edges of these rules are beveled and divided into **Drafting Scales** ⅛, ¼, ⅜ and ½ inch
to the foot. The beveling brings the edges close to the surface being scaled, which is a great convenience
in laying out work or when used with a pencil.

[STANLEY]
(S.W.)

STANLEY BOXWOOD RULES

TWO FOOT   FOUR FOLD   1⅜ INCHES WIDE

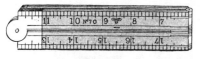

No.   Each
70 Square Joint, Middle Plates, Drafting
Scales. Graduated 8ths and 16ths
Inches   **.50**

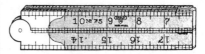

No.   Each
75 Arch Joint, Edge Plates, Drafting Scales
Garduated 8ths, 10ths and 16ths Inches **.75**

72 Square Joint, Edge Plates, Drafting
Scales. Graduated 8ths, 10ths and
16ths Inches   **.65**

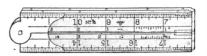

76 Arch Joint, Full Bound, Drafting Scales
Graduated 8ths, 10ths and 16ths Inches **1.30**

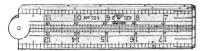

72½ Square Joint, Full Bound, Drafting
Scales. Graduated 8ths, 10ths and
16ths Inches   **1.15**

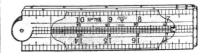

78½ Double Arch Joint, Full Bound,
Drafting Scales. Graduated 8ths, 10ths
16ths Inches   **1.50**

*BLINDMAN'S RULE

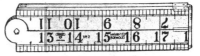

7 Square Joint, Edge Plates, Large Figures.
Graduated 8ths and 16ths Inches **1.00**

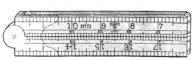

73 Arch Joint, Middle Plates, Drafting
Scales. Graduated 8ths, 10ths and
16ths Inches   **.65**

¾ INCH WIDE

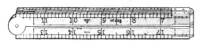

63½ Square Joint, Edge Plates
Graduated 8ths, 10ths and 16ths Inches   **.50**

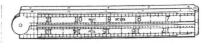

62½ Square Joint, Full Bound. Graduated
8ths, 10ths, 12ths and 16ths Inches   **.90**

*So called on account of the large figures designating the inches. These figures are nearly twice as large as those on the regular rule, and both figures and graduations are extra wide and black. Made expressly for use by persons with poor eyesight or when working in poorly lighted places.

[STANLEY]
(S.W.)

STANLEY BOXWOOD RULES

ONE FOOT—FOUR FOLD—⅝ INCH WIDE

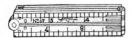

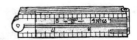

No.		Each
69 Round Joint, Middle Plates		
Graduated 8ths and 16ths Inches		**.20**
64 Square Joint, Edge Plates		
Graduated 8ths and 16ths Inches		**.35**

No.		Each
65 Square Joint, Middle Plates		
Graduated 8ths and 16ths Inches		**.25**
65½ Square Joint, Full Bound		
Graduated 8ths and 16ths Inches		**.70**

THREE FOOT—FOUR FOLD—1 INCH WIDE

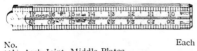

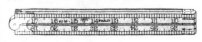

No.		Each
66½ Arch Joint, Middle Plates		
Graduated 8ths and 16ths Inches		**.70**

No.		Each
66¼ Arch Joint, Edge Plates		
Graduated 8ths and 16ths Inches		**.85**

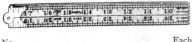

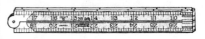

No.		Each
66½A Arch Joint, Middle Plates, Extra		
Large Figures. Graduated 8ths and		
16ths Inches		**.70**

No.		Each
66¾ Arch Joint, Full Bound		
Graduated 8ths and 16ths Inches		**1.80**

TWO FOOT—TWO FOLD—1½ INCHES WIDE

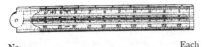

No.		Each
***5** Arch Joint, Full Bound, Drafting and		
Octagonal Scales. Graduated 8ths,		
10ths and 16ths Inches		**1.20**

No.		Each
18 Square Joint		
Graduated 8ths and 16ths Inches		**.50**

FOUR FOOT—FOUR FOLD—1½ INCHES WIDE

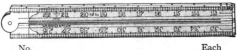

No.		Each
94 Arch Joint, Full Bound		
Graduated 8ths and 16ths Inches		**3.35**

*Octagonal Scales are used to lay out Eight-Square work, from 1 inch to 24 or 32 inches diameter. Outline on the board, or stick, a square diagram of the dimensions desired. The Scale marked M (Middle) is for setting a pair of Dividers from a point midway from the two corners of any one side of this diagram. The Scale E (Edge) is used for setting the Dividers so as to prick on the sides of the square, the distance from the four corners at which to saw for an Eight-Square.

STANLEY BOXWOOD CALIPER RULES

Boxwood Caliper Rules have the caliper slide made of brass and machined to accurately fit the "T" slot in the leg of the rule. The slides are graduated in 16ths and 32nds of inches except No. 83C which is graduated in 32nds of inches both sides.

All Caliper Rules are regularly made with caliper left hand as shown in the illustrations. They can be furnished with caliper right hand, that is, with the caliper slide in the other leg of the rule, the caliper head or end piece being turned the other way, for $0.05 extra each.

SIX INCH—TWO FOLD
7/8 Inch Wide

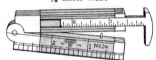

No.		Each
36 Square Joint. Graduated 8ths, 10ths, 12ths and 16ths Inches		**.60**

1 1/8 Inches Wide

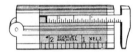

13 Square Joint Graduated 8ths and 16ths Inches		**.75**

1 1/2 Inches Wide

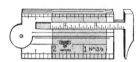

13 1/2 Square Joint Graduated 8ths and 16ths Inches		**.85**

ONE FOOT—FOUR FOLD
1 Inch Wide

No.		Each
32 Arch Joint, Edge Plates. Graduated 8ths, 10ths, 12ths and 16ths Inches		**.90**

1 Inch Wide

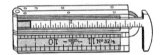

32 1/2 Arch Joint, Full Bound. Graduated 8ths, 10ths, 12ths and 16ths Inches		**1.30**

ONE FOOT—TWO FOLD
1 3/8 Inches Wide

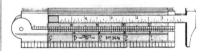

36 1/2 Square Joint, Bitted. Graduated 8ths, 10ths, 12ths and 16ths Inches		**.85**

TWO FOOT—FOUR FOLD

1 Inch Wide

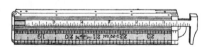

No.		Each
62C Square Joint, Full Bound, Drafting Scales. Graduated 8ths, 10ths, 12ths and 16ths Inches		**1.80**

1 3/8 Inches Wide

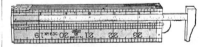

No.		Each
83C Arch Joint, Edge Plates, Drafting Scales. Graduated 8ths, 10ths and 16ths, Slide 32nds Inches		**1.60**

[STANLEY]
(S.W.)

STANLEY PATTERN MAKERS BOXWOOD SHRINKAGE RULES

All castings shrink in cooling, depending on the kind of metal, the thickness and the condition under which cast. The shrinkage per foot of castings where the thickness runs about 1 inch, cast under ordinary conditions, is shown in the table at bottom of the page. Thicker castings under the same conditions will shrink less, and thinner ones more than this average.

To allow for shrinkage, patterns must be made larger than castings are wanted. Shrinkage rules are graduated to allow for shrinkage in different metals. The spacing of graduations are based for work on patterns, the figuring of graduations refer to castings.

2 FEET LONG—1½ INCHES WIDE—BRASS TIPS

No.		Each	No.		Each
30½	A-$\frac{1}{16}$ Inch Shrinkage per Foot	1.65	30½	F-$\frac{3}{16}$ Inch Shrinkage per Foot	1.65
	B-$\frac{1}{12}$ " " " "	1.65		K-$\frac{7}{32}$ " " " "	1.65
	C-$\frac{1}{10}$ " " " "	1.65		G-$\frac{1}{4}$ " " " "	1.65
	E-$\frac{1}{8}$ " " " "	1.65		L-$\frac{5}{16}$ " " " "	1.65
	H-$\frac{5}{32}$ " " " "	1.65		M-$\frac{3}{8}$ " " " "	1.65

Graduated 8ths, 10ths, 12ths, 16ths of inches, or 8ths and 16ths only if so ordered.

2 FEET LONG—1¼ INCHES WIDE—BRASS TIPS

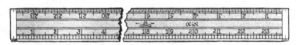

No.		Each
30	$\frac{1}{8}$ Inch Shrinkage per Foot—Graduated 8ths and 16ths of inches	1.45

AVERAGE SHRINKAGE OF CASTINGS

	Shrinkage per Foot		Shrinkage per Foot
Cast Iron	$\frac{1}{8}$ in.	Aluminum	$\frac{3}{16}$ in.
Brass	$\frac{3}{16}$ "	Britannia	$\frac{1}{32}$ "
Steel	$\frac{1}{4}$ "	Lead	$\frac{5}{16}$ "
Mal. Iron	$\frac{1}{8}$ "	Copper	$\frac{3}{16}$ "
Zinc	$\frac{5}{16}$ "	Bismuth	$\frac{5}{32}$ "
Tin	$\frac{1}{12}$ "		

STANLEY
(S.W.)

STANLEY MISCELLANEOUS RULES

EXTENSION RULES
Maple—Brass Trim—1 Inch Wide

These Rules are very useful for accurately measuring the distance between two fixed points. When extended to required length, the sections may be secured by the set screw. To read this rule, add to the number of feet indicated by large figure, nearest left end of rule, the inches and fractions of inches exposed from under left hand end of the upper section.

No.					
240 2 to 4 feet—Graduated 8ths of inches				Each **1.55**
360 3 " 6 "	"	" " "			**1.75**
480 4 " 8 "	"	" " "			**1.95**
510 5 " 10 "	"	" " "			**2.40**
612 6 " 12 "	"	" " "			**3.05**

YARD STICKS

Graduated in 8ths of inches on one side and yard measure on the other. The illustration shows a No. 41 Yard Stick.

No.				
33 Maple ¾ inches wide			Each	**.35**
41 " 1 " " Brass Tips				**.50**
50 Hickory ¾ " "				**.70**

STEEL YARD MEASURES

Made of tempered steel $\frac{1}{16}$ in. thick, ¾ in. wide, 36 in. long, and heavily nickel plated. The graduations are deep and plainly defined.

The tacks for holding the measure have polished oval heads and as they project about $\frac{3}{32}$ in. above the surface of the measure, serve as markers of the yard, ¼ yard, ½ yard and ¾ yard. They are smooth and have no corners to catch.

No. **450** Unmounted. This can be placed on either the surface of the counter or countersunk so as to lie flush with the surface.

No. **550** Mounted. This is the same measure as No. 450, but it is countersunk in a wood mount and is designed to screw to the inside edge of the counter.

No.		
450 Unmounted	Each	**1.40**
550 Mounted		**1.75**

GAUGING ROD

Made of maple one-half inch square and three feet long with one end wedge shaped, this end being covered by a brass cap to prevent its wearing. On one beveled side are graduations giving the capacity of a barrel or cask from 1 to 120 gallons. The opposite side is graduated to show the quantity of liquid in a barrel having a capacity of 42 gallons and a bung diameter of 22 inches. The third side is graduated in regular inches and tenths of inches the entire length. The fourth side is blank.

No. **45** Maple—3 feet long   Each **.75**

STANLEY MISCELLANEOUS RULES

DESK RULES

One foot long, ¾ of an inch wide—One edge is Beveled—Graduated in inches, or inches and metric, as desired.

Boxwood

No.		Each
98	Graduated 8ths and 16ths Inches	**.15**

Boxwood

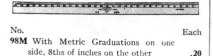

No.		Each
98M	With Metric Graduations on one side, 8ths of inches on the other	**.20**

BENCH RULE

Made of Maple—2 feet long—1¼ inches wide Brass Tips

No.		Each
34	Graduated 8ths of inches on one side, 16ths on the other	**.50**

SADDLERS RULE

Made of Maple — 3 feet long — 1½ inches wide — Brass Tips

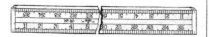

No.		Each
80	Graduated 8ths of inches on one side, 16ths on the other	**.95**

SCHOOL RULES

1 foot long—1⅛ inches wide—Brass Tips. These Rules are not beveled.

Maple

No.		Each
34¼	Graduated 8ths and 16ths inches on both sides	**.35**

Boxwood

No.		Each
34½	Graduated 8ths and 16ths inches on both sides	**.40**

FLAT WOOD RULES

Made of Maple—1½ inches wide and with Brass Tips—Graduated 8ths inches on one side, 16ths on the other

No.		Each
71	3 feet long	**.90**
4	" "	**1.15**
5	" "	**1.60**
6	" "	**2.40**

METER RULES

These Rules are one meter long—1 inch wide —Have metric graduations on one side, 8ths of inches on the other

No.		Each
141	With brass tips	**.65**
142	Without tips	**.55**

STANLEY TRAMMEL POINTS AND PLUMB BOBS

TRAMMEL POINTS

Used by Millwrights, Carpenters, Machinists and all Mechanics having occasion to strike arcs or circles larger than can be done with ordinary compass dividers.

Machinists Adjustable Trammel Points

These are made with long and short points, one each of which is adjustable by means of set screws. No. 6 Points have, in addition, a roller marker and four special curved points for use as outside or inside calipers. For Straight Edge up to 1½ in. Nickel Plated.

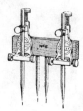

No.	Per Set
5 With 4 Points	3.60

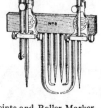

No.	Per Set
6 With 8 Points and Roller Marker	4.95

Bronze Trammel Points

These Trammel Points have steel points, on either of which an accompanying pencil socket can be clamped.

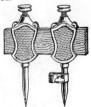

No.					Per Set
1 For	⅝ inch Straight Edge				1.60
2 "	1	"	"	"	2.05
3 "	1¼	"	"	"	2.80

Rule Trammel Points

These can be attached to carpenters' rules of any ordinary width. They have movable steel points and a pencil socket.

No.	Per Set
99 For Straight Edge up to ¾ inch	1.00

Nickeled Trammel Points

They can be attached to one side of a straight stick. The pencil socket will take an ordinary sized pencil, or a full sized oval shaped carpenters' pencil.

No.	Per Set
4 For Straight Edge up to 1¼ inches	1.15

ADJUSTABLE PLUMB BOBS

These Plumb Bobs have a reel at the upper end containing a suitable length of line. A spring which has its bearing on the reel, will check and hold the Bob firmly at any point on the line.

No.				Per Set
1—3½ in. Long, Bronze, Polished				2.40
2—4 "	"	"	"	2.80
5—4½ "	"	Iron, Nickeled		1.60

STANLEY ZIG-ZAG RULES

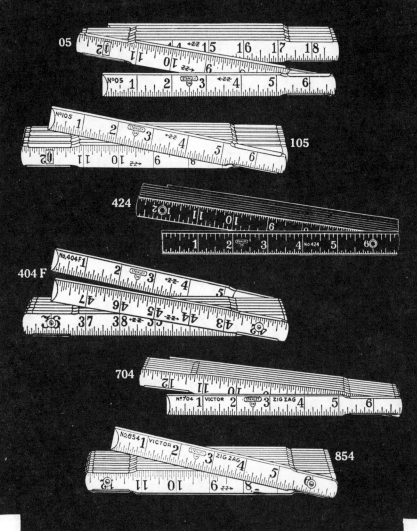

STANLEY "ZIG ZAG" RULES

The term "ZIG ZAG" as applied to folding rules made of flexible wood is a trade-mark belonging to this company.   This trade-mark is stamped on the rules either in full length or in its abbreviated form "ZZ."

JOINTS used in "Zig Zag" Rules are made in two distinct styles: The Concealed Joint "A" in which there is no hole through the wood, and the Rivet Joint "B" in which the rivet is carried through both wood and joint.

Both styles of joints contain a stiff spring which holds the rule rigid when open, even in the long lengths.

DIRECTION ARROWS "E" enable the user to tell at a glance from which end of the rule to commence measuring.   They are located near the end of each leg and add materially to the value of the rule.

STRIKE PLATES "D" are small pieces of metal fastened to the flat surfaces of each section which prevent the wearing away of the graduations when opening and closing.   These are used only in connection with the Concealed Joint type, as the form of the rivet on the Rivet Joint type is such that the rivet itself acts as a Strike Plate.

TIPS "C" are semi-circular in form, allowing graduations to be run to the extreme end of the rule and are securely fastened to the wood.

Figures are of several varieties as are here described and illustrated.

REGULAR MARKING—In which the rule is continuously marked with the numbers, 1, 2, 3, etc., commencing on the outside of the rule.

See Nos. 02, 102, 403, 503, 703, 753, 802, 852, 342, 642, 423, 204 lines.

STYLE "F" MARKING—The numbers 1, 2, 3, etc., commence on the inside of the rule, allowing the rule to lie flat when open.   The figures 12, 24, 36, etc., are made extra large.

See Nos. 403F, 503F, 803F, 853F lines.

STYLE "M" MARKING—In which the rules are Inches on one side and Metric on the other. All rules having Metric graduations have enlarged figures at 10, 20, 30, etc., centimeters.   All Metric graduations are millimeters.

See Nos. 803M, 804M, 805M, 806M, 853M, 854M, 855M, 856M.   See note on page 19.

STANLEY "ZIG ZAG" RULES

Stanley "Zig Zag" Rules have an especially fine finish. All numbers have direction arrows and the Concealed Joint type have strike plates which prevent the wearing away of the graduations when opening and closing the rule. The form of Rivet on the Rivet Joint Type is such that the rivet itself acts as a Strike Plate. Graduated in 16ths of inches on both sides. The Joints, Tips and Strike Plates are brass plated.

SIX INCH FOLDS 5/8 INCH WIDE

YELLOW ENAMEL FINISH	WHITE ENAMEL FINISH
Concealed Joints, Regular Figuring	Concealed Joints, Regular Figuring

No.		Each	No.		Each
02	2 feet long	.20	102	2 feet long	.25
03	3 " "	.35	103	3 " "	.40
04	4 " "	.45	104	4 " "	.50
05	5 " "	.55	105	5 " "	.60
06	6 " "	.70	106	6 " "	.75
08	8 " "	.90	108	8 " "	.95

Rivet Joints, Regular Figuring	Rivet Joints, Regular Figuring

 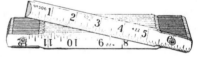

No.		Each	No.		Each
403	3 feet long	.30	503	3 feet long	.35
404	4 " "	.40	504	4 " "	.45
405	5 " "	.50	505	5 " "	.55
406	6 " "	.65	506	6 " "	.70
408	8 " "	.85	508	8 " "	.90

Rivet Joints, "F" Figuring	Rivet Joints, "F" Figuring

No.		Each	No.		Each
403F	3 feet long	.30	503F	3 feet long	.35
404F	4 " "	.40	504F	4 " "	.45
405F	5 " "	.50	505F	5 " "	.55
406F	6 " "	.65	506F	6 " "	.70
408F	8 " "	.85	508F	8 " "	.90

STANLEY
S.W.

STANLEY "VICTOR" "ZIG ZAG" RULES

"Victor" "Zig Zag" Rules do not have the direction arrows or the strike plates as are on the Stanley Concealed Joint type. They are graduated in 16ths of inches on both sides. The Joints and Tips are brass plated.

SIX INCH FOLDS ⅝ INCH WIDE

YELLOW ENAMEL FINISH	WHITE ENAMEL FINISH
Concealed Joints, Regular Figuring	**Concealed Joints, Regular Figuring**

No.		Each	No.		Each
703	3 feet long	.25	753	3 feet long	.30
704	4 " "	.35	754	4 " "	.40
705	5 " "	.45	755	5 " "	50
706	6 " "	.55	756	6 " "	.60
708	8 " "	.70	758	8 " "	.75

Rivet Joints, Regular Figuring	**Rivet Joints, Regular Figuring**

 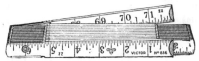

No.		Each	No.		Each
802	2 feet long	.20	852	2 feet long	.25
803	3 " "	.25	853	3 " "	.30
804	4 " "	.35	854	4 " "	.40
805	5 " "	.45	855	5 " "	.50
806	6 " "	.55	856	6 " "	.60
808	8 " "	.70	858	8 " "	.75

The 3, 4, 5 and 6 foot lengths of the No. 802 and 852 lines of rules can be furnished with metric graduations as described on page 17 without extra charge. In ordering add "M" to the number of the Rule wanted, as 803M—853M, etc.

Rivet Joints, "F" Figuring	**Rivet Joints, "F" Figuring**

No.		Each	No.		Each
803F	3 feet long	.25	853F	3 feet long	.30
804F	4 " "	.35	854F	4 " "	.40
805F	5 " "	.45	855F	5 " "	.50
806F	6 " "	.55	856F	6 " "	.60
808F	8 " "	.70	858F	8 " "	.75

STANLEY
(S.W.)

STANLEY "ZIG ZAG" RULES

WITH THE NEW HOOK FEATURE

The new Stanley hook feature facilitates the use of a Zig Zag Rule when employed in measuring beyond one's normal reach. Joints, tips and strike plates are brass plated and the finish is exceptionally fine, being of white or yellow enamel as specified.

SIX INCH FOLDS ⅝ INCH WIDE

YELLOW ENAMEL FINISH	WHITE ENAMEL FINISH
Concelaed Joints, Regular Figuring	Concealed Joints, Regular Figuring

 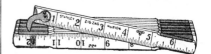

No.		Each	No.		Each
H04	4 ft.	.50	H104	4 ft.	.55
H05	5 "	.60	H105	5 "	.65
H06	6 "	.75	H106	6 "	.80
H08	8 "	.95	H108	8 "	1.05

STANLEY "VICTOR" "ZIG ZAG" RULES

WITH THE NEW HOOK FEATURE

These rules are like the Stanley "Zig Zag" Rules except that they have no direction arrows or strike plates.

SIX INCH FOLDS ⅝ INCH WIDE

YELLOW ENAMEL FINISH	WHITE ENAMEL FINISH
Rivet Joints, Regular Figuring	Rivet Joints, Regular Figuring

No.		Each	No.		Each
H804	4 ft.	.40	H854	4 ft.	.45
H805	5 "	.50	H855	5 "	.55
H806	6 "	.60	H856	6 "	.65
H808	8 "	.75	H858	8 "	.80

STANLEY AND "VICTOR" SPECIAL "ZIG ZAG" RULES

EXTRA NARROW

Concealed Joints—Four inch folds—$^7/_{16}$ inches wide—Graduated in 16ths of inches on both sides

YELLOW ENAMEL FINISH	WHITE ENAMEL FINISH

No.		Each	No.		Each
342	2 feet long	.20	642	2 feet long	.25
343	3 " "	.35	643	3 " "	.40
344	4 " "	.45	644	4 " "	.50

"ZIG ZAG" RULES	BLACKSMITH'S SPRING BRASS RULE

Graduated in 10ths and 100ths

These Rules have Rivet Joints, Six Inch Folds and are $^5/_8$ of an inch wide. They are graduated in 10ths and 100ths of a foot on one side and in 16ths of inches on the other.

BLACKSMITH'S SPRING BRASS RULE

This Rule consists of two legs made from spring brass, joined together by a brass joint containing a stiff spring which holds the rule rigid when open. Particularly adapted for measuring hot metal, as it can be cooled by plunging in water without rusting. They have a rivet joint and are $^5/_8$ of an inch wide— Graduated in 16ths of inches.

No.		Each
814	4 feet long	.35
815	5 " "	.45
816	6 " "	.55

No.		Each
17	2 feet long	1.00

{STANLEY} (S.W.)

STANLEY SPECIAL "ZIG ZAG" RULES

ALUMINUM

Aluminum "Zig Zag" Rules are recommended on account of their strength and the fact that they will not rust.

They have Rivet Joints with stiff springs which hold the rule rigid when open.

The figures and graduations are raised above the surface of the rule and are white. As the surface has a black finish both the figures and graduations can easily be read especially in places where there is but little light.

Six inch folds, ½ inch wide, graduated in 16ths of inches on both sides.

No.			Each
423	3 feet long		1.00
424	4 " "		1.35
425	5 " "		1.70
426	6 " "		2.00

EXTENSION "ZIG ZAG" RULES

These Rules have an extra leg termed by us an Extension Slide, making the rule an inside "Caliper" with which inside measurements can be easily obtained, as for instance, the inside dimensions of window or door openings, up to the length of the rule plus the length of the extension. Rule No. 204 will caliper 4 feet, 6 inches; No. 206, 6 feet, 6 inches. In the cut the rule shows the distance between the sides of the frame to be $9\frac{3}{8}$ inches, i.e. 6 inches shown at end of rule plus $3\frac{3}{8}$ inches shown on the slide.

Concealed Joints—Six inch folds—⅝ inch wide—Yellow Enamel Finish

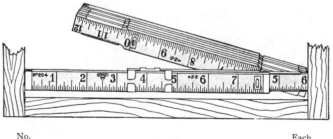

No.		Each
204	4 feet long	.70
206	6 " "	.95

STANLEY IMPROVED LEVELING STAND

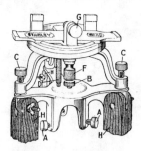

A Leveling stand used in connection with a wood or iron Level and a pair of Level Sights will be found in many cases a very satisfactory and inexpensive substitute for the more expensive surveyor's instruments.

By its use one can readily determine levels from a given point to one at a distance, such as locating or setting the profiles for foundation work, ascertaining the proper grades for drains, ditches, etc.

In use the stand may be placed on any reasonably flat surface such as a wall or box and by means of the adjusting screws (C) the swivel part of the stand can be made exactly level.

The Metal Base that is furnished with each stand enables the user to place same on a stake or crow bar and adjust it to a horizontal position even though the stake or crow bar may not be exactly perpendicular. It can thus be properly located by means of the three horizontal screws "A", and when so located, held securely in place by tightening the vertical screw "B".

A Bolt "D" passes through the Stand and is screwed into the Base, securely holding the two parts together when the Level is adjusted for use.

The Base is provided with three wings (H) so that the tool can also be attached to the legs of a tripod.

The swivel is accurately machined so that it works freely and easily and can be firmly locked in any position desired by the small knurled screw (F) located immediately under the center.

The Screw (G) holds the level in its position on the Swivel, a slight pressure only being required to accomplish this.

All parts of the stand are made of Metal—nickel plated.

No. 38 Leveling Stand is for use in connection with a Stanley Metal Level. No. 48 for use in connection with an ordinary wood level.

No. 39 Leveling Set is a combination of the No. 38 Stand, a No. 36 12" Stanley Metal Level and a pair of No. 2 Stanley Level Sights.

No.		Each
38	For Metal Levels	3.15
48	For Wood Levels	3.15
		Per Set
39	Leveling Set	7.15

STANLEY WOOD LEVELS

104½

3

30

15

1093

95

STANLEY WOOD PLUMBS AND LEVELS

The cuts below illustrate the principal mechanical features of Stanley Wood Plumbs and Levels which are used in combination with the various woods, types of glasses and different forms of brass trim, which make up the most complete line of Wood Levels on the market.

D

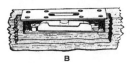

B

NON-ADJUSTABLE LEVELS have the level and plumb set solid in plaster and cannot be adjusted. Level Glass Cut D. Plumb Glass Cut A.

ADJUSTABLE LEVELS have the level glass set in plaster in a metal case. This case is fastened to a steel base on one end by a screw and bushing and on the other (adjusting end) by a special spring and adjusting screw. The case complete is fastened securely in the level by two wood screws. The top plate is independent of the level case thus permitting the level to be easily adjusted. Cut B.

The PLUMB GLASS in adjustable levels is set in a case flanged at one end, and is secured to a specially formed cap so made that there is leeway for rotating the flanged case for the proper adjustment. Cut C.

A

C

DUPLEX PLUMBS have the glasses close to one surface of the level, Cut E, giving an increased angle of vision as compared with the regular form shown above. The flange holding the Plumb Glass case in the level is made with slots, as shown, permitting it to be slightly rotated and adjusted. Cut F.

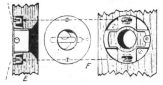

E

F

THREE PLY (Cut H) AND FIVE PIECE (Cut G) LEVELS have a novel method of securely holding the sections of the level in place by a series of tongues and grooves running the entire length of the level. BRASS BOUND LEVELS have the corner bindings dovetailed into the wood and are forced in under pressure.

H   G

THE "HAND-Y" GRIP, a feature of all Stanley Wood Levels, gives the workman a secure hold of his level and decreases the chance of dropping the tool. Both Plumb and Level side views are blackened, a trade mark and exclusive Stanley feature, which concentrates the light directly on the bulb, thus enabling the user to quickly locate its position.

STANLEY WOOD PLUMBS AND LEVELS
SMALL STOCK (2⅜ x 1¼) NON ADJUSTABLE PROVED GLASSES

Small Stock Levels are especially adapted for use by Millwrights or Plumbers, or for any work where a Level of greater length and cross section cannot be readily used.

LEVELS ONLY

Hardwood

No.		Each
102	10 inches long	.80
	12 " "	.80
	14 " "	.90
	16 " "	.90

Hardwood

No.		Each
103	18 inches long	1.10
	20 " "	1.10
	22 " "	1.15
	24 " "	1.15

PLUMBS AND LEVELS

Hardwood

No.		Each
104	12 inches long	1.20
	14 " "	1.20
	16 " "	1.25
	18 " "	1.25

Hardwood—Special Stock (1⅞ x ¾)

No.		Each
107	9 inches long	.90
	12 " "	1.00

Hardwood—Brass Tips

No.		Each
104½	12 inches long	1.90
	14 " "	1.90
	16 " "	1.95
	18 " "	1.95

STANDARD STOCK (3⅛ x 1⅜) NON ADJUSTABLE PROVED GLASSES
PLUMBS AND LEVELS

Hardwood

No.		Each
00	18 inches long	1.60
	20 " "	1.60
	22 " "	1.65

Hardwood

No.		Each
02	24 inches long	2.20
	26 " "	2.20
	28 " "	2.35
	30 " "	2.35

Hardwood

No.		Each
0	24 inches long	1.70
	26 " "	1.70
	28 " "	1.85
	30 " "	1.85

Hardwood—Brass Tips

No.		Each
03	24 inches long	2.55
	26 " "	2.55
	28 " "	2.65
	30 " "	2.65

STANLEY (S.W.)

STANLEY WOOD PLUMBS AND LEVELS
ADJUSTABLE PROVED GLASSES STANDARD STOCK (3⅛ x 1⅜)
SINGLE PLUMB

These Plumbs and Levels are similar to the Standard Stock Plumbs and Levels shown on the previous page, but both the Plumb and Level Glasses are adjustable. For detail of adjustments, see page 25.

Hardwood

Hardwood, Brass Tips

No.		Each	No.		Each
2	24 inches long	2.50	3	24 inches long	2.80
	26 " "	2.50		26 " "	2.80
	28 " "	2.60		28 " "	2.90
	30 " "	2.60		30 " "	2.90

Hardwood, 3 Ply, Brass Tips, Brass Lips
For description of 3 Ply Plumbs and Levels see page 25.

Mahogany, Brass Tips, Brass Lips

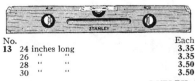

No.		Each	No.		Each
5	24 inches long	3.65	9	24 inches long	3.55
	26 " "	3.65		26 " "	3.55
	28 " "	3.80		28 " "	3.75
	30 " "	3.80		30 " "	3.75

DOUBLE PLUMBS

A high grade Level, only surpassed by the ground glass and brass bound levels. They have heavy top plates and corner tips, and two plumb glasses so set that the user can plumb from either end of the Level without reversing.

Hardwood, Brass Tips

Hardwood, 3 Ply, Brass Tips, Brass Lips
For description of 3 Ply Plumbs and Levels see page 25.

No.		Each	No.		Each
13	24 inches long	3.35	15	24 inches long	4.05
	26 " "	3.35		26 " "	4.05
	28 " "	3.50		28 " "	4.20
	30 " "	3.50		30 " "	4.20

DUPLEX ADJUSTABLE

These can be read conveniently, even if held above the head. They have three glasses; a level glass set in the top in the usual way, a plumb glass, and a second level glass set in the side. The second level glass can be readily reversed to form a second plumb, if desired.

Hardwood, Brass Tips

Mahogany, Brass Tips, Brass Lips

No.		Each
25	24 inches long	4.65
	26 " "	4.65
	28 " "	4.85
	30 " "	4.85

No.		Each
30	24 inches long	3.65
	26 " "	3.65
	28 " "	3.80
	30 " "	3.80

Hardwood, 3 Ply, Brass Tips, Brass Lips

No.		Each
50	24 inches long	4.35
	26 " "	4.35
	28 " "	4.60
	30 " "	4.60

STANLEY WOOD PLUMBS AND LEVELS

BRASS BOUND   ADJUSTABLE

The life of a wooden Level is greatly increased by having the edges brass bound, which prevents the surface and edges from becoming damaged.   The four edges are each protected by one piece of brass of special form, dovetailed the entire length into the wood and through the solid brass tips.   The wearing parts are of solid brass to prevent rusting.

All brass lipped levels have brass plumb rings.   Made from especially selected, carefully polished and finished stock.

STANDARD STOCK (3⅛ x 1⅜)
Mahogany, Brass Tips, Proved Glasses

No.		Each
93	24 inches long	4.60
	26 " "	4.80
	28 " "	5.00
	30 " "	5.25

Mahogany, Brass Tips, Brass Lips, Ground Glasses

No.		Each
95	24 inches long	6.85
	26 " "	7.10
	28 " "	7.45
	30 " "	7.70

Rosewood, 5 Piece, Brass Tips, Brass Lips, Ground Glasses

For description of 5-Piece Plumbs and Levels, see page 25.

No.		Each
96	24 inches long	8.50
	26 " "	8.80
	28 " "	9.10
	30 " "	9.70

SMALL STOCK (2⅛ x 1¹⁄₁₆)
Rosewood, Brass Tips, Brass Lips, Ground Glasses

No.		Each
98	6 inches long	2.50
	9 " "	3.15
	12 " "	3.90
	18 " "	5.10

Mahogany, Brass Tips, Proved Glasses

No.		Each
1093	12 inches long	2.70
	18 " "	3.30
	24 " "	3.90

Mahogany, Brass Tips, Two Plumbs, Proved Glasses

No.		Each
1193	12 inches long	3.70
	18 " "	4.25
	24 " "	4.85

LEVEL GLASSES

Proved

Made of extra thick tubing.   The Glass is marked at its central or crowning point by two indelible lines, enabling the user to very quickly center the bubble.

No.	Each
1 to 1¾ inches long	.10
2 inches long	.10
2¼ " "	.10
2½ " "	.10
3 " "	.15
3½ " "	.15
4 " "	.15
4½ " "	.20

Ground

The inside surface is ground smooth and true, making the bubble extremely sensitive.   The same system of marking is used on these Glasses as on Proved Glasses.

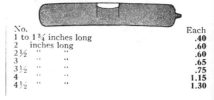

No.	Each
1 to 1¾ inches long	.40
2 inches long	.60
2½ " "	.60
3 " "	.65
3½ " "	.75
4 " "	1.15
4½ " "	1.30

STANLEY
(S.W.)

STANLEY MASONS PLUMBS AND LEVELS

DOUBLE PLUMBS

These Levels follow the general design of the Carpenters Plumbs and Levels in appearance, trim and adjustments, but are of greater length. They have Proved Glasses.

HARDWOOD, (2¾ x 1⅜), NON-ADJUSTABLE

No.		Each
7½	36 inches long	**3.10**
8	42 " "	**3.65**

COMBINED PLUMB RULES AND LEVELS

These are made in two styles, No. 35 having one non-adjustable plumb and one opening for use of plumb bob line, and No. 45½ having two adjustable plumbs and two openings for use of plumb bob and line. Both have proved glasses. The Level Glasses are adjustable.

LIGHT WOOD, (3⅝ x 1⅜)
Adjustable, Opening For Plumb Bob

No.	Each
35 42 inches long	**3.15**

LIGHT WOOD, (3¾ x 1¹⁄₁₆)
Adjustable, Double Plumb, Opening for Plumb Bob

No.	Each
45½ 48 inches long	**4.90**

Note—A further line of Masons Plumbs and Levels in both Aluminum and Wood are shown on pages 30 to 34.

STANLEY ALUMINUM AND WOOD LEVELS

257 - 24"

258 - 24"

232 - 30"

235 - 42"

250 - 42"

253 - 48"

STANLEY ALUMINUM AND WOOD PLUMBS AND LEVELS

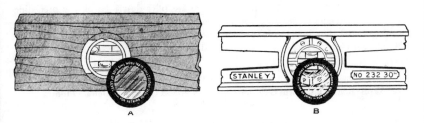

Particular attention is called to this new line of Plumbs and Levels, both as regards general appearance and the several special features incorporated in both the Aluminum and Wood types.

Those made of Aluminum are highly recommended, as they combine light weight and great strength and are guaranteed against rusting or warping.

The Truss form of construction (a patented feature) adds materially to the strength of the level frame, overcoming the liability of its being sprung out of true by accident.

The tops and bottoms are milled and ground to insure perfectly parallel surfaces.

Both the Aluminum and Wood Levels are fitted with "Proved" Glasses, so arranged that no matter how the tool is taken up, one or more of them are available to level or plumb.

The openings for both level and plumb glasses are protected by heavy glass covers, thus preventing damage to the bulbs and keeping out the dirt.

If a glass should be broken we would recommend that the level be returned to the factory for repairs, thus insuring the accurate adjustment of the new glass. However, if the owner has a perfect standard by which to set the new glass, a new glass set in its case can be sent from the factory.

The cases holding the level and plumb glass in the non-adjustable levels are set solid in plaster in a brass case (Cut A). The adjustable are set in an adjustable aluminum case (Cut B) and are fastened to the level stock by screws under the glass covers on the side of the level where directions for removing appears. To remove the level or plumb glass, cut out the putty holding the cover. The cover can then be removed and the broken glass in its case taken out by loosening the screws holding it to the level stock.

STANLEY ALUMINUM AND WOOD PLUMBS AND LEVELS

The Plumbs and Levels shown on this page are fully described on the preceding page and are especially designed for Carpenters' and Mechanics' use. The Glasses are so arranged that no matter how the tool is taken up, one or more of them are available with which to level or plumb. All Glasses are protected by heavy glass covers.

ALUMINUM

Adjustable—Aluminum Cases Fitted with 6 Proved Glasses—2 Double Plumbs and 1 Double Level

No.				Each
232	24 inches long	Weight 2 ¼ lbs.		**6.40**
	26 " "	" 2 ⅜ "		**6.70**
	28 " "	" 2 ½ "		**7.00**
	30 " "	" 2 ⅝ "		**7.50**

EXTRA QUALITY—LIGHT WOOD (1³⁄₁₆ x 2⅜)

Non-Adjustable—Brass Cases Fitted with 4 Proved Glasses—2 Single Plumbs and 1 Double Level

They have the "Hand-y" feature and are made in two styles, unbound and without Tips and Full Aluminum Bound and Tipped.

Not Bound—No Tips

No.				Each
257	24 inches long	Weight 1 ⅛ lbs.		**2.40**
	26 " "	" 1 ¼ "		**2.45**
	28 " "	" 1 ⅜ "		**2.50**
	30 " "	" 1 ½ "		**2.55**

Aluminum Bound—Aluminum Tips

No.				Each
258	24 inches long	Weight 1 ⅝ lbs.		**4.50**
	26 " "	" 1 ¾ "		**4.60**
	28 " "	" 1 ⅞ "		**4.70**
	30 " "	" 2 "		**4.80**

STANLEY WOOD PLUMBS AND LEVELS

Non-Adjustable Brass Cases—Extra Quality—Light Wood ($2\frac{3}{8}$ x $1\frac{3}{16}$)

Fitted with 2 proved glasses—1 plumb and 1 level—"Handy" feature

No.		Each
257 18 Inches long		**1.60**

Adjustable Aluminum Cases, Extra Quality ($2\frac{3}{4}$ x $1\frac{1}{16}$)

Fitted with 4 proved glasses—2 single plumbs and 1 double level

These levels are made of cherry and have an unusually fine hand rubbed finish and have the "Handy" feature.

Not Bound—No Tips

No.		Each
260 24 in. long.		**3.75**
28 " "		**3.85**

Aluminum Tips

No.		Each
261 24 in. long.		**4.20**
28 " "		**4.35**

Full Aluminum Bound with Aluminum Tips

No.		Each
262 24 in. long.		**6.30**
28 " "		**6.55**

STANLEY ALUMINUM AND WOOD PLUMBS AND LEVELS

The Plumbs and Levels shown on this page are fully described on page 31 and are especially designed for MASONS use. The Glasses are so arranged that one or more of them are available with which to level or plumb, no matter how the tool is taken up. All glasses are protected by heavy glass covers.

ALUMINUM
Adjustable—Aluminum Cases Fitted with 6 Proved Glasses—2 Double Plumbs and 1 Double Level

No.			Each
235 42 in. long		Weight 4¼ lbs.	**12.00**

EXTRA QUALITY—LIGHT WOOD (2¾ x 1¹⁄₁₆)
Non-Adjustable Iron Cases Fitted with 6 Proved Glasses, 2 Double Plumbs and 1 Double Level
Two hand holes are provided for convenience and safety in handling

No.		Each
250 42 in. long,	Weight 2 lbs.	**5.00**
48 " "	" 2¼ "	**5.50**

EXTRA QUALITY—LIGHT WOOD (1³⁄₁₆ x 2⅜)
Fitted with 6 Proved Glasses—4 Single Plumbs and 1 Double Level
Two hand holes are provided for convenience and safety in handling. Made in three styles, as noted below.

Not Bound—No Tips

No.		Each
252 42 in. long	Weight 2 lbs.	**4.50**
48 " "	" 2¼ "	**5.00**

Not Bound—Aluminum Tips

No.	Each
254 48 in. long	**5.50**

Aluminum Bound—Aluminum Tips

No.		Each
253 42 in. long	Weight 2¾ lbs.	**6.50**
48 " "	" 3 "	**7.50**

Other Masons Plumbs and Levels are shown on page 29

┤STANLEY├
(S.W.)

STANLEY METALLIC LEVELS

HEXAGON POCKET LEVELS
Nickel Plated—Proved Glasses

These are very handy for leveling up clocks, cameras, etc.

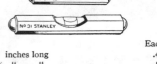

No.			Each
31	2 inches long		.45
	2½ " "		.50
	3 " "		.60
	3½ " "		.75

STRAIGHT EDGE POCKET LEVELS
Proved Glasses

So called for the reason that they can be readily attached to any Straight Edge or Carpenter's Square. By means of the thumb screw it can be held firmly in place. The body is of iron and is japanned.

No.		Each
40	Japanned, Japan Top Plate	.20
41	" Brass " "	.25

BIT AND SQUARE LEVEL
Proved Glasses

This tool has three pairs of V slots on its edges. The shank of a Bit will lie in these slots, either horizontal, vertical or at an angle of 45 degrees, and boring can be done with perfect accuracy. It can also be attached to a Carpenter's Square, making it an accurate Plumb or Level.

No.		Each
44	Brass Frame	.55

STANLEY LEVEL SIGHTS

For sighting from one given point to another a distance away. Can be attached to any level. When not in use, will pack away in a small space. Furnished in pairs.

No.		Per Pair
1	For Wood Levels, Black Finish	1.25

No.		Per Pair
2	For Metal Levels, Black Finish	1.25

For use on either wood or metal levels.

Made of wrought brass with black nickel finish.

To use on wood levels place thumb screw in the lower tapered hole, for metal levels in the upper tapered hole.

No.		Per Pair
138	For Wood and Metal Levels	1.50

STANLEY METALLIC LEVELS

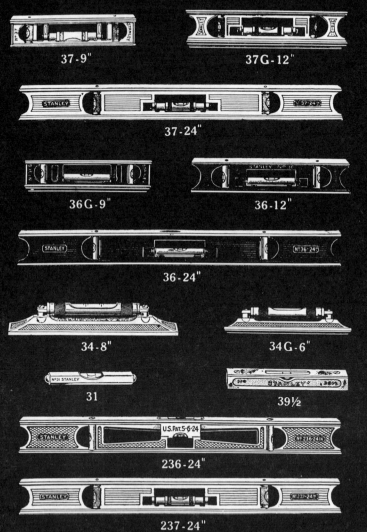

37-9"

37G-12"

37-24"

36G-9"

36-12"

36-24"

34-8"

34G-6"

31

39½

236-24"

237-24"

STANLEY
S.W.

STANLEY METALLIC PLUMBS AND LEVELS

THE FRAMES of both Nos. 36 and 37 are of corrugated I section, insuring lightness, strength and rigidity. The tops and bottoms of the levels are milled and wet ground to insure two perfectly parallel surfaces so that they can be used to level by placing the bottom on the work in the ordinary way, or the top under the work as required in leveling ceiling beams, girders, overhead piping, etc.

THE ADJUSTMENT of both level and plumb glasses on Levels No. 36 and No. 37, described on pages 38 and 39, is clearly shown in the above cut. The nickel plated brass case containing level or plumb glass is plugged at both ends. Each plug is provided with a tapered hole, drilled above the center line of the case. Taper pointed screws engage in these holes, thus bringing the tube firmly down onto the two milled seats. Slight adjustment, when necessary, is obtained by loosening one or the other of the screws and placing thin paper between the seat and the tube.

THE ECLIPSE COVER is an outer shell or tube fitting over the level case, which can be turned, either to expose the level glass when in use, or to protect it when not in use. The cut above shows cover partially closed.

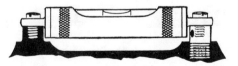

IN THE No. 34 LEVEL (see page 41) the glass is suspended in the case between supports, one of which is a part of the casting and therefore fixed, the other a stud which can be moved up or down as required. On both supports the level glass container is held by fastening screws.

STANLEY METALLIC PLUMBS AND LEVELS
No. 36

These Plumbs and Levels have tops and bottoms milled and wet ground to insure two perfectly parallel surfaces. The glasses are so set that either surface may be used to level or plumb. They are set in metal cases which fit accurately on supports cast in the frame of the level. The cases are held on the supports by means of eccentric cone centers at each end, with screw adjustment.   See page 37.

These levels are also made with a grooved bottom for working on shafting, piping, etc.

JAPANNED   NICKEL TRIM   ADJUSTABLE   PROVED GLASSES

Smooth Bottoms		Grooved Bottoms	
No.	Each	No.	Each
36 6 inches long	1.90	36G 6 inches long	1.90
36 9 inches long	2.30	36G 9 inches long	2.30
36 12 inches long	2.75	36G 12 inches long	2.75
36 18 inches long	3.30	36G 18 inches long	3.30
36 24 inches long	3.70	36G 24 inches long	3.70

STANLEY (S.W.)

STANLEY METALLIC PLUMBS AND LEVELS
No. 37

These are of the same general design as the No. 36 line described on previous page. They have, however, ground glasses, are full nickel plated, and the glasses are protected. This latter feature consists of a shell or cover, termed by us "Eclipse Case." When the level is not in use this case can be turned so as to completely protect the glass from damage. They are also made with a grooved bottom for working on shafting, piping, etc.

NICKEL PLATED   ADJUSTABLE   GROUND GLASSES   ECLIPSE COVERS

Smooth Bottoms		Grooved Bottoms	
No.	Each	No.	Each
37 6 inches long	2.70	37G 6 inches long	2.70
37 9 inches long	3.20	37G 9 inches long	3.20
37 12 inches long	3.70	37G 12 inches long	3.70
37 18 inches long	4.45	37G 18 inches long	4.45
37 24 inches long	5.15	37G 24 inches long	5.15

STANLEY ALUMINUM PLUMBS AND LEVELS

The Aluminum Plumbs and Levels shown below are, by reason of their light weight, great strength, and the fact that they will not rust or warp, especially adapted for carpenters use.

No. 236

The No. 236 Level is of the "Truss" construction (patented) adding exceptional strength. The tops and bottoms are milled and ground to insure two perfectly parallel surfaces. It is fitted with two level and two plumb "Proved Glasses." Particular attention is called to the distinctive arrangement of the level glasses, one being on the top of the frame and the other directly beneath it, allowing the user to level from above or below the work with equal facility.

No.		Each
236 24 in. long	Weight 1 ½ lbs.	**6.00**

No. 237

In this line of Aluminum Plumbs and Levels the tops and bottoms are milled and ground insuring two parallel surfaces. They are fitted with three "Proved Glasses" (one level and two plumbs) and both level and plumb glasses are protected by "Eclipse" covers and are adjustable.

The finish is Japan with Nickel Trimmings.

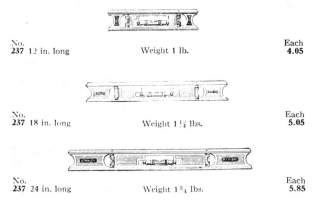

No.		Each
237 12 in. long	Weight 1 lb.	**4.05**

No.		Each
237 18 in. long	Weight 1 ¼ lbs.	**5.05**

No.		Each
237 24 in. long	Weight 1 ¾ lbs.	**5.85**

STANLEY MACHINISTS LEVELS
NICKEL PLATED—GROUND GLASSES—ECLIPSE COVERS

These Levels are exceptionally fine tools. The bottoms are milled true on both the smooth and grooved patterns. They are fitted with ground glasses which are extra long and of large diameter. This makes them extremely sensitive consequently particularly adapted for machinists' use. The glass is fitted in a metal case. An outer shell, termed by us "Eclipse Cover" is fitted over the case, which can be turned so as to completely protect the Glass. The case is screwed to a substantial metal base. The levels may be adjusted by these screws. For leveling up shafting, piping, etc., they are made with grooved bottoms.

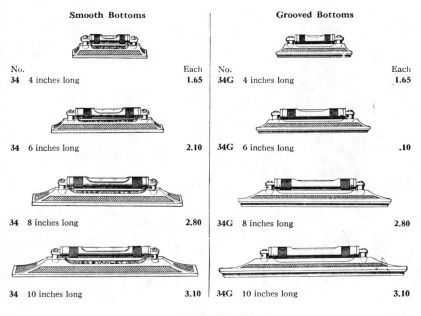

Smooth Bottoms		Grooved Bottoms	
No.	Each	No.	Each
34 4 inches long	**1.65**	**34G** 4 inches long	**1.65**
34 6 inches long	**2.10**	**34G** 6 inches long	**.10**
34 8 inches long	**2.80**	**34G** 8 inches long	**2.80**
34 10 inches long	**3.10**	**34G** 10 inches long	**3.10**

SQUARE IRON LEVELS
Nickel Plated—Proved Glasses

These are fitted with Proved Glasses set solid in plaster. The top plate is entirely separate from the glass.

No.	Each	No.	Each
38½ 4 inches long	**.75**	**39½** 6 inches long	**.95**

STANLEY SQUARES AND BEVELS

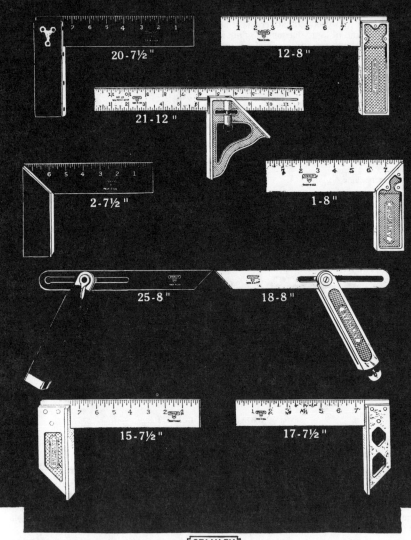

20-7½"

12-8"

21-12"

2-7½"

1-8"

25-8"

18-8"

15-7½"

17-7½"

STANLEY TRY AND MITRE SQUARES

TRY SQUARES

The edges of the blades are machined and are square inside and out. Regularly graduated 8ths of inches but can be furnished with metric graduations without additional charge.

ROSEWOOD HANDLES
"Hand-y" Feature, Brass Face Plates, Blued Blades

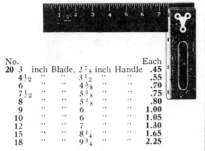

No.					Each
20 3	inch Blade, 2$^7_8$ inch Handle				.45
4$\frac{1}{2}$	"	"	3$^1_2$	" "	.55
6	"	"	4$^5_8$	" "	.70
7$\frac{1}{2}$	"	"	5$^3_8$	" "	.75
8	"	"	5$^3_8$	" "	.80
9	"	"	6	" "	1.00
10	"	"	6	" "	1.05
12	"	"	7	" "	1.30
15	"	"	8$^1_4$	" "	1.65
18	"	"	9$^3_4$	" "	2.25

15 and 18 inch have Handle Rests

IRON HANDLES
Nickel Plated

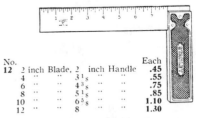

No.					Each
12	2 inch Blade, 2	inch Handle			.45
4	"	"	3$^1_8$	" "	.55
6	"	"	4$^3_8$	" "	.75
8	"	"	5$^1_8$	" "	.85
10	"	"	6$^5_8$	" "	1.10
12	"	"	8	" "	1.30

ALUMINUM HANDLES
Special Blued Finish Blade Rust Resisting

No.					Each
312	6 inch Blade, 4$^3_8$ inch Handle				1.00
8	"	"	5$^1_2$	"	1.04
10	"	"	6$^5_8$	" "	1.34

TRY AND MITRE SQUARES

Can be used with equal convenience and accuracy as a Try Square or a Mitre Square. The edges of blades are machined and are square inside and out. Graduated 8ths of inches, but can be furnished with metric graduations without additional charge.

ROSEWOOD HANDLES
"Hand-y" Feature, Brass Face Plates, Blued Blades

No.					Each
2	4$^1_2$ inch Blade, 3$^1_8$ inch Handle				.70
6	"	"	4	" "	.80
7$^1_2$	"	"	5	" "	.95
9	"	"	5$^3_4$	" "	1.15
12	"	"	5$^3_4$	" "	1.40

IRON HANDLES
Nickel Plated

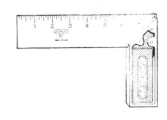

No.					Each
1	4 inch Blade, 3 inch Handle				.65
6	"	"	4	" "	.80
8	"	"	5	" "	.95
10	"	"	5	" "	1.15
12	"	"	5	" "	1.30

STANLEY TRY AND MITRE SQUARES

ADJUSTABLE SQUARES

The edges of the Blades are machined and square inside and out. The Blade can be firmly locked at any point. Can be furnished with metric graduations without additional charge.

COMBINATION TRY AND MITRE SQUARES	TRY SQUARES

Iron Handles, Nickel Plated. Graduated 8ths, 16ths, 32nds.

Iron Handle, Nickel Plated. Graduated 8ths, 16ths.

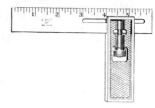

No.				Each
21	6 inch Blade, 2⅝ inch Handle			1.00
9	"	" 3⅛ "	"	1.20
12	"	" 3⅝ "	"	1.40

No.			Each
14	4 inch Blade, 2¾ inch Handle		.65
6	"	" 3⅝ " "	.75

NON-ADJUSTABLE SQUARES

TRY SQUARES	MITRE SQUARES

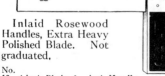

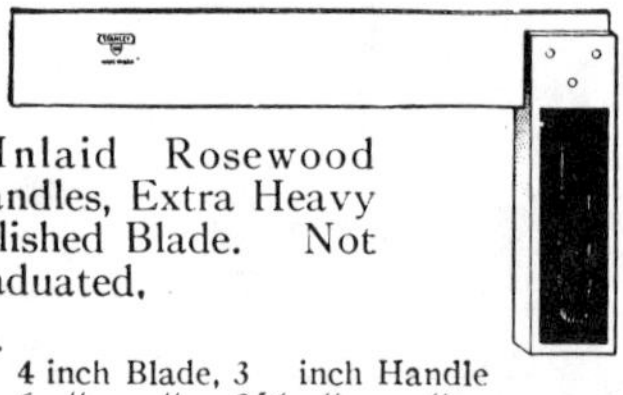

Inlaid Rosewood Handles, Extra Heavy Polished Blade. Not graduated,

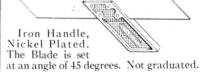

Iron Handle, Nickel Plated. The Blade is set at an angle of 45 degrees. Not graduated.

No.			Each
10	4 inch Blade, 3 inch Handle		.80
6	"	" 3⅝ " "	1.05
8	"	" 5⅜ " "	1.35
10	"	" 6½ " "	1.85

No.			Each
16	8 inch Blade, 4⅜ inch Handle		1.00
10	"	" 5⅛ " "	1.15
12	"	" 5⅝ " "	1.35

TRY AND MITRE SQUARES	TRY AND MITRE SQUARES

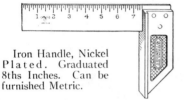

Iron Handle, Nickel Plated. Graduated 8ths Inches. Can be furnished Metric.

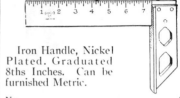

Iron Handle, Nickel Plated. Graduated 8ths Inches. Can be furnished Metric.

No.		Each
15	7½ inch Blade, 5¼ inch Handle	1.20

No.		Each
17	7½ inch Blade, 5 inch Handle	.95

STANLEY BEVELS AND ANGLE TOOLS

SLIDING "T" BEVELS

These bevels have an improved locking device which prevents the Blade from slipping. Blades are machined and are ground on both sides and edges.

ROSEWOOD HANDLE
Blued Blade

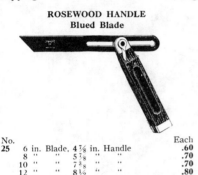

No.						Each
25	6 in.	Blade, 4⅞ in. Handle				.60
	8 "	" 5⅞ "	"	"		.70
	10 "	" 7⅜ "	"	"		.70
	12 "	" 8½ "	"	"		.80
	14 "	" 10¼ "	"	"		.85

ANGLE DIVIDERS

To lay out the cut bisecting an angle with an ordinary bevel necessitates the use of dividers and a second handling of the bevel, making three operations. The Stanley Angle Divider is designed for performing this work at one setting and is practically a double bevel. The two blades each fit one side of an angle and the handle gives the center line. The cut is marked from the center.

The handle is graduated on the under side for laying out 4, 6 or 8-sided work, and, by means of a removable "T" head, it can also be used as a "T" square.

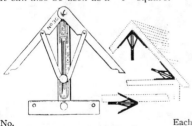

No.		Each
30	7⅜ inches long, Nickel Plated	2.20

IRON HANDLE
Nickel Plated

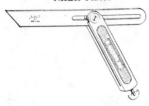

No.					Each
18	6 in.	Blade, 4¼ in. Handle			.90
	8 "	" 5⅛ "	"	"	1.15
	10 "	" 6¼ "	"	"	1.25
	12 "	" 6¼ "	"	"	1.40

"ODD JOBS"

It combines a Level, Plumb, Try Square, Mitre Square, Bevel, Scratch Awl, Depth Gauge, Marking Gauge, Mortise Gauge, Beam Compass and a One-Foot Rule. The rule is graduated in sixteenths of inches.

All parts of the tool are carefully machined so that in using same for any purpose where any of the above mentioned tools are required, sufficient accuracy may be obtained for all practical purposes.

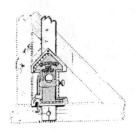

No.		Each
1	4 inches long, Nickel Plated	1.40

STANLEY
S.W.

STANLEY STEEL SQUARES

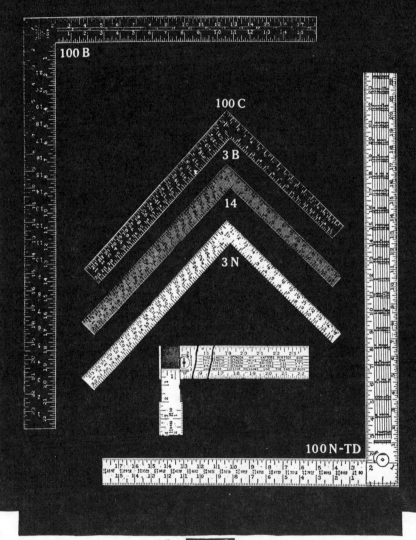

100 B

100 C

3 B

14

3 N

100 N-TD

STANLEY STEEL SQUARES

Stanley Steel Squares combine the highest quality of workmanship and material. They are made from one piece of steel, and unless otherwise specified, all two-foot Squares are tapered in thickness from the angle outward, and have specially hardened corners.

On the opposite page, the two larger cuts show the general appearance and proportions of the Square, although the cuts are so small that the graduations or the tables can not be clearly shown. The smaller cuts are intended to show colors of finishes. Graduations on blued and copper Squares are filled with white.

The Steel Square has essentially two parts—the tongue and the body—the tongue being the shorter, narrower part; and the body the longer, wider part.

The cuts on this page give in reduced size and in detail, portions of the well-known tables or scales which are stamped on the Squares.

Complete details of the method of using these tables will be found in a booklet which is packed with each Square.

RAFTER OR FRAMING TABLE

This is always found on the body of the Square. It is used for determining the length of common, valley, hip and jack rafters and the angles at which they must be cut to fit at the ridge and plate.

The appearance of this table is a column six lines deep under each inch graduation from 2 to 18 inches.

The 12-inch section only of this table is shown here, but at the left of the table on the Square will be found letters indicating the application of the figures given.

The symbols X and V as applied to this table, are a patented feature designed to do away with the possibility of making errors in laying out angles for cuts.

ESSEX TABLE

This is always found on the body of the Square. This table shows the board measure in feet and 12ths of feet of boards one inch thick of usual lengths and widths.

On Stanley Squares, it consists of a table 8 lines deep under each inch graduation as shown by the cut at the right which represents the 12-inch section of this table.

BRACE TABLE

This table is found on the tongue of the Square. It shows the length of the brace to be used where the rise and run are from 24 inches to 60 inches and are equal.

OCTAGON SCALE

This is located on the tongue of the Square, and is used for laying out a figure with eight equal sides on a square piece of timber. It is a scale, the graduations of which are represented by 65 dots located $5/_{24}$ ths of an inch apart.

HUNDREDTHS SCALE

This scale is found on the tongue of the Square and by means of a divider, decimals of an inch may be obtained. It is used particularly in reference to brace measure.

STANLEY STEEL SQUARES

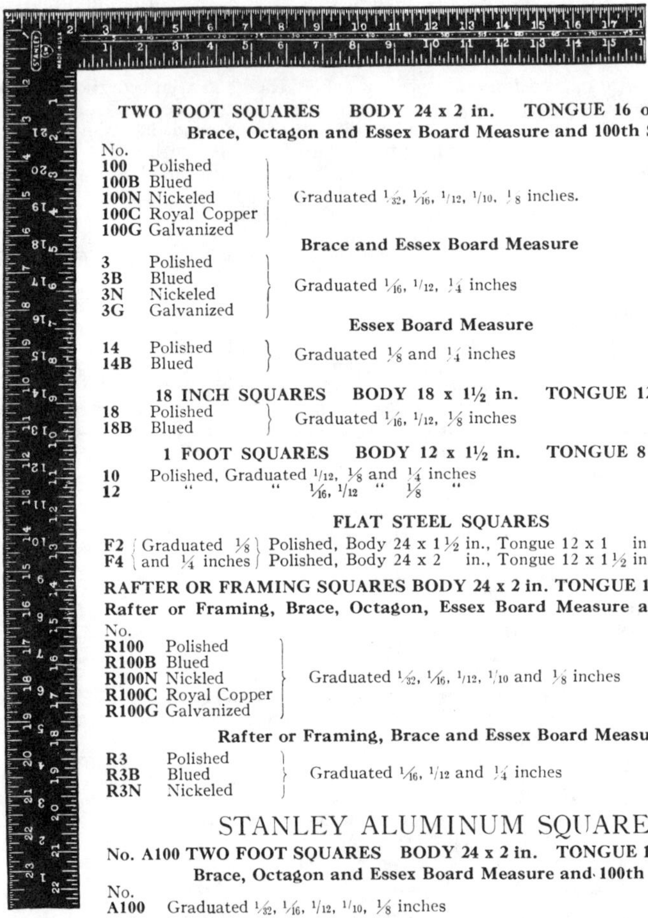

TWO FOOT SQUARES   BODY 24 x 2 in.   TONGUE 16 or 18 x 1½ in.

Brace, Octagon and Essex Board Measure and 100th Scale

No.			Each
100	Polished		2.80
100B	Blued		3.40
100N	Nickeled	Graduated ¹⁄₃₂, ¹⁄₁₆, ¹/₁₂, ¹/₁₀, ¹⁄₈ inches.	3.30
100C	Royal Copper		3.80
100G	Galvanized		3.40

Brace and Essex Board Measure

3	Polished		2.50
3B	Blued	Graduated ¹⁄₁₆, ¹/₁₂, ¹⁄₄ inches	3.10
3N	Nickeled		3.00
3G	Galvanized		3.10

Essex Board Measure

14	Polished	Graduated ⅛ and ¼ inches	2.25
14B	Blued		2.85

18 INCH SQUARES   BODY 18 x 1½ in.   TONGUE 12 x 1 in.

18	Polished	Graduated ¹⁄₁₆, ¹/₁₂, ⅛ inches	2.25
18B	Blued		2.85

1 FOOT SQUARES   BODY 12 x 1½ in.   TONGUE 8 x 1 in.

10	Polished, Graduated ¹/₁₂, ⅛ and ¼ inches	1.70
12	" " ¹⁄₁₆, ¹/₁₂ " ⅛ "	1.95

FLAT STEEL SQUARES

F2	Graduated ⅛	Polished, Body 24 x 1½ in., Tongue 12 x 1 in.	1.35
F4	and ¼ inches	Polished, Body 24 x 2 in., Tongue 12 x 1½ in.	1.50

RAFTER OR FRAMING SQUARES BODY 24 x 2 in. TONGUE 16 or 18 x 1½ in.

Rafter or Framing, Brace, Octagon, Essex Board Measure and 100th Scale

No.			Each
R100	Polished		3.55
R100B	Blued		4.15
R100N	Nickled	Graduated ¹⁄₃₂, ¹⁄₁₆, ¹/₁₂, ¹/₁₀ and ⅛ inches	4.05
R100C	Royal Copper		4.55
R100G	Galvanized		4.15

Rafter or Framing, Brace and Essex Board Measure

R3	Polished		2.75
R3B	Blued	Graduated ¹⁄₁₆, ¹/₁₂ and ¼ inches	3.35
R3N	Nickeled		3.25

STANLEY ALUMINUM SQUARES

No. A100 TWO FOOT SQUARES   BODY 24 x 2 in.   TONGUE 16 or 18 x 1½ in.

Brace, Octagon and Essex Board Measure and 100th Scale

No.		Each
A100	Graduated ¹⁄₃₂, ¹⁄₁₆, ¹/₁₂, ¹/₁₀, ⅛ inches	3.85

**No. AR100 RAFTER OR FRAMING SQUARES   BODY 24 x 2 in.
TONGUE 16 or 18 x 1½ in.**

Rafter or Framing, Brace, Octagon, Essex Board Measure and 100th Scale

No.		Each
AR100	Graduated ¹⁄₃₂, ¹⁄₁₆, ¹/₁₂, ¹/₁₀, ⅛ Inches	4.75

Unless otherwise specified, squares having a 16-inch tongue will be sent.

STANLEY
S.W.

STANLEY "TAKE DOWN" STEEL SQUARES

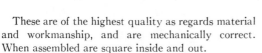

These are of the highest quality as regards material and workmanship, and are mechanically correct. When assembled are square inside and out.

The tongue is dovetailed into the body of the square and drawn up against the shoulder to insure its proper position.

The cam locking device draws the tongue firmly against the shoulder, by turning the cam, as indicated in the small cut, either with the key furnished with the square, or with a screw driver or coin.

The cam and tongue are so designed that any wear will be taken care of automatically and the square will be always correct when the tongue is locked into position.

TWO FOOT SQUARES. BODY 24 x 2 in. TONGUE 16 x 1½ in.
Brace, Octagon and Essex Board Measure and 100ths Scale

No.			Each
100-TD Polished			5.25
100N-TD Nickeled	Graduated ¹⁄₃₂, ¹⁄₁₆, ¹⁄₁₂, ¹⁄₁₀ and ⅛ inches		5.75
100B-TD Blued			5.85

RAFTER SQUARES. BODY 24 x 2 in. TONGUE 16 x 1½ in.
Rafter, Brace, Octagon and Essex Board Measure and 100ths Scale

No.			Each
R100-TD Polished			5.65
R100N-TD Nickeled	Graduated ¹⁄₃₂, ¹⁄₁₆, ¹⁄₁₂, ¹⁄₁₀, and ⅛ inches		6.15
R100B-TD Blued			6.25

Packed 1 in a water-proof, canvas case

[STANLEY]
(S.W.)

STANLEY WOOD MORTISE AND MARKING GAUGES

The bars in all numbers are oval in form and are graduated in 16ths of inches for 6 inches from the point, except Nos. 68, 73 and 77 graduated for 3 inches.   Gauges having a brass thumb screw have the bar protected by a brass shoe and the head is prevented from falling off by a brass stop screw. Face plates are brass plates inserted in the head to prevent wear.

MARKING GAUGES

Square Heads

Oval Heads

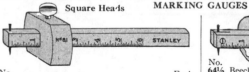

No.		Each
61	Beech, Boxwood Screw	.20
62	Beech, Polished, Boxwood Screw, Adjustable Point	.35

No.		Each
64½	Beech, Polished, Brass Screw, Adjustable Point, Face Plate, Stop Screw	.60
65½	Boxwood, Polished. Brass Screw, Adjustable Point, Face Plate, Stop Screw	1.00
264½	Same as 64½ except not figured or marked	.60

65	Boxwood, Polished, Brass Screw, Adjustable Point, Face Plate, Stop Screw	.90
265	Same as 65 except not figured or marked	.90

65¾	Boxwood, Polished, Brass Screw, Adjustable point and Pencil, Face Plate	1.10

MORTISE AND MARKING GAUGES

Double Bar Gauges

These have two independent bars working in the same head. One pin is affixed to each bar. One side of the mortise is marked and the Gauge turned over for marking the other side.

Slide Gauges

These have a slide working in the bar. One point is affixed to the slide, the other to the bar itself. Both sides of the mortise are marked at the same time.

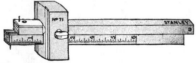
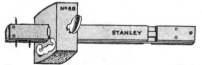

No.		Each
71	Beech, Polished, Brass Screw, Head Plated, Stop Screw	.95

No.		Each
68	Beech, Polished, Brass Screw, Wood Slide, Face Plate, Stop Screw	.75

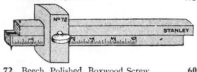

72	Beech, Polished, Boxwood Screw	.60

73	Boxwood, Polished, Brass Screw, Brass Slide, Face Plate, Stop Screw	1.15

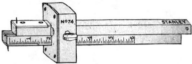

74	Boxwood, Polished, Brass Screw, Head Full Plated, Stop Screw	1.50

77	Rosewood, Brass Adjustable Slide, Brass Screw, Face Plate, Stop Screw	1.65

STANLEY SPECIAL GAUGES

CUTTING GAUGE

This cutting Gauge will be found very useful for slitting up thin stock. The Blade is specially tempered and sharpened and is adjustable.

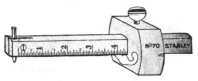

No.   Each
70   Beech, Polished, Boxwood Screw, Adjustable Blade, Face Plate   **.60**

PANEL GAUGES

These Gauges are mainly used for marking door panels and such wide work where an extra long bar is needed. The steel marking points are well tempered and adjustable. They have an extra wide head that is rabbeted to prevent slipping.

No.   Each
85   Beech, Polished, 17 ½ in. Long, Adjustable Point   **.45**
85½   Rosewood, Polished, 20 ½ in. Long, Adjustable Point   **3.35**

CIRCULAR FACE PLATES FOR WOOD GAUGES

Any Wood Gauge may be fitted with this attachment. It consists of a brass face with two ribs, and when attached to one side of a gauge head will enable the user to run a gauge line with perfect steadiness and accuracy around curves of any degree, either concave or convex. In ordering any Gauge with this attachment, simply prefix 1 to the number, as 161, 162, 165, etc. For price, add .10 to the regular price given for the corresponding number of Gauge.

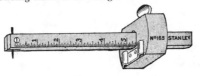

Convex Work   Concave Work

STANLEY BUTT GAUGES

In hanging doors there are three measurements to be marked—the location of the butt on the casing, the location of the butt on the door, and the thickness of butt on both casing and door. STANLEY BUTT GAUGES have three separate cutters arranged with the necessary clearances so that no change of setting is necessary when hanging a number of doors. They are also Rabbet Gauges, Marking Gauges, and Mortise Gauges and have a scope sufficient for all door trim including lock plates, strike plates, etc.

The illustrations below show the method of using Stanley Butt Gauges on doors having rabbeted jambs or nailed on strikes.

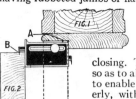

For Gauging Casings with Rabbeted Jambs

Set Cutter A to gauge from back of rabbeted jamb (Fig. 1); Cutter B is then in correct position for gauging from edge of door (Fig. 2) which engages in closing. These Cutters are made so as to allow sufficient clearance to enable the door to close properly, without catching or binding. (See dotted line Fig. 1.)

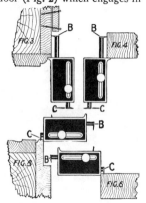

For Gauging Jambs to Which Strike is Nailed after Door is Hung

Reverse Bar to which Cutter B is attached, place Flange against edge of casing, and mark with Cutter B (Fig. 3). Use same setting of Cutter B for marking door, placing Flange against the outer edge (Fig. 4).

To Gauge for Thickness of Butt

Set Cutter C to depth required; gauge from depth of jamb (Fig. 5) and from edge of door (Fig. 6).

To Square for Mortise

On Rabbeted jamb place end of gauge against the rabbet or strike, and mark along edge of bottom (Fig. 8). On nailed-on jamb or strike or edges of door, place either one of the two Flanges against the edge and mark along bottom (Fig. 7).

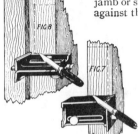

To Gauge for Mortise for Lock or Lock Strike

Set Cutter B to mark distance from edge of door or casing to mortise. Set Cutter C for width of mortise (Fig. 9). The bar to which Cutter C is attached can be turned to give a wider gauging face if desired. The bevel of the Cutters allow for working either front or back.

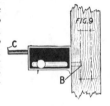

STANLEY BUTT GAUGES

Directions for using these Gauges are given on opposite page.
The letters indicating the use of the several cutters apply to all numbers of Stanley Butt Gauges.

RABBETED JAMBS OR NAILED STRIKES

For rabbeted jambs Cutter "A" marks from the jamb in the rabbet—Cutter "B" from the edge of the door engaged in closing—Cutter "C" the thickness of the butt.

For nailed on strikes Cutter "B" when reversed marks for the butt on both door and jamb—Cutter "C" the thickness of the butt.

It can also be used as a Marking and Mortise Gauge and as an inside or outside Square for squaring the edge of the butt on either door or jamb.

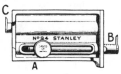

No. Each
94 Nickel Plated, Graduated in 16ths of Inches for 2 Inches **1.75**

FOR RABBETED JAMBS

Cutter "A" marks from the jamb in the rabbet—Cutter "B" from the edge of the door engaged in closing—Cutter "C" the thickness of the butt. It can also be used as a Marking and Mortise Gauge and as an inside or outside Square for squaring the edge of the butt on either door or jamb.

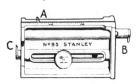

No. Each
95 Nickel Plated, Graduated in 16ths of Inches for 2 Inches **1.60**

RABBETED JAMBS OR NAILED STRIKES

For Rabbeted jambs Cutter "A" marks from the jamb in the rabbet—Cutter "B" from the edge of the door engaged in closing—Cutter "C" the thickness of the butt.

For nailed on strikes Cutter "B" marks for the butt on both door and jamb—Cutter "C" the thickness of the butt.

Can also be used as a Marking and Mortise Gauge.

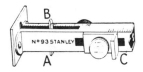

No. Each
93 Steel Head, Brass Slide, Nickel Plated, Graduated in 16ths of Inches for 2 Inches **1.55**

FOR RABBETED JAMBS

Cutter "A" marks from the jamb in the rabbet—Cutter "B" from the edge of the door engaged in closing—Cutter "C" the thickness of the butt.

It can also be used as a Marking and Mortise Gauge.

The dotted line shows Gauge when set to be used as a Mortise Gauge.

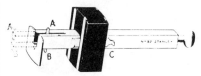

No. Each
92 Rosewood Head, Brass Slide, Screw Adjustment. Graduated in 16ths of Inches for 3 inches **2.50**

STANLEY
S.W.

STANLEY METAL BAR GAUGES

These Gauges have steel bars, and the heads are either machined castings, or selected rosewood with brass face plates inserted. Two types of markers are used— one a pin point; the other a roller cutter which can be used close into rabbets or corners and which is recommended for working across the grain, over knots, etc. Some numbers combine both styles of markers by having one at each end of the bar. Where there is a marker at each end of the bar, the heads are double faced. The bars in those Gauges having a metal head can be set so that either a narrow or wide gauging surface is obtained. Where two cutters are fitted on one bar, there are graduations for each cutter.

All parts are finely finished, and the metal bars and heads are nickel plated.

The bars are 6½ inches long, graduated in sixteenths of an inch for five inches.

Marking—Nickel Plated **Single Bar**	**Marking and Mortise—Nickel Plated** **Double Bar**
	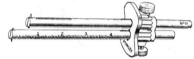
No. Each **90** Metal Head, Pin Point **.70**	No. Each **91** Metal Head, Pin Point **1.25**
	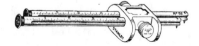
97 Metal Head, Pin Point and Roller Cutter **1.10**	**98** Metal Head, Pin Point and Roller Cutter **1.65**

197 Rosewood Head, Pin Point and Roller Cutter **1.49**	**198** Rosewood Head, Pin Point and Roller Cutter **2.00**

HOLLOW HANDLE TOOL SETS

The Screw Cap which covers the recess containing the tools has a steel strike plate. Jaws case hardened and held open by a spring. Chuck Body of large diameter. Shell extra heavy knurled and nickel plated.

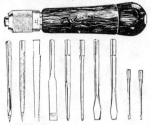

10 tools are furnished: 1 each, Gimlet, File, Saw, Chisel, Reamer, Scratch Awl; 2 Brad Awls and 2 Screw Drivers. Made of steel, hardened, tempered and polished. Approximately 4 inches long.

An extra Saw 6¾ inches long is furnished if desired at .10 each.

No.		Each
300	Cocobolo Handle, 7⅜ in. long, 10 tools	3.80

Jaws are of Malleable Iron polished and case hardened.
Shell knurled and nickel plated.

10 tools are furnished: 1 each, Gimlet, Chisel, Reamer, Scratch Awl, Tack Puller, 2 Screw Drivers and 3 assorted Brad Awls, hardened and tempered and with polished shanks and points. Approximately 2½ inches long.

No.		Each
303	Cocobolo Handle, 5¾ in. long	2.25
304	Hardwood Handle, 5¾ in. long	1.25

Jaws are of Malleable Iron. Polished and case hardened. Shell knurled and nickel plated.

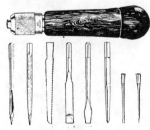

8 tools are furnished, 1 each: Gimlet, File, Saw, Chisel, Reamer, Screw Driver, and 2 Brad Awls. Made of special tool steel, hardened, tempered and polished. Approximately 4 inches long. An extra Saw 6¾ inches long is furnished if desired, at .10 each.

No.		Each
301	Cocobolo Handle, 7⅜ in. long	2.90
302	Hardwood Stained, 7⅜ in. long	2.60

The extra tools are placed in the Ferrule around the Socket in plain view for selection. Caps are Nickel Plated.

12 tools are furnished, 1 each: Chisel, Reamer, Scratch Awl, Screw Driver, Tack Puller, Belt Awl, and 6 Brad Awls assorted, hardened, tempered and the shanks and points are polished. Approximately 1⅝ inches long.

No.		Each
305	Cocobolo Handle, 4½ in. long	1.75
306	Hardwood Handle, 4½ in. long	1.55

STANLEY BIT BRACES

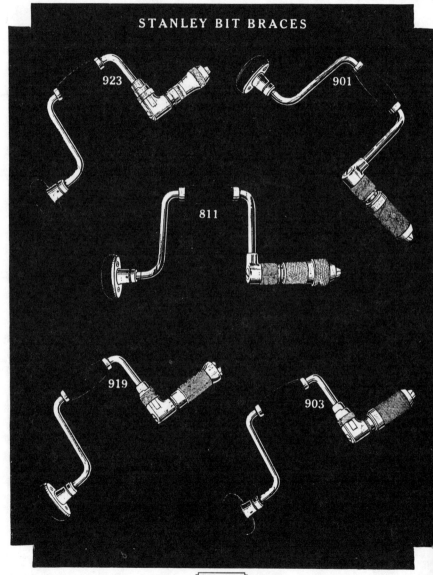

STANLEY BIT BRACES

Combinations of HEADS, RATCHETS and JAWS, with the trims and finishes make up the different numbers of Bit Braces described on pages immediately following.

The Heads are known as: METAL CLAD BALL BEARING HEAD, cut "A"; REGULAR BALL BEARING HEAD, cut "B"; PLAIN HEAD, cut "C".

CONCEALED RATCHET—Cut "D"—in which the Ratchet is in alignment with the Bit. The Ratchet parts are entirely enclosed, keeping out moisture and dirt, and retaining lubrication. The two-piece Clutch is machined and hardened, is backed by a spring, insuring a secure lock. Never less than five teeth are in engagement.

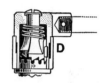

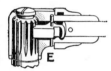

BOX RATCHET—Cut "E"—in which the gear teeth are cut on an extra heavy spindle and encased so that the user's hands are protected from the teeth. The Pawls work at right angles to the line of the spindle.

OPEN RATCHET-Cut "F"—in which the gear is cut on a separate piece of steel and pinned to the spindle in assembly. The Ratchet mechanism is exposed.

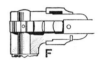

BALL BEARING CHUCK—Cut "K"—of especial advantage in holding round shanks. The ball bearings enable the user to firmly fasten any kind of bit easier and quicker than is possible with the ordinary form of chuck.

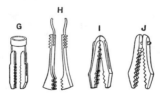

UNIVERSAL JAWS—Cut "G"—for both wood and metal workers, hold round shank bits and drills from ⅛ inch to ½ inch, and taper shanks as large as No. 2 Clark Expansive Bit.

SPRING ALLIGATOR JAWS—Cut "I," which hold ordinary size taper shank bits, also small and medium size drills.

INTERLOCKING JAWS—Cut "H"—the best Jaw for taper shanks, which they hold up to No. 2 Clark's Expansive Bit, and are, therefore, particularly recommended for carpenters.

TWO-PIECE ALLIGATOR JAWS—Cut "J"—suitable for ordinary size taper shank bits.

STANLEY RATCHET BIT BRACES

These Braces are of the highest quality as regards workmanship and material.

Their distinctive feature lies in the Ball Bearing Chuck. The details of construction of these chucks as well as of the Heads, Ratchet Ends and Jaws are clearly shown in the sectional cuts on the preceding page.

CONCEALED RATCHET

In this style of ratchet end the Cam Ring which governs the ratchet is in line with the bit, making it more convenient in handling than where it is at right angles. The jaws are forged, machined and hardened.

Ball Bearing Chuck—Universal Jaws—Metal Clad Ball Bearing Head—Cocobolo Head and Handle—
Nickel Plated

No.		Each
811	10 inch sweep	**7.05**
	12 " "	**7.25**
	14 " "	**7.40**

Extra Jaws **.50** per pair

BOX RATCHET

These Braces are the most improved form of construction, where the Ratchet Ring is at right angles to the bit. The Jaws are forged, machined and hardened.

Ball Bearing Chuck—Universal Jaws—Metal Clad Ball Bearing Head—Cocobolo Head and Handle—
Nickel Plated

No.		Each
813	8 inch sweep	**6.05**
	10 " "	**6.15**
	12 " "	**6.35**
	14 " "	**6.50**
	16 " "	**6.85**

Extra Jaws **.50** per pair

For Prices of Bit Brace Parts see page 181

STANLEY RATCHET BIT BRACES

These Braces are of the highest quality as regards workmanship and material.

The advantages of the Concealed Ratchet type of Ratchet mechanism is fully described on page 57. The jaws in all styles shown below are forged, machined and hardened.

CONCEALED RATCHET

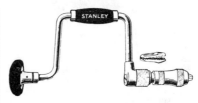

Nickel Plated, Universal Jaws, Metal Clad Ball Bearing Head, Cocobolo Head and Handle.

Nickel Plated, Alligator Jaws, Ball Bearing Head, Cocobolo Head and Handle.

No.		Each
901	8 inch sweep	6.05
	10 " "	6.15
	12 " "	6.35
	14 " "	6.50

Extra Jaws .50 per pair

No.		Each
921	8 inch sweep	5.15
	10 " "	5.25
	12 " "	5.40
	14 " "	5.70

Extra Jaws .50 per pair

BOX RATCHET

Nickel Plated, Universal Jaws, Ball Bearing Head, Cocobolo Head and Handle.

Polished, Alligator Jaws, Metal Clad Head, Aluminum Head and Handle, Case Hardened Shell.
This construction renders it practically unbreakable.

No.		Each
903	8 inch sweep	5.15
	10 " "	5.25
	12 " "	5.40
	14 " "	5.70

Extra Jaws .50 per pair

No.		Each
929	6 inch sweep	4.80
	8 " "	4.80
	10 " "	4.85
	12 " "	4.95

For Prices of Bit Brace Parts see page 181

STANLEY RATCHET BIT BRACES

These Braces are of the highest quality as regards workmanship and material. The Jaws are machined and hardened.

A detailed description of the various kinds of Ratchet Ends, Jaws and Heads, is clearly shown on page 57.

BOX RATCHET

Nickel Plated, Forged Alligator Jaws, Metal Clad Ball Bearing Head, Cocobolo Head and Handle.

No.		Each
913	8 Inch Sweep	4.90
	10 " "	5.00
	12 " "	5.20
	14 " "	5.40

Extra Jaws **.50** per pair

BOX RATCHET

Nickel Plated, Forged Alligator Jaws, Ball Bearing Head, Cocobolo Head and Handle.

No.		Each
923	6 Inch Sweep	4.80
	8 " "	4.80
	10 " "	4.85
	12 " "	4.95
	14 " "	5.15

Extra Jaws **.50** per pair

BOX RATCHET

Nickel Plated, Forged Interlocking Jaws, Metal Clad Ball Bearing Head, Cocobolo Head and Handle.

No.		Each
919	6 Inch Sweep	5.00
	8 " "	5.00
	10 " "	5.05
	12 " "	5.25
	14 " "	5.40

Extra Jaws **.50** per pair

OPEN RATCHET

Nickel Plated, Alligator Jaws, Metal Clad Head, Ebonized Head and Handle.

No.		Each
915	8 Inch Sweep	3.65
	10 " "	3.75
	12 " "	3.90

Extra Jaws **.40** per pair

For prices of Bit Brace Parts see page 181

STANLEY RATCHET BIT BRACES

For a moderate priced Brace this line is recommended for working qualities, strength and general finish. A detailed description of the various kinds of Ratchet Ends, Jaws and Heads, is clearly shown on page 57.

OPEN RATCHET

Nickel Plated, Machined and Hardened Alligator Jaws, Hardwood Head and Handle.

No.		Each
945	8 Inch Sweep	**2.95**
	10 " "	**3.00**
	12 " "	**3.05**

Extra Jaws **.30** per pair

OPEN RATCHET

Nickel Plated, Alligator Jaws, Hardwood Head and Handle.

No.		Each
965N	8 Inch Sweep	**2.00**
	10 " "	**2.05**
	12 " "	**2.10**

Extra Jaws **.20** per pair

"LATCH PAWL" RATCHET

Nickel Plated, Alligator Jews, Hardwood Head and Handle.

No.		Each
975N	10 Inch Sweep	**1.95**

Extra Jaws **.20** per pair

OPEN RATCHET

Polished, Machined and Hardened Alligator Jaws, Hardwood Head and Handle.

No.		Each
955	8 Inch Sweep	**2.60**
	10 " "	**2.65**
	12 " "	**2.70**

Extra Jaws **.30** per pair

OPEN RATCHET

Polished, Alligator Jaws, Hardwood Head and Handle.

No.		Each
965	8 Inch Sweep	**1.85**
	10 " "	**1.90**
	12 " "	**1.95**

Extra Jaws **.20** per pair

"LATCH PAWL" RATCHET

Polished, Alligator Jaws, Hardwood Head and Handle.

No.		Each
975	8 Inch Sweep	**1.75**
	10 " "	**1.80**
	12 " "	**1.85**

Extra Jaws **.20** per pair

For Prices of Bit Brace Parts see page 181

STANLEY
S.W.

STANLEY NON-RATCHET BIT BRACES

A detailed description of the various kinds of Ratchet Ends, Jaws and Heads, is clearly shown on page 57.

NON-RATCHET

These braces correspond in quality and finish with the line of Ratchet Braces shown on pages 58, 59 and 60. The jaws are machined and hardened.

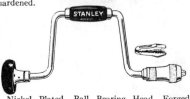

Nickel Plated, Ball Bearing Head, Forged Alligator Jaws, Cocobolo Head and Handle.

No.			Each
924	6 Inch Sweep		**3.55**
	8 ''		**3.55**
	10 ''		**3.65**

Extra Jaws **.50** per pair

Nickel Plated, Metal Clad Head, Alligator Jaws, Ebonized Head and Handle.

No.			Each
916	8 Inch Sweep		**2.30**
	10 '' ''		**2.35**
	12 '' ''		**2.50**

Extra Jaws **.40** per pair

SPOFFORD

Black Finish, Nickel Trim, Cocobolo Head and Handle

No.			Each
108	8 Inch Sweep		**4.15**
110	10 '' ''		**4.45**
112	12 '' ''		**4.75**
114	14 '' ''		**5.25**

NON-RATCHET

These braces correspond in quality and finish with the line of Ratchet Braces shown on page 61.

Nickel Plated, Machined and Hardened Alligator Jaws, Hardwood Head and Handle.

No.			Each
945	8 Inch Sweep		**1.90**
	10 '' ''		**1.95**
	12 '' ''		**2.00**

Extra Jaws **.30** per pair

Polished, Machined and Hardened Alligator Jaws, Hardwood Head and Handle.

No.			Each
956	8 Inch Sweep		**1.50**
	10 '' ''		**1.55**
	12 '' ''		**1.60**

Extra Jaws **.30** per pair

ROLLED FINISH

Shell Polished, Alligator Jaws, Hardwood Head and Handle.

No.			Each
966	8 Inch Sweep		**1.10**
	10 '' ''		**1.15**
	12 '' ''		**1.20**

Extra Jaws **.30** per pair

For Prices of Bit Brace Parts see page 181

STANLEY
S.W.

STANLEY CORNER BIT BRACES

For corner work, when using a bit of ordinary size, these braces will work much faster than a regular ratchet brace.

The gears are of bevel type, the teeth carefully cut, and the whole mechanism enclosed to protect same from dirt as well as to guard the user's hands.

The quill is fastened to the head by three screws, one of which goes through that part of the frame where it enters the head, securely fastening all three together.

These braces are made in two styles of chucks or jaws; otherwise are the same and of the following specifications: Nickel plated, metal clad head, cocobolo head and handles, jaws forged, machined and hardened, with springs for automatic release.

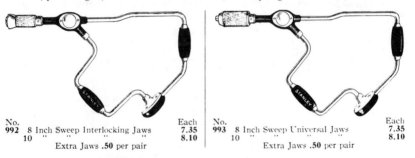

No.   Each
992 8 Inch Sweep Interlocking Jaws   7.35
  10   "   "   "   "   8.10
      Extra Jaws .50 per pair

No.   Each
993 8 Inch Sweep Universal Jaws   7.35
  10   "   "   "   "   8.10
      Extra Jaws .50 per pair

STANLEY CORNER RATCHET BIT BRACES

This style of Ratchet Bit Brace is designed particularly for Electricians, Plumbers and Gas Fitters, but many other Mechanics who have occasion to work close up into corners find it a very useful tool.

The knurled ring between the head and the ratchet mechanism, operated by the thumb and finger of the hand holding the head, is for the purpose of starting and holding the bit until it is far enough in the wood, so that it will not reverse when the handle is turned back.

The peculiar shape of the head enables the user to place the Brace close up to horizontal or perpendicular surfaces.

These Braces are made in two styles of chucks or jaws; otherwise, are the same and of the following specifications:

Nickel plated, ball bearing head, cocobolo head and handle, jaws forged, machined and hardened, with springs for automatic release.

No.   Each
982 Interlocking Jaws   4.60
      Extra Jaws .50 per pair

No.   Each
984 Alligator Jaws   4.40
      Extra Jaws .50 per pair

STANLEY (S.W.)

STANLEY EXTENSION BIT HOLDERS

These Tools extend the Bit, enabling the user to bore through walls, floors, etc., where the ordinary bit will not reach. They are so made that it is impossible for the bit to work loose and come out of the chuck while in use. All numbers can be quickly taken apart if necessary.

SECTIONAL VIEW No. 1

Jaws for holding bit and shank are in one piece, drop forged, hardened and spring tempered. All parts Nickel Plated except Sleeve and Nut, which are blued.

Will Follow Up a ⅝ inch Bit

No.		Each
1	12 inches long	2.15
	16 " "	2.20
	18 " "	2.25
	20 " "	2.30
	24 " "	2.40
	30 " "	2.55

SECTIONAL VIEW Nos. 3 AND 4

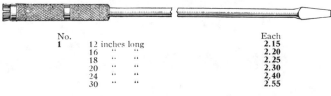

The jaws of Nos. 3 and 4 are of two piece construction, drop forged and tempered and are held in position by springs which permit the easy inserting or removal of the bit. All parts Nickel Plated except Jaws and anti-friction Ring, which are blued.

Will Follow Up a ⅝ inch Bit

No.		Each
3	12 inches long	2.15
	16 " "	2.20
	18 " "	2.25
	20 " "	2.30
	24 " "	2.40
	30 " "	2.55

Will Follow Up a ¾ inch Bit

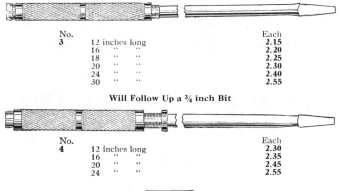

No.		Each
4	12 inches long	2.30
	16 " "	2.35
	20 " "	2.45
	24 " "	2.55

STANLEY BIT BRACE TOOLS

COUNTERSINKS FOR WOOD

These tools cut very rapidly and can be readily resharpened. The Depth Gauge is a very convenient attachment.

No.		Each
18	Malleable Iron, Nickel Plated	.35

| 20 | Malleable Iron with Gauge, Nickel Plated | .45 |

| 23 | Steel Forging, Blued Finish | .45 |

| 24 | Steel Forging with Gauge, Blued Finish | .55 |

DOWEL SHARPENER

Has a keen cutting edge and can be readily resharpened.

No.		Each
22	Nickel Plated	.40

SCREW DRIVER BITS

These Bits are forged from crucible steel, oil tempered and polished.

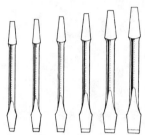

No.		Each
26	$\frac{3}{16}$ in. Tip, 4½ in. long	.25
	¼ " " 4½ " "	.25
	$\frac{5}{16}$ " " 4¾ " "	.25
	⅜ " " 5 " "	.25
	½ " " 5 " "	.25
	⅝ " " 5 " "	.30
	¾ " " 5 " "	.35

STANLEY ADJUSTABLE BIT GAUGE

This Gauge can be attached to bits of any size up to one inch in diameter. Two projections engage with the twist of the bit, so that it can be accurately set for the bit to bore to any depth required. Stops on both sides of the bit insure it remaining upright when the desired depth is reached.

No.		Each
49	2½ in. long, Nickel Plated	.90

STANLEY HAND DRILLS AND BREAST DRILLS

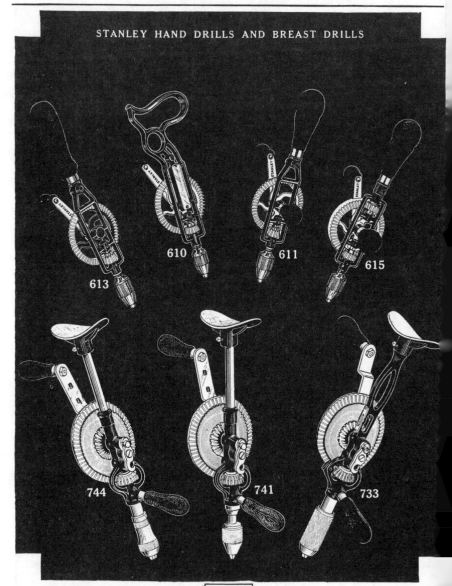

STANLEY HAND DRILLS

This is a new line of Hand Drills, being of special design and having several important features not ordinarily found in tools of this description.

The Frames are of Malleable Iron or Steel. The Malleable Iron Frames have parallel sides, providing a handy means of attaching the Drill to a Drill Frame.

The Chucks are of steel and are fitted with hardened tool steel Jaws. They are securely locked on the spindle end, so are not likely to get mislaid or lost.

The Spindles are provided with a keyway, so that an ordinary nail can be used to prevent turning when inserting a drill in the Chuck.

All Gears are machine cut, the teeth being pitched so as to insure the Spindle running quietly and smoothly.

Special attention is called to the finish of all parts of these tools.

"PISTOL GRIP" PARALLEL FRAME, SINGLE PINION

$3\frac{1}{4}$ in. Speed Gear. Chuck takes drills up to $\frac{1}{4}$ in. diameter.

No.		Each
610	With 6 Drill Bits	3.00
	(1 Each: $\frac{1}{16}$, $\frac{5}{64}$, $\frac{3}{32}$, $\frac{7}{64}$, $\frac{4}{32}$, $\frac{9}{64}$)	

PARALLEL FRAME, DOUBLE PINIONS

$3\frac{1}{4}$ in. extra wide Flanged Speed Gear. Tropical Hardwood Handles and Side Knob. Chuck takes drills up to $\frac{1}{4}$ in. diameter.

No.	Each
612	3.60

PARALLEL FRAME, SINGLE PINION

$3\frac{1}{4}$ in. Speed Gear, Hardwood Handles stained red. Chuck takes drills up to $\frac{1}{4}$ in. diameter.

No.	Each
613	2.50

PARALLEL FRAME, SINGLE PINION

4 in. Speed Gear. Hardwood Handles and Side Knob stained red. Chuck takes drills up to $\frac{3}{8}$ in. diameter.

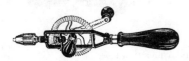

No.	Each
623	4.30

STANLEY HAND DRILLS

PARALLEL FRAME, SINGLE PINION

3¼ in. Speed Gear. Tropical Hardwood Handles and Side Knob. Chuck takes drills up to ¼ in. diameter.

No.		Each
611	With 8 Drill Bits	**3.50**

(1 Each: $\frac{1}{16}$, $\frac{5}{64}$, $\frac{3}{32}$, $\frac{7}{64}$, $\frac{4}{32}$, $\frac{9}{64}$, $\frac{5}{32}$, $\frac{11}{64}$)

PARALLEL FRAME, DOUBLE PINIONS

3¼ in. Speed Gear. Tropical Hardwood Handles and Side Knob. Chuck takes drills up to ¼ in. diameter.

No.		Each
614	With 8 Drill Bits	**3.80**

(1 Each: $\frac{1}{16}$, $\frac{5}{64}$, $\frac{3}{32}$, $\frac{7}{64}$, $\frac{4}{32}$, $\frac{9}{64}$, $\frac{5}{32}$, $\frac{11}{64}$)

PARALLEL FRAME, DOUBLE PINIONS

3¼ in. extra wide flanged Speed Gear. Tropical Hardwood Handles and Side Knob. Chuck takes drills up to ¼ in. diameter.

No.		Each
615	With 8 Drill Bits	**4.00**

(1 Each: $\frac{1}{16}$, $\frac{5}{64}$, $\frac{3}{32}$, $\frac{7}{64}$, $\frac{4}{32}$, $\frac{9}{64}$, $\frac{5}{32}$, $\frac{11}{64}$)

PARALLEL FRAME, DOUBLE PINIONS

4 in. Speed Gears. Tropical Hardwood Handles and Side Knob. Chuck takes drills up to ⅜ in. diameter.

No.		Each
624	With 8 Drill Bits	**5.02**

(1 Each: $\frac{1}{16}$, $\frac{5}{64}$, $\frac{3}{32}$, $\frac{7}{64}$, $\frac{4}{32}$, $\frac{9}{64}$, $\frac{5}{32}$, $\frac{11}{64}$)

STANLEY (S.W.)

STANLEY HAND DRILLS

STEEL FRAME, DOUBLE PINIONS

3¼ in. Speed Gear. Tropical Hardwood Handles. Chuck takes drills up to ¼ in. in diameter.

No.
616

Each
3.10

STEEL FRAME, DOUBLE PINIONS

3¼ in. extra wide flanged Speed Gear. Tropical Hardwood Handles and Side Knobs. Chuck takes drills up to ¼ in. diameter.

No.
617

Each
3.60

STEEL FRAME, DOUBLE PINIONS

4 in. Speed Gear. Tropical Hardwood Handles and Side Knob. Chuck takes drills up to ³⁄₈ in. diameter.

No.
626

Each
3.90

STEEL FRAME, SINGLE PINION

3¼ in. Speed Gear. Hardwood Handles and side Knobs. Chuck takes drills up to ¼ in. diameter.

No.
618

Each
2.00

STEEL FRAME, SINGLE PINION

3¼ in. Speed Gear. Hardwood Handles and side Knobs. Chuck takes drills up to ¼ in. diameter.

No.
619 With 8 Drill Bits
(1 Each: ¹⁄₁₆, ⁵⁄₆₄, ³⁄₃₂, ⁷⁄₆₄, ⁴⁄₃₂, ⁹⁄₆₄, ⁵⁄₃₂, ¹¹⁄₆₄)

Each
2.60

STANLEY
S.W.

STANLEY BREAST DRILLS

All bright parts are nickel plated. Other parts are finished in black and orange. Handles are Cocobolo. A Level is set in the frame to assist the user to maintain a horizontal position of the drill while working. The Breast Plate is adjustable. The Handle can be set for three different sweeps. All Jaws are forgings, machined and hardened. The Breast Drills with 3 jaw chuck are particularly adapted for metal work.

STEEL FRAME, SINGLE SPEED

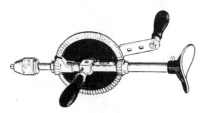
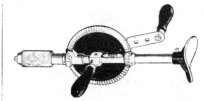

No.		Each
711	Fitted with Three Jaw Chuck, which will take round shank twist drills from ½ inch down	**8.00**

No.		Each
713	Fitted with Universal Jaws which are adapted for round shanks ⅛ in. to ½ in. diameter as well as taper shank bits	**7.15**

Extra Jaws **.50** per pair

STEEL FRAME, DOUBLE SPEED

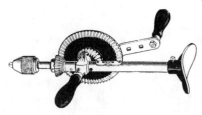
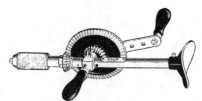

No.		Each
721	Three Jaw Chuck, which will take round shank twist drills from ½ in. down	**7.65**

No.		Each
723	Fitted with Universal Jaws which are adapted for round shanks ⅛ in. to ½ in. diameter, as well as taper shank bits	**7.40**

Extra Jaws **.50** per pair

"D" OR SPADE HANDLES

All of the above Drills can be furnished with "D" Handles instead of Breast Plate without extra charge. Letter "D" added to number designates "D" Handle.

STANLEY
(S.W.)

STANLEY BREAST DRILLS

The Frame is of one piece, made of malleable iron, giving strength with light weight. All bright parts are nickel plated, other parts are finished in black and orange. Handles are Cocobolo. A Level is set in the frame to assist the user to maintain a horizontal position of the drill while working. The Breast Plate is adjustable. The Handle can be set for three different sweeps. All Jaws are forgings, machined and hardened. The Breast Drills with 3 Jaw Chuck are particularly adapted for metal work.

IRON FRAME, DOUBLE SPEED

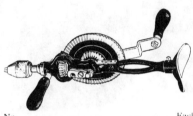 

No.   Each
731 Fitted with Three Jaw Chuck, which will take round shank twist drills from ½ in. down   **6.50**

No.   Each
733 Fitted with Universal Jaws which are adapted for round shanks ⅛ in. to ½ in. diameter as well as taper shank bits   **5.75**
Extra Jaws .50 per pair

"VICTOR" BREAST DRILLS, DOUBLE SPEED

All bright parts are polished, other parts are finished in black and orange. The Handles are ebonized, the Breast Plate is adjustable. The Handle can be set for three different sweeps. All Jaws are forgings, machined and hardened. The Breast Drills with 3 Jaw Chuck are particularly adapted for metal work.

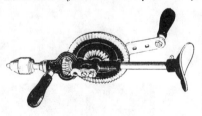 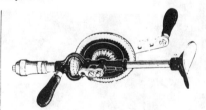

No.   Each
741 Fitted with Three Jaw Chuck, which will take round shank twist drills from ½ in. down   **5.45**

No.   Each
744 Fitted with Alligator Jaws, which are adapted for small and medium round shanks as well as taper shank bits   **4.55**
Extra Jaws .50 per pair

"D" OR SPADE HANDLES

All of the above Drills can be furnished with "D" Handles instead of Breast Plate without extra charge. Letter "D" added to number designates "D" Handle.

"BAILEY"-"BED ROCK" AND GAGE PLANES

4

A 4

5

605

G 6

7 C

STANLEY BENCH PLANES

The Planes described on the pages immediately following, generally known as Bench Planes, are divided into four classes, namely *Smooth—Jack—Fore* and *Jointer*.

A SMOOTH PLANE is used for finishing or smoothing off flat surfaces. Where uneven spots are of slight area, its short length will permit it to locate these irregularities, leaving the work with a smooth surface when finished.

A JACK PLANE is used to true up the edges of a board in the rough and prepare it for the Fore or Jointer.

(Attention is called to No. 5¼ "Junior" Jack Plane, described on page 75. Its size makes it especially desirable for all work requiring a lighter Jack Plane than the No. 5 or 5½. Particularly well adapted for Manual Training Work.)

A FORE PLANE is simply a short Jointer, and being lighter, is preferred by some workmen to the longer Plane.

A JOINTER is a finishing Plane for large surfaces and is invariably used to true up the edges of boards so that they can be closely fitted or joined together.

The color plate on the opposite page illustrates a few numbers of Stanley "Bailey," "Bed Rock," and "Gage" Iron Bench Planes. A complete description including sizes, prices, etc., of all three styles will be found on pages 74 to 81.

Particular attention is called to the Cutters, which are thin and of uniform thickness.

This permits: 1. Ease in grinding. 2. Less grinding as a thin cutter can be kept in condition by honing. 3. Less tendency to "stub off" the cutting edge when honing, hence the original bevel is kept much longer.

They are made of the highest grade steel obtainable, the cutting and wearing qualities being known the world over.

The adjustments of both Cutters and Frogs, while differing in detail are in each case the result of long years of study and provide a range of adjustment that will satisfy all requirements.

STANLEY "BAILEY" ADJUSTABLE IRON PLANES

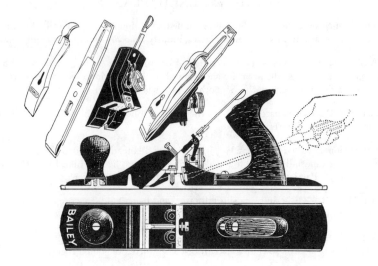

STANLEY "BAILEY" IRON PLANES have been in use for nearly sixty years and are the recognized standard for planes of this type. While retaining all the original features, many valuable improvements in construction have been added from time to time. Only the finest materials and the best workmanship are used in their manufacture.

In the illustration the detail of construction is very clearly shown. Note that the frog has a support directly at the rear of the mouth, making practically one solid piece from the cap to the bottom. The sides and bottom of the plane are stiffened by means of the cross ribs. The screw bosses on each side of the center rib are very deep, allowing a number of threads to engage, thereby securely holding the frog. The design prevents the plane being drawn out of true when the face of the frog is screwed up hard.

The width of the mouth may be regulated and made wider or narrower as coarse or fine work may require. First remove the lever and cutter and loosen the two frog screws that fasten the frog to its seat. With a screw driver turn the center adjusting screw (see cut) to the right to close the mouth, and to the left to open it. When the frog is in the position desired, tighten the frog screws and replace the cutter and lever.

STANLEY
(S.W.)

STANLEY "BAILEY" ADJUSTABLE IRON PLANES

These Planes have Rosewood Handles and Knobs. The Cutters are adjustable endwise and sidewise.

SMOOTH BOTTOMS

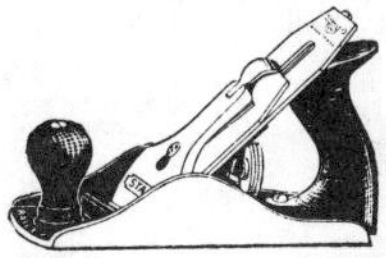

No.		Each
1	Smooth, 5½ in. long. 1¼ in. Cutter	3.00
2	" 7 " " 1⅝ " "	3.85
3	" 8 " " 1¾ " "	4.00
4	" 9 " " 2 " " (Weight No. 4 Plane, 3½ lbs.)	4.40
4½	Smooth, 10 in. long, 2⅜ in. Cutter	5.00

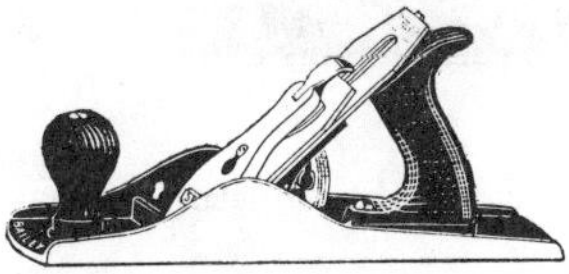

5	Jack, 14 in. long, 2 in. Cutter (Weight No. 5 Plane, 4½ lbs.)	5.00
5¼	"Junior" Jack, 11½ in. long, 1¾ in. Cutter	4.50
5½	Jack, 15 in. long, 2¼ in. Cutter	5.70

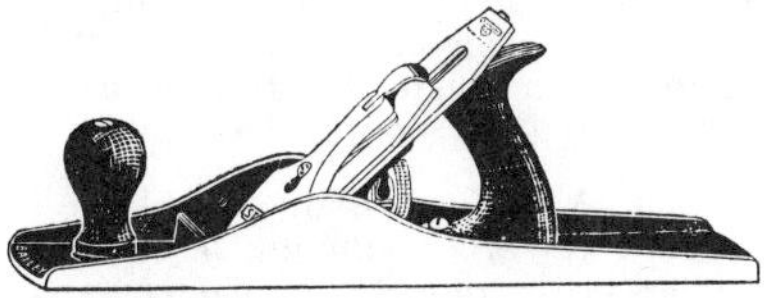

6	Fore, 18 in. long, 2⅜ in. Cutter (Weight No. 6 Plane, 6¼ lbs.)	6.50
7	Jointer, 22 in. long, 2⅜ in. Cutte	7.40
8	" 24 " " 2⅝ " "	8.85

CORRUGATED BOTTOMS

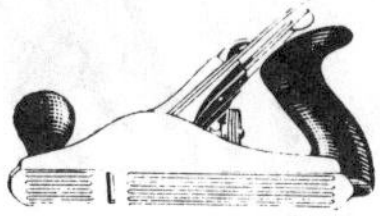

No.		Each
2C	Smooth, 7 in. long, 1⅝ in. Cutter	4.05
3C	" 8 " " 1¾ " "	4.20
4C	" 9 " " 2 " "	4.60
4½C	" 10 " " 2⅜ " "	5.30

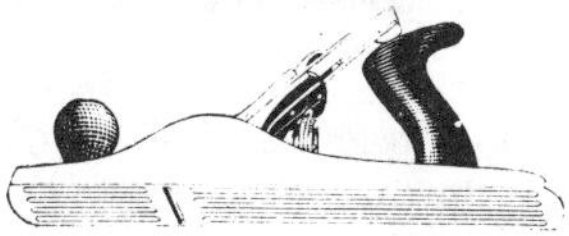

5C	Jack, 14 in. long, 2 in. Cutter	5.30
5¼C	"Junior" Jack, 11½ in. long, 1¾ in. Cutter	4.75
5½C	Jack, 15 in. long, 2¼ in. Cutter	6.00

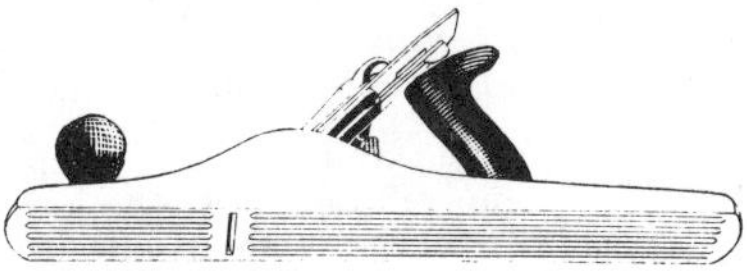

6C	Fore, 18 in. long, 2⅜ in. Cutter	6.80
7C	Jointer, 22 in. long. 2⅜ in. Cutter	7.80
8C	" 24 " " 2⅝ " "	9.30

For Prices of Plane Irons and Plane Parts see page 170

STANLEY "BED ROCK" ADJUSTABLE IRON PLANES

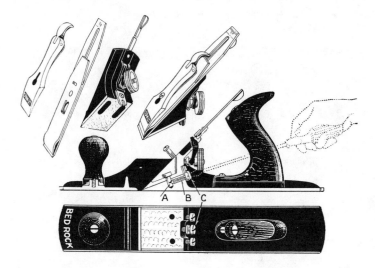

The "Bed Rock" Plane owing to its solidity and variety of adjustments makes an ideal tool for fine work on all woods.

The cutter, frog and bottom are so designed, machined and fitted that they are practically one solid piece of metal, thus preventing any chance of vibration.

Particular attention is called to the shape of the sides. This distinctive feature adds greatly to the strength of the plane as well as affording large bearing surfaces when the plane is used on its sides.

The frog may be adjusted either forward or backward without removing the lever and cutter; simply slacken the tension of the two frog clamping screws "B", and with a screw driver adjust the frog as desired by means of the frog adjusting screw "C" in the center, and then tighten the frog clamping screws. (See cut).

The frog is held to its seat by means of two pins "A" of large diameter. Each of these has a tapered hole near the lower end. The two frog clamping screws "B" have tapered points. These points fit in the holes in the pins "A." The center of the tapered hole in these pins is slightly above the center line of the frog clamping screws, so that when these screws are driven in, they produce the effect of a wedge, drawing the pins downward, and clamping the frog absolutely rigid in its place.

If, for any reason, these frog pins "A" should be taken out of the plane, care must be used in replacing them to see that the tapered holes come in line with the points of the frog clamping screws "B".

STANLEY
S.W.

STANLEY "BED ROCK" ADJUSTABLE IRON PLANES

These Planes have Rosewood Handles and Knobs. The Cutters are adjustable endwise and sidewise.

SMOOTH BOTTOMS

No.		Each
602	Smooth, 7 in. long. 1 ⅝ in. Cutter	4.25
603	" 8 " " 1 ¾ " "	4.40
604	" 9 " " 2 " "	4.85
604½	" 10 " " 2 ⅜ " "	5.55

605	Jack, 14 in. long. 2 in. Cutter	5.55
605¼	" 11 ½ " " 1 ¾ " "	5.00
605½	" 15 " " 2 ¼ " "	6.25

606	Fore 18 in. long, 2 ⅜ in. Cutter	7.10
607	Jointer, 22 in. long, 2 ⅜ in. Cutter	8.15
608	" 24 " " 2 ⅝ " "	9.70

CORRUGATED BOTTOMS

No.		Each
603C	Smooth, 8 in. long, 1 ¾ in. Cutter	4.65
604C	" 9 " " 2 " "	5.10
604½C	" 10 " " 2 ⅜ " "	5.85

605C	Jack, 14 in. long, 2 in. Cutter	5.85
605½C	" 15 " " 2 ¼ " "	6.60

606C	Fore, 18 in. long, 2 ⅜ in. Cutter	7.50
607C	Jointer, 22 in. long, 2 ⅜ in. Cutter	8.55
608C	" 24 " " 2 ⅝ " "	10.20

For Prices of Plane Irons and Plane Parts see page 171

STANLEY (S.W.)

GAGE SELF-SETTING PLANES

Gage Self-Setting Planes do not chatter because the cutter iron is held rigid at the cutting edge by the cap; at the same time the lever screw used for tightening the cap is pressing against the binder plate on top of the cutter iron. This pressure against the binder plate holds the cutter firm its entire length.

The Self-Setting Features are:

First—The relation of the edge of the steel cap to the edge of the Iron is automatically adjusted when setting the Plane for fine or coarse work.

Second—The Plane Iron and Cap goes back in the same position after being removed for honing.

The Lever and Cap (A) is the same in Iron and Wood Planes. The upper part of the Lever has a hardened steel cap fastened to it by two screws, by means of which it may be adjusted to the cutting iron to make either a single or double plane iron, as desired, for various kinds of work.

A

C

The Plane Iron (B) consists of three pieces—the cutter, the adjustment slide fastened to the under side of the cutter (shown black), and the binder plate fastened above the cutter—all three being fastened by one screw.

The Adjustment Silde (C) is machined on its sides to accurately fit the groove machined in the frog and is also machined to fit the adjusting screw. This is the same in both Iron and Wood Planes.

B

The Frog (D)—In the iron plane the Frog is fitted to the plane bottom and then permanently attached by screw and pins. A continuous cutter seat is obtained clear to the plane mouth.

In the wood plane the Frog (E) is a part of an iron throat which fits into the plane wood and is there fastened by screws. This iron throat is adjustable as the plane bottom wears, thus eliminating any difficulty of the mouth (F) wearing large. The bottom of this throat is ground a little rounding and may be set slightly below the plane bottom, which enables the plane to cut very fast with a fine shaving.

There is an endwise screw adjustment to the cutter in both the Iron and Wood Planes.

D

E

F

GAGE SELF-SETTING IRON PLANES

The Self-Setting feature of these Planes is fully explained on the opposite page. The handles and knobs are made of Rosewood.

SMOOTH BOTTOMS	**CORRUGATED BOTTOMS**

No.	Each	No.	Each
G3 Smooth 8¾ inches long, 1¾ inch Cutter	**4.25**	**G3C** Smooth 8¾ inches long, 1¾ inch Cutter	**4.45**
G4 Smooth 9 inches long, 2 inch Cutter	**4.60**	**G4C** Smooth 9 inches long, 2 inch Cutter	**4.85**

G5 Jack 14 inches long, 2 inch Cutter	**5.30**	**G5C** Jack 15 inches long, 2 inch Cutter	**5.55**

G6 Fore 18 inches long, 2¼ inch Cutter	**6.80**	**G6C** Fore 18 inches long, 2¼ inch Cutter	**7.15**
G7 Jointer 22 inches long, 2½ inch Cutter	**7.80**	**G7C** Jointer 22 inches long, 2½ inch Cutter	**8.15**

For prices of Plane Irons and Plane Parts see page 172

STANLEY "BAILEY" AND GAGE WOOD PLANES

Every Carpenter needs two or more wood planes in his kit, for rough outside work. Both the Stanley "Bailey" and the Gage Self-Setting Planes supply the demand for a wood plane of superior quality.

The bottoms are made from selected, well seasoned beech.

STANLEY "BAILEY"	GAGE SELF-SETTING
Cutters adjustable endwise and sidewise. The Frog is held in place by two machine screws which pass through the top iron and screw into brass lugs. These lugs are screwed and securely pinned into the wood bottom. Handles and Knobs of Beech.	The Self-Setting feature of these planes is fully explained on page 78. Handles and knobs stained black.

No.   Each
22 Smooth 8 in. long, 1 ¾ in. Cutter   **3.40**
24   "   9 "   "   2   "   "   **3.60**

No.   Each
G22 Smooth 10 in. long, 1 ¾ in. Cutter   **4.50**
G35   "   10 "   "   2   "   "   **4.80**

No.   Each
35 Handled Smooth, 9 in. long, 2 in. Cutter **4.20**
36 Handled Smooth, 10 in. long, 2 ⅜ in.
     Cutter   **4.75**

No.   Each
G26 Jack 14 in. long, 2 in. Cutter   **5.25**

No.   Each
26   Jack 15 in. long, 2   in. Cutter   **3.70**
27½ Jack 15 "   "   2 ¼ "   "   **4.30**
28   Fore 18 "   "   2 ⅜ "   "   **4.70**
31   Jointer 24 in. long, 2 ⅜ in. Cutter   **5.05**
32   "   26 "   "   2 ⅝ "   "   **5.45**

No.   Each
G28 Fore 10 in. long, 2 ¼ in. Cutter   **6.00**
G30 Jointer 22 in. long, 2 ¼ in. Cutter   **6.40**

For prices of Plane Irons and Plane Parts see pages 172 and 173

[STANLEY]
(S.W.)

STANLEY ALUMINUM BENCH PLANES

The Aluminum Planes shown below are of the same general design and construction as the regular line of Stanley "Bailey" Planes described on pages 73-74 and 75.

This includes the well known Bailey adjustments of both frogs and cutters. The bottoms and frogs, however, are made of Aluminum, which provides a tool that is highly recommended on account of its light weight and the fact that it will not rust.

The handles and knobs are made of Rosewood.

No.		Each
A4	Smooth, 9 in. long, 2 in. Cutter, Weight 2¼ lbs.	**5.80**

No.		Each
A5	Jack, 14 in. long, 2 in. Cutter, Weight 2⅝ lbs.	**6.60**

No.		Each
A6	Fore, 18 in. long, 2³⁄₈ in. Cutter, Weight 3½ lbs.	**8.80**

For prices of Plane Irons and Plane Parts see page 170

STANLEY STEEL BENCH PLANES

These Steel Planes of the regular Stanley "Bailey" type of bench planes have a malleable iron frog and lever cap and a steel base. These combined features render the planes practically indestructable and give them an entirely new appearance. Knobs and handles are of selected Rosewood.

No.		Each	No.		Each
S4	**Steel** Smooth, 9 in. long, 2-in. Cutter	**4.85**	S5	**Steel** Jack, 14 in. long, 2-in. Cutter	**5.55**

STANLEY READY EDGE BLADES

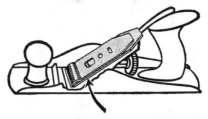

Ready Edge Blade and Double Iron in Position

Stanley Ready Edge blades are attached by screws to specially constructed blade holders. A plane iron cap of special design fits over this and is held in place by a cap screw.

These blades assure a sharp cutting edge. Whenever an old blade becomes dull a new one can be quickly substituted.

Stanley Ready Edge blades are furnished with double Plane Irons in the $1\frac{3}{4}$, 2 and $2\frac{3}{8}$ inch sizes for use on the regular Stanley "Bailey", "Bed Rock" and Aluminum Planes.

Each

One Special Plane Iron with six Ready Edge Blades   **2.00**
Extra blades. Package of five   **.80**

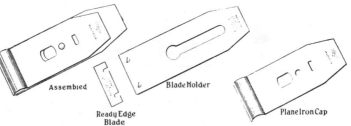

Assembled   Blade Holder

Ready Edge
Blade

Plane Iron Cap

Cap Screw

For prices of Plane Irons and Plane Parts see page 170

STANLEY PLANES
CIRCULAR PLANES

These Planes have flexible steel faces which can be accurately adjusted for planing the inside or outside of circles. The cutters are adjustable endwise and sidewise. There are two designs, varying in the method of adjusting the face.

In the No. 113 the face is fastened at its center to the Plane Body, and adjusted at the ends by means of a screw and levers. It has a graduated scale for setting the face.

In the No. 20 the face is fastened at each end to the Body, and adjusted by a screw at the center. This gives great strength and accuracy.
The design of the frame provides convenient and firm handles for both hands.

No.		Each
113	10 inches long, 1¾ inch Cutter, Japanned	7.45

No.		Each
20	10 inches long, 1¾ inch Cutter, Japanned	9.15

CARRIAGE MAKERS RABBET PLANES

Especially adapted for heavy framing required in mining work, for carriage or wagon building, or in any work of a similar nature. The Cutters are adjustable endwise and sidewise. In the No. 10¼ Plane both the handle and knob can be tilted to either side and held by a set screw. This permits of the Plane being worked with ease close up to perpendicular sides of any height without hurting the hands of the user. It is also fitted with spurs on both sides, so that it will rabbet across the grain equally as well as with it.

No.		Each
10½	9 inches long, 2⅛ inch Cutter	5.30
10	13 " " 2⅛ " "	6.40

No.		Each
10¼	13 inches long, 2⅛ inch Cutter	7.65

SCRUB PLANES

For planing down to a rough dimension any board that is too wide to conveniently rip with a hand saw, an operation that is sometimes called "hogging." This is made possible by reason of the shape of the extra heavy cutter, the cutting edge of which is round instead of square. Handle and Knob of Beech.

BELT MAKERS PLANE

For chamfering down the ends or laps of a belt before fastening them together. Used by belt manufacturers, also a valuable tool for all users of belting, enabling them to make repairs that otherwise would require that the belt be sent to the makers. Fitted with an adjustable throat. The cutter is adjustable endwise. Hardwood Handle.

No.		Each
40	9½ inches long. 1¼ inch Cutter, Japanned	2.45
40½	10½ inches long, 1½ inch Cutter, Japanned	3.25

No.		Each
11	5¾ inches long, 2⅜ inch Cutter, Japanned	4.30

For prices of Plane Irons and Plane Parts see page 177

STANLEY
S.W.

STANLEY BLOCK PLANES

9½

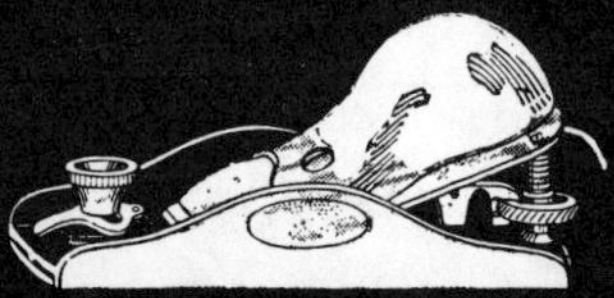

18

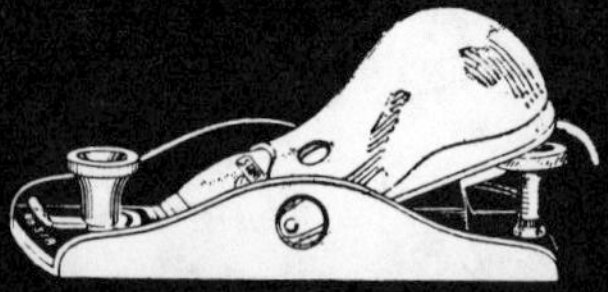

S 18

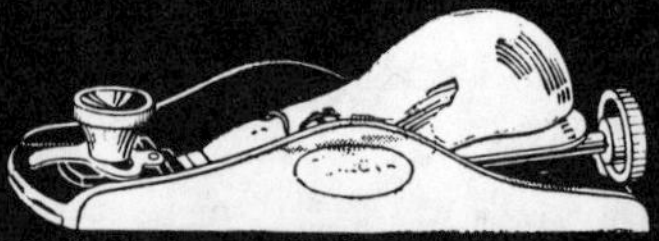

65

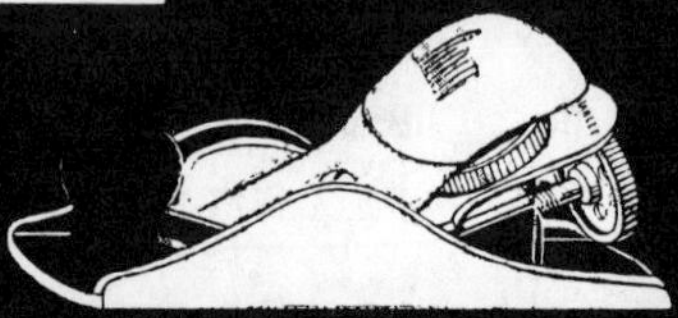

140

60½

220

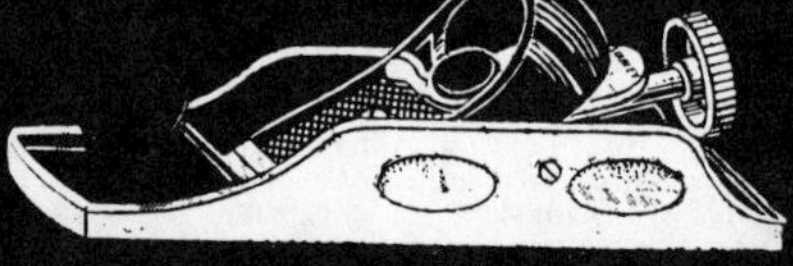

131

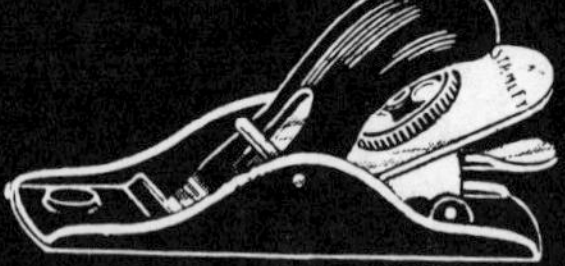

103

110

STANLEY AND "BAILEY" BLOCK PLANES

A Block Plane was first made to meet the demand for a Plane which could be easily held in one hand while planing across the grain, particularly the ends of boards, etc. This latter work many Carpenters call "Blocking in", hence the name "Block" Plane.

The Cutter rests on its seat at an angle of 20 degrees as against 45 degrees in the ordinary Bench Plane, and the cutter bevel is made on the upper instead of on the lower side.

To meet a demand for Block Planes having the cutters lying at a still lower angle than 20 degrees, a line of low Angle Planes are offered. In these the cutter rests on its seat at an angle of only 12 degrees, permitting of great ease in working across the grain on hard wood.

Those planes having adjustable throat are especially recommended, as this feature allows the mouth to be easily and quickly opened or closed as coarse or fine work may require.

The "Hand-y" feature on the sides will also be found of benefit as they form a convenient grip for the hand and give a feeling of security to the workman.

On the following pages will be found a number of different styles, varying as to size, method of adjustment and trim.

SKEW CUTTERS

When the cutter is set on a skew or angle with the bottom of the Plane as in Planes Nos. 39-46-95-140-196 and 289, the shaving or drawing cut necessary in working across the grain is obtained while still using the plane straight with the work.

This cut is less liable to break the fibre than a straight cut and leaves the work in better condition.

STANLEY "BAILEY" BLOCK PLANES

The cutters are adjustable endwise and sidewise and rest on their seats at an angle of 20 degrees. The Throats are adjustable for coarse of fine work. Fitted with "Hand-y" feature.

JAPAN TRIMMINGS

No.		Each
9½	6 inches long, 1 ⅝ inch Cutter	2.30
15	7 " " 1 ⅝ " "	2.40

Handled

These Planes have an iron handle with rosewood knob extending from the rear making it convenient to work the plane with both hands.

No.		Each
9¾	6 inches long, 1 ⅝ inch Cutter	2.65
15½	7 " " 1 ⅝ "	2.90

STEEL

Similar in design to the regular No. 18 Block Plane, but the bottom and Adjustable Front are made of steel, making the plane practically indestructible.

No.		Each
S18	6 inches long, 1 ⅝ inch Cutter	3.50
	Weight 1 ⅛ lbs.	

NICKEL TRIMMINGS

No.		Each
16	6 inches long, 1 ⅝ inch Cutter	2.60
17	7 " " 1 ⅝ " "	2.80

Knuckle Joint

Fitted with a new and patented form of lever or cap called "knuckle joint," which, being entirely of steel, is practically indestructible.

No.		Each
18	6 inches long, 1 ⅝ inch Cutter	3.00
	Weight 1 ⅜ lbs.	
19	7 inches long, 1 ⅝ inch Cutter	3.20

ALUMINUM

Similar in construction to the regular No. 18 Block Plane, but the Bottom and Adjustable Front are made of Aluminum, making it extremely light in weight and rust proof.

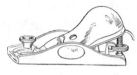

No.		Each
A18	6 inches long, 1 ⅝ inch Cutter	3.50
	Weight ⅞ lbs.	

For prices of Plane Irons and Plane Parts see page 174

STANLEY
S.W.

STANLEY LOW ANGLE BLOCK PLANES

The cutters are adjustable endwise by means of the adjusting wheel at the rear of the plane. In these planes the cutter rests on its seat at an angle of only 12 degrees, which permits of great ease in working across the grain on hard woods. All numbers except No. 62, have the "Hand-y" feature.

| ADJUSTABLE THROAT
Nickel Trimming | | ADJUSTABLE THROAT
Knuckle Joint | |

No.		Each	No.		Each
60	6 inches long, 1 ⅜ inch Cutter	2.65	65	7 inches long, 1 ⅝ inch Cutter Nickel Trimming	3.15

| ADJUSTABLE THROAT | | NON-ADJUSTABLE THROAT | |

No.		Each	No.		Each
60½	6 inches long, 1 ⅜ inch Cutter Japan Trimming	2.40	61	6 inches long, 1 ⅜ inch Cutter Nickel Trimming with Rosewood Knob	2.30
65½	7 inches long, 1 ⅝ inch Cutter Japan Trimming	2.60	63	7 inches long, 1 ⅝ inch Cutter Nickel Trimming with Rosewood Knob	2.75

ADJUSTABLE THROAT

Especially adapted for use in cutting across the grain on heavy work, where more power is required than can be obtained by the use of the ordinary Block Plane. It is fitted with a rosewood handle and knob, and is designed to be operated with both hands. No. 164 has an overhead adjustment. It is short in length, making it an ideal plane for working into small places.

No.		Each	No.		Each
62	14 inches long, 2 inch Cutter, Black Nickel Trimming	5.60	164	9 inches long, 2 inch Cutter,	5.00

For prices of Plane Irons and Plane Parts see page 174

[STANLEY]
(S.W.)

STANLEY BLOCK PLANES

For those desiring a plane for ordinary work that does not require that the tool be frequently adjusted, we strongly recommend this line.

ADJUSTABLE

No. 103 is for light work. The cutter is adjustable endwise. The bottom is ground true and the sides neatly japanned.

No.		Each
103	5½ inches long, 1⅜ inch Cutter, Lever Adjustment	**1.20**

No. 120 is similar in design to the No. 103, having the same form of cutter adjustment and cutter fastening device. However, in this plane the sides are ground.

No.		Each
120	7 inches long, 1⅝ inch Cutter, Lever Adjustment. Rosewood Knob	**1.65**

No. 220 is in many ways better adapted for average use than any of the cheaper block planes made. It is ground on both bottom and sides. The cutter is fastened by a lever and cam, and is adjustable endwise.

No.		Each
220	7 inches long, 1⅝ inch Cutter, Screw Adjustment. Rosewood Knob	**1.70**

NON-ADJUSTABLE

Nos. 100 and 101 are very handy little planes for household use and many mechanics carry one in their kits for odds and ends of light work. No. 100 has an iron handle.

No. 100   No. 101

No.		Each
100	3½ inches long, 1 inch Cutter, Handled	**.55**
101	3½ " " 1 " "	**.45**

No. 102 is a light, serviceable plane, 5½ inches long. The bottom is ground and the sides japanned.

No.		Each
102	5½ inches long, 1⅜ inch Cutter	**.85**

No. 110 is the most popular of all the non-adjustable block planes. Both the bottoms and sides are ground and in place of the boss on the front for a finger rest, it has a rosewood knob.

No.		Each
110	7 inches long, 1⅝ inch Cutter	**1.20**

For prices of Plane Irons and Plane Parts see page 174

[STANLEY S.W.]

STANLEY BLOCK PLANES

BLOCK AND RABBET

A detachable slide will easily change it from a block plane to a rabbet plane, and vice-versa. The cutter is adjustable endwise, and set on a skew. (See page 85.)

No.		Each
140	7 inches long, 1¾ inch Cutter, Japan Trimming, Rosewood Knob	3.00

DOUBLE END ADJUSTABLE

A combination block and bull nose plane. It has two slots and a movable cutter seat. Use center cutter seat and slot for ordinary block plane work. For use as a bull nose plane, reverse the cutter seat by throwing over the adjusting wheel. It is fitted with the "Hand-y" feature, and the cutter is adjustable endwise.

No.		Each
131	8 inches long, 1⅝ inch Cutter, Japan Trimming, Rosewood Knob	2.80

ADJUSTABLE BLOCK

Designed especially for manual training use. It is fitted with the "Hand-y" feature. The cutter is secured in its place by a lever fastened with a cam. Cutter adjustable endwise.

No.		Each
203	5½ inches long, 1⅜ inch Cutter, Rosewood Knob	1.50

EDGE TRIMMING BLOCK

For trimming or smoothing the edge of boards for a square or close fit. The cutter works on a skew (see page 85). Wood blocks of various bevels may be attached, enabling the user to make a slanting cut.

No.		Each
95	6 inches long, ⅞ inch Cutter, Japanned	1.90

DOUBLE END NON-ADJUSTABLE

It has two slots and two cutter seats. The center seat and slot to be used for ordinary block plane work, the other slot and seat for use when it is desired to work same as a bull nose plane.

No.		Each
130	8 inches long, 1⅝ inch Cutter, Hardwood Knob	1.70

BULL NOSE RABBET

This plane will be found very useful for working close up into corners or other difficult places. The mouth can be adjusted for different widths by means of the set screw on top of the plane.

No.		Each
75	4 inches long, 1 inch Cutter, Japanned	.75

For Prices of Plane Irons and Plane Parts see pages 174 and 175

STANLEY
(S.W.)

STANLEY MISCELLANEOUS PLANES

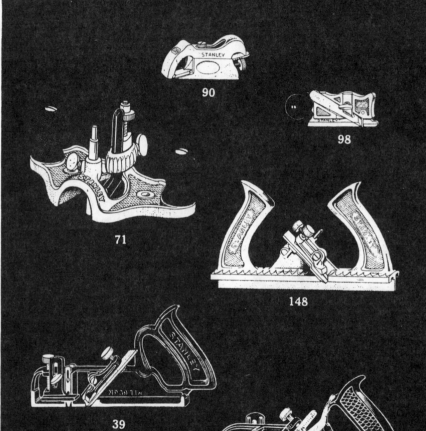

STANLEY RABBET AND FILLETSTER PLANES

DUPLEX RABBET AND FILLETSTER PLANES

They have two seats for the cutter, one for regular and the other for bull-nose work. Also a spur and a removable depth gauge. The adjustable fence can be used on either side of the Plane and slides under the bottom for regulating the width of the cut. The rear cutter is adjustable endwise.

No. A78 is the same in every respect as the No. 78 except that the body and fence are made of aluminum, making it considerably lighter in weight and rust proof.

No.   Each
78   8 1⁄2 in. long, 1 1⁄2 in. Cutter. Wgt. 2 3⁄4 lbs. **3.30**

No.   Each
A78   8 1⁄2 in. long, 1 1⁄2 in. Cutter. Wgt. 1 1⁄4 lbs. **4.20**

SKEW CUTTER RABBET AND FILLETSTER PLANE

It has an extra wide skew cutter described on page 85, and an adjustable spur on each side. Can be used either right or left hand. The fence and depth gauge can be attached to either side; the fence sliding under the bottom. Remove arms and fence, and a Skew Cutter Rabbet Plane is obtained.

RABBET AND FILLETSTER PLANE

This plane will lie perfectly flat on either side to work either right or left hand and has an adjustable fence for regulating the width of the cut. It is fitted with two spurs and an adjustable depth gauge. The front of the plane can be detached for bull-nose work. The cutter is adjustable endwise.

No.   Each
289   8 1⁄2 inches long, 1 3⁄4 inch Cutter   **3.85**

No.   Each
278   6 3⁄4 inches long, 1 inch Cutter   **3.20**

For Prices of Plane Irons and Plane Parts see page 175

For Prices of Plane Irons and Plane Parts see page 175

STANLEY
S.W.

STANLEY RABBET AND DADO PLANES

HANDLED IRON RABBET PLANES

These planes will lie flat on either side and can be used with right or left hand while planing into corners or up against perpendicular surfaces.

They are fitted with a spur and a detachable depth gauge.

No.					Each
190	8 inches long,	$1\frac{1}{2}$ inch Cutter			2.95
191	" "	$1\frac{1}{4}$ "	"		2.80
192	" "	1 "	"		2.60

HANDLED IRON DADO PLANES

They will keep true even in the narrowest widths. They have skew cutters (see page 85), an adjustable depth gauge, and two adjustable spurs.

In ordering, always give the number (39) and width of cutter desired.

No.					Each
39	8 inches long,	$\frac{1}{4}$ inch Cutter			2.90
	8 " "	$\frac{3}{8}$ "	"		3.10
	8 " "	$\frac{1}{2}$ "	"		3.30
	8 " "	$\frac{5}{8}$ "	"		3.45
	8 " "	$\frac{3}{4}$ "	"		3.60
	8 " "	$\frac{13}{16}$ "	"		3.80
	8 " "	$\frac{7}{8}$ "	"		3.80
	8 " "	1 "	"		3.95

CORNER ROUNDING PLANE

This plane is designed for rounding corners on wall board battens, casings, shelving, etc.

It is made in three sizes, to cut $\frac{1}{4}$ inch, $\frac{3}{8}$ inch and $\frac{1}{2}$ inch circles. The cutters are sharpened ready for use.

No.					Each
144	$7\frac{1}{2}$ inches long,	$\frac{1}{4}$ inch Cutter			1.50
	$7\frac{1}{2}$ "	"	$\frac{3}{8}$ "	"	1.50
	$7\frac{1}{2}$ "	"	$\frac{1}{2}$ "	"	1.50

SPECIAL DADO PLANE

For blind wire grooving as well as for many other purposes. Fitted with a double spur, which prevents splintering, and a depth gauge, allowing a groove to be cut up to the limit of the plane—$\frac{1}{2}$ of an inch. The fence is adjustable.

No.					Each
239	$7\frac{1}{2}$ inches long,	$\frac{1}{8}$ inch Cutter			5.10
	$7\frac{1}{2}$ "	"	$\frac{3}{16}$ "	"	5.10
	$7\frac{1}{2}$ "	"	$\frac{1}{4}$ "	"	5.10

For Prices of Plane Irons and Plane Parts see page 175

STANLEY
S.W.

STANLEY MATCHING PLANES

These planes cut a tongue on the edge of one board to fit a groove in the edge of another so that when put together the surfaces of the boards come true. The straightness of both tongue and groove, and their distance from the surface, is governed by a fence. This fence is so designed that the distance of the groove from the side the fence engages is practically the same as the width of the groove.

SWINGING FENCE MATCH PLANES

This form has two plow cutters of the same width, and one extra wide cutter. The fence in one setting exposes two cutters for cutting the tongue, and when reversed, leaves only one exposed for cutting the groove. On thicker boards than the plane works on center, the extra wide cutter is substituted for groove cutter when cutting tongue. Nickel plated. Rosewood knob.

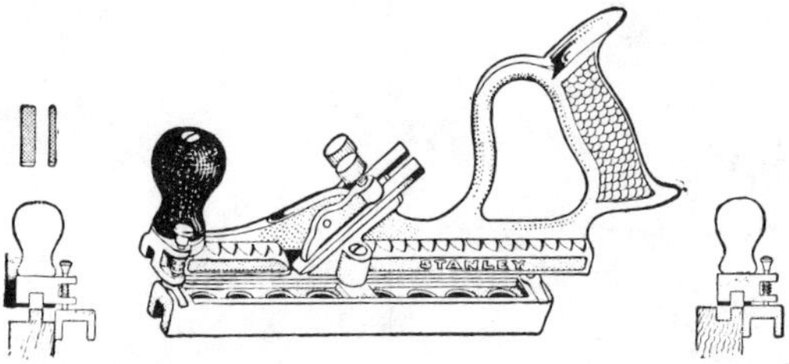

No.			Each
48	Cuts 5/16 Groove, on boards 3/4 in. to 1 1/4 in.	Centers on 7/8 in.	5.30
49	" 3/16 " " " 1/2 " " 3/4 "	" " 1/2 "	5.30

DOUBLE END MATCH PLANES

These planes have two separate cutters, a plow, and a tongue tool, both governed by one permanent fence. The tongue tool has one edge wider than the other, which overhangs one side when tonguing on center. Both tongue and groove are cut by working the tool in the same direction, by merely reversing it end for end. Nickel plated. Iron handles cast with the body.

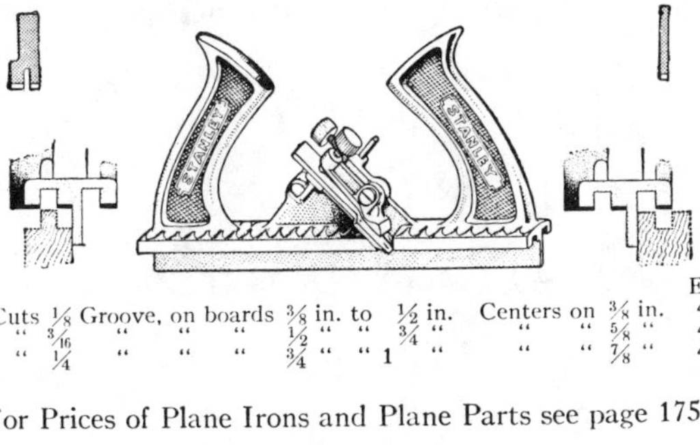

No.			Each
146	Cuts 1/8 Groove, on boards 3/8 in. to 1/2 in.	Centers on 3/8 in.	4.00
147	" 3/16 " " " 1/2 " " 3/4 "	" " 5/8 "	4.25
148	" 1/4 " " " 3/4 " " 1 "	" " 7/8 "	4.50

For Prices of Plane Irons and Plane Parts see page 175

STANLEY ROUTER PLANES

These Planes are for surfacing the bottom of grooves or other depressions parallel with the general surface of the work. The bottoms are designed so that an extra wooden bottom of any size desired can be screwed on, enabling the user to router on large openings.

OPEN THROAT

Cutters are adjustable and can be held on the front of the cutter post for regular work, or on the back for bull-nose work. An attachment for closing the throat, for use on narrow surfaces and regulating depth of cut, is furnished.

CLOSED THROAT

Cutters are adjustable and can be held on the front of the cutter post for regular work or on the back for bull-nose work.

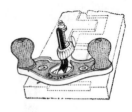

No.		Each
71	7½ inches long, Nickel Plated, Maple Knobs, with a ¼ and ½ inch Cutter and a patented smoothing cutter	4.10

No.		Each
71½	7½ inches long, Nickel Plated, Maple Knobs, with a ¼ and ½ inch Cutter and a patented smoothing cutter	3.20

ROUTER PLANE WITH FENCE

This Plane will make mortises for butts, face plates, strike plates, escutcheons, etc., up to a depth of $\frac{3}{16}$ and a width of 3 inches. Its original feature is the method of mounting the cutter, which can be instantly set to work from either end of the Plane or across it. In addition, the cutter is cushioned by a spring which prevents taking a heavier chip than can be easily carried. A fence regulates the position of the cut and insures the sides of the cut being parallel. The depth of the cut is governed by a positive stop.

An extra wooden bottom of any size desired can be screwed on, enabling the user to router on large openings.

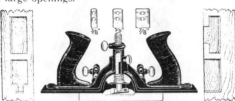

No.		Each
171	11 inches long, Japanned, Rosewood Handles, with three forged steel Cutters ¼, ½ and ⅞ inch wide	5.85

For Prices of Plane Irons and Plane Parts see page 175

[STANLEY]
(S.W.)

STANLEY MISCELLANEOUS PLANES

ROUTER PLANE

Because of its small size it is useful on very narrow work for pattern and Cabinet Makers also Carpenters in letting in lock plates etc. It is so constructed that either a closed throat for regular work or open throat for bull nose work, can be had. By reversing cutter it can be used as a depth gauge.

No. | | Each
271 | 3 inches long, Nickel Plated, ¼ inch cutter. Case hardened Thumb Screw | .75

CABINET MAKERS RABBET PLANES

For fine cabinet or other work where extreme accuracy is required. Both sides of these planes are square with the bottom, and sides and bottoms are machine ground.

They will lie perfectly flat on either side and can be worked either right or left hand.

The width of the throat opening or mouth is adjustable so that it can be widened or narrowed as coarse or fine work may require. Cutters are adjustable endwise. By removing the front a chisel plane is obtained.

They have the "Hand-y" feature.

Plane No. 90 is of the bull nose pattern so that it can be used close up into corners or other difficult places.

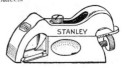

No. | | Each
90 | 4 inches long, 1 inch Cutter, Nickel Plated | 4.00

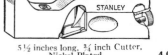

92 | 5½ inches long, ¾ inch Cutter, Nickel Plated | 4.00
93 | 6½ inches long, 1 inch Cutter, Nickel Plated | 4.80
94 | 7½ inches long, 1¼ inch Cutter, Nickel Plated | 5.55

SIDE RABBET PLANES

Made in two styles, No. 98 for right hand work and No. 99 for left hand work.

These will be found to be very convenient for side-rabbeting in trimming dados, mouldings and grooves of all sorts. A reversible nose-piece gives the tool a form whereby it will work close up into corners when required. Fitter with depth gauge. Rosewood knobs. Nickel plated.

Right Hand

No. | | Each
98 | 4 inches long, ½ inch Cutter. Nickel plated, Rosewood knob | 2.20

Left Hand

99 | 4 inches long, ½ inch Cutter, Nickel plated, Rosewood knob | 2.20

SIDE RABBET PLANE

A convenient plane for side rabbeting, in trimming dados, mouldings and grooves of all sorts. A reversible nose piece allows it to be worked up into close corners when required.

No. | | Each
79 | 5½ inches long, ½ inch Cutters, Nickel Plated | 2.75

For Prices of Plane Irons and Plane Parts see page 175

STANLEY CORE BOX PLANE

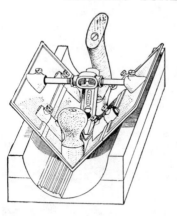

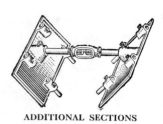

ADDITIONAL SECTIONS

This plane is designed for making circular core boxes. The sides of the plane are at right angles, consequently the point of the plane will always cut on the circumference of the circle when the sides rest on the edges of the cut.

It will make tapered core boxes as well as straight, it being merely necessary to lay out and groove to the desired taper instead of parallel.

Without additional sections the plane will work semi-circles from one inch to two and one-half inches in diameter.

With one pair of additional sections, which are regularly furnished with the plane, it will work semi-circles up to five inches in diameter.

Two pairs of additional sections with adjusting rods, by means of which the sides can be made square and held firmly in position, can be supplied. Each extra pair adds two and one-half inches to the diameter of the semi-circle that can be worked; making the diameter ten inches, the practical limit of the plane.

No.		Each
57	With one pair of Sections, to work semi-circles 1 to 5 inches. 10 inches long, ⅛ inch Cutter, Nickel Plated, Beech Handle and Knob	**8.65**

ADDITIONAL SECTIONS

No.		Per Pair
2	To work semi-circles 5 inches to 7½ inches.	**1.90**
3	" " " " 7½ " " 10 "	**1.90**

In ordering, give number of section wanted. If no number is given on order, No. 2 will be sent.

For Prices of Plane Irons and Plane Parts see page 176

STANLEY MISCELLANEOUS PLANES

ADJUSTABLE CHAMFER PLANE

This Plane will do perfect chamfer or stop-chamfer work. It has a ninety degree V bottom which acts as a mitre guide. To this is attached an adjustable front, "A," having a flat bottom which carries the cutter. This front can be set for different sizes of chamfer. Front "A," can be readily detached and a bull-nose front, "B," (furnished with the Plane) substituted, permitting the Plane to be worked close up into corners.

No.   Each
72 Rosewood Handle and Knob, 9 in. long, 1 ⅝ in. Cutter. Weight
      each 3 ⅜ lbs.   **4.30**

CABINET MAKERS BLOCK PLANE

For piano makers and workmen in kindred trades who require an extra fine tool for finishing hard woods, etc. The metallic handle can be attached to the top of either edge, and the sides, being accurately machined, it can be used for work with a shoot board in planing mitres, etc. The mouth is adjustable for coarse or fine work and the cutter is adjustable endwise.

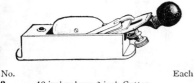

No.   Each
9   10 inches long, 2 inch Cutter,
            Rosewood Knob   **8.40**

CABINET MAKERS EDGE PLANE

For piano makers and all cabinet workers. It has a cutter resting on a solid bed practically its entire length. The cutting edge being located at the extreme end of the plane, gives the tool the form of a chisel. No other plane can be worked in such a small space or so close up into corners. The cutter is adjustable endwise. Rosewood knob.

No.   Each
97   10 inches long, 2 ¼ inch Cutter   **4.40**

STANLEY
S.W.

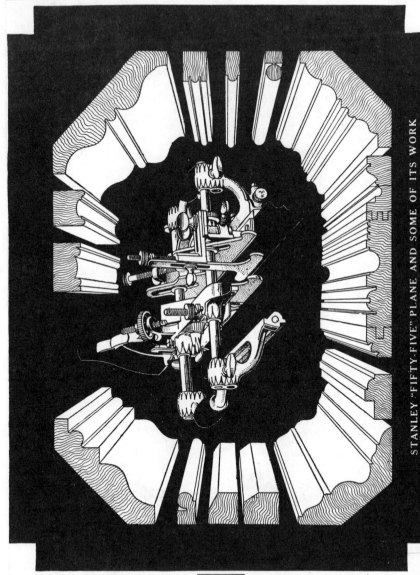

STANLEY "FIFTY-FIVE" PLANE AND SOME OF ITS WORK

STANLEY
S.W.

STANLEY "FIFTY-FIVE" PLANE

"A Planing Mill Within Itself"

This tool, in addition to being a beading and center beading plane, a plow, dado, rabbet, filletster, and match plane, a sash plane and a slitting plane, is also a superior moulding plane, and will accommodate cutters of almost any shape and size.

The samples of work illustrated, show some of the mouldings that can be made with cutters regularly furnished with this plane.

When it is considered, that in addition to the fifty-five regular cutters and the forty-one special cutters (carried in stock). the plane will take practically any form of cutter desired, its wide range of work will be appreciated.

The plane has: A main stock, which carries the cutter adjustment, a handle, a depth gauge, a slitting gauge, and has a steel bottom forming a bearing for one edge of the cutter. A sliding section, with a steel bottom gives bearing for the other edge of the cutter and slides on arms secured in the main stock. This bottom can be raised or lowered so that, in addition to allowing the use of cutters of different widths, cutters can be used having one edge higher or lower than the edge supported in the main stock.

The main fence has a lateral adjustment for extra fine work. The fences can be used on either side of the plane, and the rosewood guides can be tilted to any desired angle up to forty-five degrees. The second fence can be reversed for center beading wide boards.

The plane is fitted with spurs for working across the grain, and a special cam rest, to be located on the front arm when working at a distance from the edge of the board, to keep the fence from sagging, or on the rear arm on certain work, to prevent the possibility of the plane "rocking."

The regular equipment furnished with the plane comprises fifty-five cutters, all of which are shown on page 100.

A further line of forty-one cutters (shown on page 101) are carried in stock. Cutters of practically any form can be used in the plane, which the owner can make from blanks or order from sketch.

All metal parts of the plane are nickel plated. The handle and fences are made of selected rosewood, and every part is well finished.

The cutters, together with the plane and all its attachments are packed in a neat substantial box.

No.   Each

55   Nickel Plated with 55 Cutters. Weight 15¼ lbs.   **30.00**

A special booklet covering the use of this plane will be sent on request.

For Prices of Plane Parts see page 178

STANLEY "FIFTY-FIVE" PLANE

REGULAR CUTTERS FOR "FIFTY-FIVE" PLANE

The following cutters are furnished with each plane. The prices are given in case duplicates should be required:

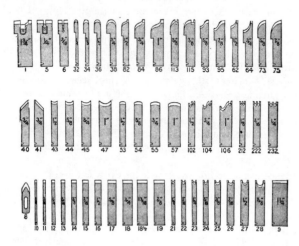

No.		Each	No.		Each	No.		Each
1	1½ in. Sash Tool	1.00	23	¼ in. Beading Tool	.30	57	1 in. Round	.40
5	¼ " Match Tool	1.00	24	⁵⁄₁₆ " " "	.40	62	½ in. Quarter Hollow	.90
6	³⁄₁₆ " " "	1.00	25	³⁄₈ " " "	.40	64	¾ " " "	1.00
8	Slitting Tool	.60	26	⁷⁄₁₆ " " "	.50	73	⁵⁄₈ " " Round	.90
9	Filletster	.50	27	½ " " "	.50	75	⁷⁄₈ " " "	1.00
10	⅛ in. Plow DadoTool	.30	28	⅝ " " "	.60	82	½ " Reverse Ogee	.90
11	³⁄₁₆ " " " "	.30	32	¼ " Fluting Tool	.60	84	¾ " " "	1.00
12	¼ " " " "	.30	34	³⁄₈ " " "	.60	86	1 " " "	1.00
13	⁵⁄₁₆ " " " "	.30	36	½ " " "	.60	93	⅝ " Roman Ogee	.90
14	³⁄₈ " " " "	.40	38	¾ " " "	.60	95	⅞ " " "	1.00
15	⁷⁄₁₆ " " " "	.40	40	¾ " Chamfer Tool	.60	102	½ " Grecian Ogee	.90
16	½ " " " "	.40	41	¾ " " "	.60	104	¾ " " "	1.00
17	⅝ " " " "	.40	43	½ " Hollow	.40	106	1 " " "	1.00
18	¾ " " " "	.40	44	⅝ " "	.40	113	⅝ " ¼Rd.with Bead	.90
18½	¹³⁄₁₆ " " " "	.50	45	¾ " "	.40	115	⅞ " " "	1.00
19	⅞ " " " "	.50	47	1 " "	.40	212	⅛ " ReedingTl.2Bd.	.40
21	⅛ " Beading Tool	.30	53	½ " Round	.40	222	³⁄₁₆ " " " 2 "	.40
22	³⁄₁₆ " " "	.30	54	⅝ " "	.40	232	¼ " " " 2 "	.40
			55	¾ " "	.40			

For Prices of Plane Parts see page 178

STANLEY
S.W.

STANLEY "FIFTY-FIVE" PLANE
SPECIAL CUTTERS FOR "FIFTY-FIVE" PLANE

These cutters are carried in stock and may be ordered by specifying the number of the cutter:

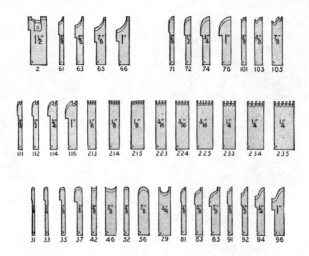

No.			Each	No.			Each	No.			Each
2	1½ in.	Sash Tool	1.00	71	⅜ in.	Quarter Round	.90	111	⅜ in.	¼ Rd. with Bead	.90
29	¾ "	Beading Cutter	.60	72	½ "	" "	.90	112	½ "	" " "	.90
31	⁵⁄₁₆ "	Fluting Tool	.60	74	¾ "	" "	1.00	114	¾ "	¼ " " "	1.00
33	⁵⁄₁₆ "	" "	.60	76	1 "	" "	1.00	116	1 "	¼ " " "	1.00
35	⁷⁄₁₆ "	" "	.60	81	⅜ "	Reverse Ogee	.90	213	⅛ "	Reeding Tl. 3 "	.60
37	⅝ "	" "	.60	83	⅝ "	" "	.90	214	⅛ "	" " 4 "	.80
42	⅜ "	Hollow	.40	85	⅞ "	" "	1.00	215	⅛ "	" " 5 "	1.00
46	⅞ "	"	.40	91	⅜ "	Roman Ogee	.90	223	⁵⁄₁₆ "	" " 3 "	.60
52	⅜ "	Round	.40	92	½ "	" "	.90	224	⁵⁄₁₆ "	" " 4 "	.80
56	⅞ "	"	.40	94	¾ "	" "	1.00	225	⁵⁄₁₆ "	" " 5 "	1.00
61	⅜ "	Quarter Hollow	.90	96	1 "	" "	1.00	233	¼ "	" " 3 "	.60
63	⅝ "	" "	.90	101	⅜ "	Grecian Ogee	.90	234	¼ "	" " 4 "	.80
65	⅞ "	" "	1.00	103	⅝ "	" "	.90	235	¼ "	" " 5 "	1.00
66	1 "	" "	1.00	105	⅞ "	" "	1.00				

For Prices of Plane Parts see page 178

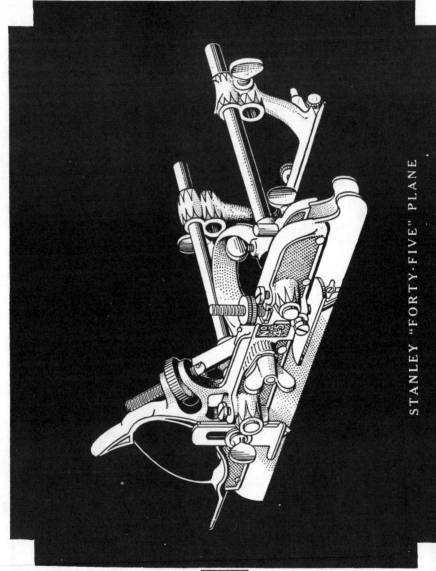

STANLEY "FORTY-FIVE" PLANE

STANLEY "FORTY-FIVE" PLANE

This well known and useful tool in reality combines *seven planes in one* in a compact and practical form. 1.—Beading and Center-beading Plane. 2.—Plow. 3.—Dado. 4.—Rabbet and Filletster. 5.—Match Plane. 6.—Sash Plane. 7.—Slitting Plane.

It has three principal parts, a *Main Stock*, a *Sliding Section*, and a *Fence* or *Gauge*.

The *Main Stock* carries the Cutter, Cutter Adjustment, Slitting Tool, Depth Gauge, Handle, and provides a bearing for one edge of the cutter.

The *Sliding Section* slides on two Arms, secured in the Main Stock and provides a bearing for the other edge of the cutter, allowing cutters of different widths to be used.

The *Fence*, which has a lateral adjustment for extra fine work, slides on these Arms and is used when working the Plane as a Plow, Beader or Filletster, to gauge the distance from the cutter to the edge of the board. The Arms slide through the Main Stock so that the Fence can be attached to either side according as the Plane is used right or left hand.

Two sets of Arms are furnished, one set 4¼ inches and the other 8¼ inches long. Longer Arms can be furnished if desired.

Spurs for working across the grain are attached to the Main Stock and Sliding Section. They can be readily turned up out of the way when not required.

For beading at a distance from the edge of a board a metal cam is furnished to go on the front arm between the sliding section and fence. This will prevent the fence from sagging. This cam can also be attached to the rear arm for work where it is desirable to keep the plane from "rocking."

Twenty-three *Cutters* are furnished with each Plane as follows: 11 Plow and Dado, 7 Beading, 1 Filletster, 1 Sash, 2 Match and 1 Slitting. Twenty-three additional cutters are regularly carried in stock and can be furnished at a slight additional cost.

All metal parts are nickel plated. The handle, knob and fence are made of selected rosewood.

The Cutters, together with the Plane, are packed in a neat substantial box.

No.		Each
45	Nickel plated, with 23 Cutters, weight 9½ lbs.	**15.00**

STANLEY ALUMINUM COMBINATION PLANE

Similar in design to the regular Stanley No. 45 Plane. Being made of aluminum it is an exceptionally light weight tool.

The Cutters for this plane are the same as used with the regular Stanley No. 45 Plane.

No.		Each
A45	Aluminum with 23 Cutters	**20.00**

For Prices of Plane Parts see page 178

STANLEY "FORTY-FIVE" PLANE
CUTTERS REGULARLY SUPPLIED WITH PLANE
The price is given in case duplicates should be required.

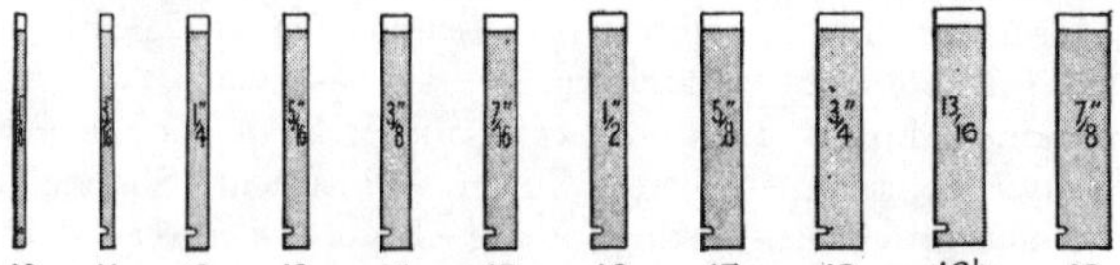

No.	Size	Style	Each	No.	Size	Style	Each	No.	Size	Style	Each
1	1½ in.	Sash Tool	1.00	13	5/16 in.	Plow&DadoTool	.30	21	⅛ in.	Beading Tool	.30
5	¼ "	Match Tool	1.00	14	3/8 "	" "	.40	22	3/16 "	" "	.30
6	3/16 "	" "	1.00	15	7/16 "	" "	.40	23	¼ "	" "	.30
8		Slitting Tool	.60	16	½ "	" "	.40	24	5/16 "	" "	.40
9	1¼ "	Filletster	.50	17	5/8 "	" "	.40	25	3/8 "	" "	.40
10	⅛ "	Plow&DadoTool	.30	18	¾ "	" "	.40	26	7/16 "	" "	.50
11	3/16 "	" "	.30	18½	13/16 "	" "	.50	27	½ "	" "	.50
12	¼ "	" "	.30	19	7/8 "	" "	.50				

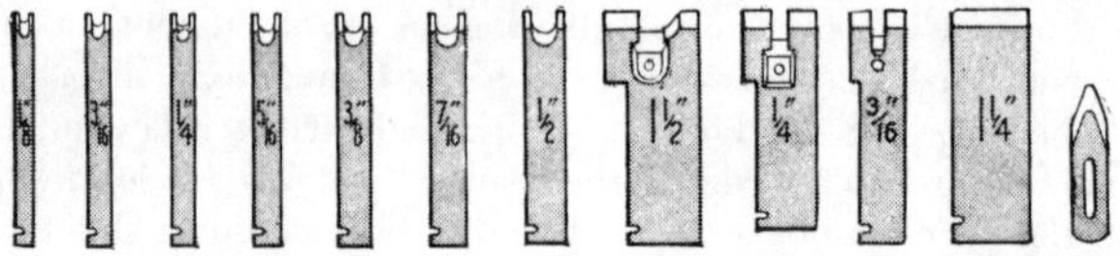

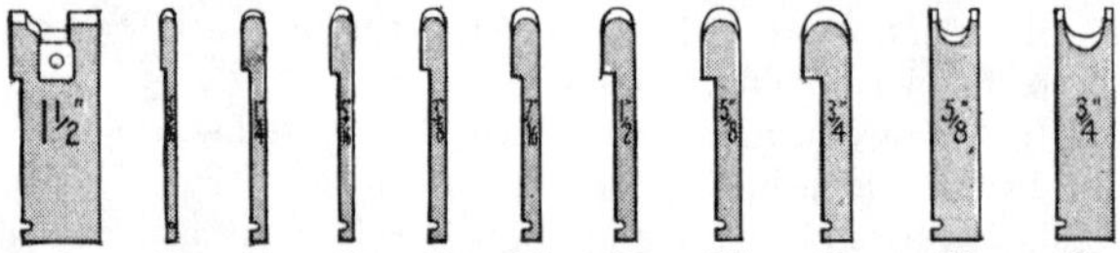

SPECIAL CUTTERS FOR "FORTY-FIVE" PLANE
Carried in stock and may be ordered by number.

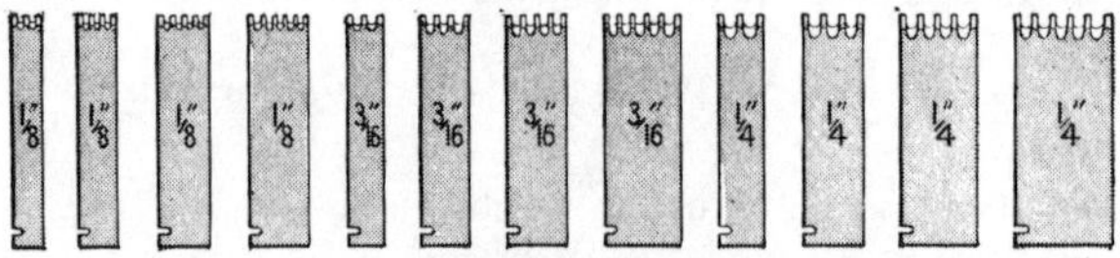

No.	Size	Style	Each	No.	Size	Style	Each
2	1½ in.	Sash Tool	1.00	212	⅛ in.	Reeding Tool 2 Beads	.40
28	5/8 "	Beading Tool	.60	213	⅛ "	" " 3 "	.60
29	¾ "	" "	.60	214	⅛ "	" " 4 "	.80
31	3/16 "	Fluting Tool	.60	215	⅛ "	" " 5 "	1.00
32	¼ "	" "	.60	222	3/16 "	Reeding Tool 2 Beads	.40
33	5/16 "	" "	.60	223	3/16 "	" " 3 "	.60
34	3/8 "	" "	.60	224	3/16 "	" " 4 "	.80
35	7/16 "	" "	.60	225	3/16 "	" " 5 "	1.00
36	½ "	" "	.60	232	¼ "	Reeding Tool 2 Beads	.40
37	5/8 "	" "	.60	233	¼ "	" " 3 "	.60
38	¾ "	" "	.60	234	¼ "	" " 4 "	.80
		For Prices of Plane Parts see page 178		235	¼ "	" " 5 "	1.00

STANLEY
(S.W.)

SPECIAL BOTTOMS FOR "FORTY-FIVE" PLANE

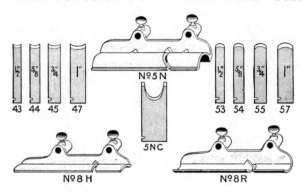

In order to work *Hollows* and *Rounds* or a *Nosing Cutter* in the No. 45 Plane, it is necessary to substitute for the sliding section furnished with the plane, specially formed bottoms as illustrated above, which are called by the same name as the cutters they are designed to carry, that is:—*Hollows, Rounds,* or *Nosing Tools.*

A *Hollow* and its cutter will form a round on the moulding being worked. A *Round* and its cutter will form a hollow. They are made in four sizes, each size being designated by a number. The dimensions given in the table below are: first, the extreme width of the cutter (both hollows and rounds), followed by the diameter of the circle each cutter is designed to work. *Hollows* and *Rounds* are usually sold in sets, a set comprising one *Hollow*, one *Round* and two *Cutters*.

A *Nosing Tool* and its cutter will form an exact half round. It is very largely used for shaping the edges of stair treads. As in the hollows and rounds, the table gives the width of the cutter and the diameter of the circle, which the cutter is designed to work. The price of the Nosing Tool includes one cutter.

No.												Per Pair
6	Hollow and Round,	½ inch Cutter,	Works	¾ inch Circle								2.30
8	"	"	"	⅝	"	"	"	1	"	"		2.30
10	"	"	"	¾	"	"	"	1¼	"	"		2.50
12	"	"	"	1	"	"	"	1½	"	"		2.50
												Each
5	Nosing Tool		1¹¹⁄₁₆"	"		"	1¼	"	"			1.90

EXTRA CUTTERS FOR HOLLOWS AND ROUNDS

No.			Each	No.			Each
43	½ inch Hollow		.40	53	½ inch Round		.40
44	⅝ " "		.40	54	⅝ " "		.40
45	¾ " "		.40	55	¾ " "		.40
47	1 " "		.40	57	1 " "		.40

No.		Each
5NC	1¹¹⁄₁₆ inch Cutter for Nosing Tool	.50

STANLEY
(S.W.)

STANLEY MISCELLANEOUS PLANES

LIGHT COMBINATION

A small combination plane for light work. Adapted for plow, beading, matching and rabbet work. Fitted with spurs, depth gauge, and a fence with a 5 inch adjustment.

The handle is metal, being a part of the main stock.

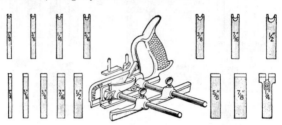

No.		Each
50	9¼ inches long, Nickel Plated	**8.50**

15 Cutters as Follows:

Plow and Dado   ¼, ⁵⁄₁₆, ⅜, ⁷⁄₁₆, ½, ⅝, ⅞ inch
Beading   ⅛, ³⁄₁₆, ¼, ⁵⁄₁₆, ⅜, ⁷⁄₁₆, ½ inch
Tonguing   ¼ inch.

BULL NOSE COMBINATION

For plow, matching and rabbet work. The tool has two interchangeable front parts that make it either an ordinary or a bull nose plane. With the bull nose attachment it will work into a ½ inch hole as in sash fitting, stair work, etc. Fitted with a depth gauge and a fence.

No.		Each
143	9¼ inches long, Nickel Plated, Rosewood Handle	**8.20**

10 Cutters as Follows:

Plows   ⅛, ³⁄₁₆, ¼, ⁵⁄₁₆, ⅜, ⁷⁄₁₆, ½, ⅝ inch
Tonguing ¼ inch and Slitting Cutter

Cutters for planes 50 and 143 have the same prices as the No. 55 plane cutters (pages 100 and 101) of same size. In ordering, specify both the number of plane and the size of the cutter. Extra parts priced on page 178.

STANLEY
S.W.

SKEW CUTTER COMBINATION

For plow, dado, filletster, matching and rabbet work. Fitted with spurs, a depth gauge and a fence with Rosewood face. A description of skew cutters is given on page 85.

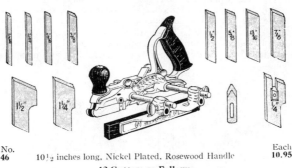

No.		Each
46	10½ inches long, Nickel Plated, Rosewood Handle	**10.95**

12 Cutters as Follows:

Plow and Dado ³⁄₁₆, ¹⁄₄, ⁵⁄₁₆, ³⁄₈, ¹⁄₂, ⁵⁄₈, ¹³⁄₁₆, ⁷⁄₈, 1 ¹⁄₄ inch
Filletster   1½ inches
Tonguing   ¼ inch and Slitting Cutter

Cutters for plane No. 46 have the same prices as the No. 55 plane cutters (pages 100 and 101) of same size. In ordering, specify both the number of plane and the size of the cutter. Extra parts priced on page 178.

CURVE RABBET

Will cut rabbets on the outside or inside of curved or straight edges.

It has two adjustable cutters, the upper acting as a spur for the lower and also cutting the side of the rabbet. The lower skew cutter (see page 85) cuts the bottom of the rabbet. Adjustable depth gauge and fence.

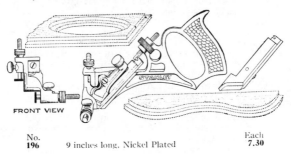

FRONT VIEW

No.		Each
196	9 inches long, Nickel Plated	**7.30**

For Prices of Extra Parts see page 175

STANLEY
S.W.

STANLEY DOVETAIL TONGUE AND GROOVE PLANE
The Only Plane Manufactured that Will Cut a Dovetail

It will cut any size grooves and tongues to fit with sides at flare of 20 degrees, where the width of the neck is more than one-quarter of an inch and the depth of groove not more than three-quarters of an inch. The tongue and groove are cut separately and can be made with parallel or tapering sides.

Its compactness is shown in the illustration, where the cut on the left shows the plane assembled for cutting the tongue, and that on the right for cutting the groove. A circular containing complete instructions for assembling and operating is packed with each tool.

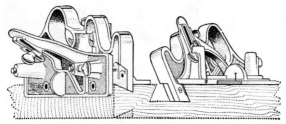

No.
444   9 inches long, Nickel Plated

Each
10.95

Extra Parts and Cutters for this Plane are Priced on page 178

SOME 444 WORK

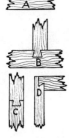

A Dovetail tongue and groove joint with the groove cut in the regular manner, and the tongue cut on a bevel, used for supports.

B Dovetail tongue and groove joint with unequal shoulders, or a joint with a regular groove, but where the tongue is offset.

C Dovetail tongue and groove joint as can very often be conveniently used when one is forming an end to end timber match.

D Dovetail tongue and groove half joint, frequently used by carpenters to a very great advantage in concealed nail work.

G Dovetail tongue and groove joint where both the groove and tongue are cut on a beveled surface, making a strong corner.

H Dovetail tongue and groove joint shown in one of its most useful applications, that of a bracket supporting a shelf.

J Dovetail tongue and groove joint as applied to the setting of gear teeth around the outer rim of any gear pattern.

STANLEY
(S.W.)

STANLEY SCRAPER PLANES

DOUBLE HANDLE SCRAPER PLANES

The handles are of rosewood with a double grip, and being placed across the center of the tool, gives it a good balance. The blades are adjustable endwise and for angle and can be firmly locked in position desired.

Plane Nos. 12—12½ and 112 can also be used as Toothing Planes.

No.		Each
12	6¼ in. long, 2⅞ in. Blade, Japanned	**4.90**
	Extra Blades	**.50**

ROSEWOOD BOTTOM

This wood bottom is especially adapted for use on very fine work, as it renders less liable the possibility of marring or scratching the surface being worked upon. The bottom is detachable, and, when worn, can be readily removed and a new one substituted.

No.		Each
12½	6¼ in. long, 2⅞ in. Blade, Japanned	**6.65**
	Extra Rosewood Bottoms	**.50**
	Extra Blades	**.50**

No.		Each
12¼	6¼ in. long, 2 in. Blade, Japanned	**4.15**
	Extra Blades	**.50**

SINGLE HANDLE SCRAPER PLANE

The handle and knob have the same form as the regular "Bailey" Plane, being preferred by some users to the two-handle or double grip form of Scraper Plane.

The blades are adjustable endwise and for angle, and can be firmly locked in position desired.

No.		Each
112	9 in. long, 2⅞ in. Blade, Japanned	**4.30**
	Extra Blades	**.50**

SPECIAL BLADE FOR PLANES Nos. 12—12½ and 112

This blade is given a special temper, permitting more of a turn being given the edge when burnishing than is practical with the blades regularly furnished.

No.		Each
12B	2⅞ inches wide	**.50**

For Prices of Parts see page 176

STANLEY
S.W.

STANLEY SCRAPER PLANES AND HAND SCRAPERS

SINGLE HANDLE SCRAPER PLANE

A small handy tool, designed to be used with one hand and well adapted for Violin Makers and all Mechanics requiring a light adjustable scraper. It has a rosewood knob but no handle. It also has the "Hand-y" feature.

CABINET MAKERS SCRAPER PLANE

In working, the blade springs backward opening the mouth and allowing the shaving to pass through it. Handle and knobs can be tilted and held with set screw. This is convenient when working into corners or up against perpendicular surfaces. Rabbet mouth.

No.		Each
212	5½ in. long, 1⅜ in. Blade, Japanned	3.10
	Extra Blades	.50

No.		Each
85	8 in. long, 2 in. Blade, Japanned	4.55
	Extra Blades	.50

For Prices of Parts see page 176

STANLEY HAND SCRAPERS AND TOOTHING CUTTERS

These Scrapers are made of high grade steel and great care is taken to give them a special temper for this work.

The Toothing Cutters are for use in Planes Nos. 12—12½ and 112.

No.						Each
0	2	inches wide,	4	inches long		.40
	2	"	6	"	"	.40
	2½	"	5	"	"	.45
	2½	"	6	"	"	.45
	2⅞	"	6	"	"	.55
	3	"	4	"	"	.40
	3	"	5	"	"	.45

No.						Each
0	3	inches wide,	6	inches long		.55
	3½	"	6	"	"	.55
600	2½	"	5	"	"	.20
	3	"	4	"	"	.20
	3	"	5	"	"	.25
	3	"	6	"	"	.30

Toothing cutters 22, 28 or 32 to the inch   Each   0.85

STANLEY SCRAPER BURNISHER No. 176

This tool is used for turning the edges on cabinet Scraper Blades. Blade oval shaped, forged from the finest tool steel and is glass hard. It is held firmly in the handle by extending nearly through it and is pinned at the end. Hardwood handle, shellac polished.

No.		Per Doz.
176	8 in. overall, Blade 3½ in.	9.00

STANLEY
(S.W.)

STANLEY SCRAPERS

DOUBLE HANDLE—IRON BOTTOM

The blade may be sprung to a slight curve by means of a thumb screw, giving ease of operation and quickness of cut. The handles are raised to protect the user's hands, and pierced so that the tool can be hung up out of the way. Body and handles are cast in one piece.

No.		Each
80	11 in. long, 2¾ in. Blade, Japanned	1.45
	Extra Blades	.30

SINGLE HANDLE—ADJUSTABLE

The Adjustable Scraper handle can be tilted to give the blade any angle desired. Blades of different forms and widths can be held in any position required, permitting the tool to be used in many places inaccessible to other Scrapers. Handle and knob of hardwood.

No.		Each
82	14½ in. long, 3 in. Blade, Japanned	1.90
	Extra Blades	.30

DOUBLE HANDLE—ROLLER BOTTOM

This Scraper has a roller back of the blade which acts as a support to relieve the strain on the wrists of the workman. Handle is made of beech and can be detached for working into corners.

No.		Each
83	9½ in. long, 3⅞ in. Blade, Nickeled	1.70
	Extra Blades	.30

DOUBLE HANDLE—ROSEWOOD BOTTOM

This Scraper has a rosewood bottom for use in the finest cabinet work. The handles are raised to protect the hands, and pierced so that it can be hung up out of the way. Body and handles cast in one piece.

No.		Each
81	10 in. long, 2½ in. Blade, Nickeled	2.35
	Extra Rosewood Bottoms	.50
	Extra Blades	.30

SINGLE HANDLE—NON-ADJUSTABLE

While this Scraper can be used for all kinds of scraping it is especially recommended for scraping floors on account of its strength and form. The body is ground smooth and japanned. Handle of hardwood securely fastened.

No.		Each
282	13 in. long, 3 in. Blade	1.50
	Extra Blades	.30

BOX SCRAPER

For removing stencils and markings from the surface of boxes, floors, etc. The handle is hinged above the surface. The face of the bottom and the edge of the cutter are slightly curved, allowing the user to scrape any uneven surface. Maple handle.

No.		Each
70	13 in. long, 2 in. Blade, Japanned	1.15
	Extra Blades	.25

STANLEY SPOKE SHAVES

These Spoke Shaves have cutters made from a high grade of steel, well tempered and sharpened ready for use.

ADJUSTABLE CUTTERS

The cutter can be quickly adjusted both endwise and sidewise by means of the adjusting screws which engage the slots near the end.

No.   Each
151 Raised Handle, 10 in. long, 2⅛ in. Cutter **.75**

152 Straight Handle, 10 in. long, 2⅛ in. Cutter **.75**

DOUBLE IRON, IMPROVED

They have a cutter and cap iron, fastened by a thumb screw, in such a manner as to bring an even pressure on the cutter edge, and at the same time allow adjustment without the use of a screw driver.

No.   Each
51 Raised Handle, 10 in. long, 2⅛ in. Cutter **.55**

52 Straight Handle, 10 in. long, 2⅛ in. Cutter **.55**

HOLLOW FACE

This Spoke Shave has a cutter with a hollow face for all kinds of round work.

No.   Each
55 Raised Handle, 10 in. long, 2⅛ in. Cutter **.50**

ADJUSTABLE MOUTH

By means of a thumb screw the mouth can be opened or closed as coarse or fine work may be required.

No.   Each
53 Raised Handle, 10 in. long, 2⅛ in. Cutter **.70**

54 Straight Handle, 10 in. long, 2⅛ in. Cutter **.70**

DOUBLE IRON, LIGHT

Designed especially for light work. They have straight handles and the cutter and japanned cap iron are fastened by a thumb screw.

No.   Each
63 Convex Bottom, 9 in. long, 1¾ in. Cutter **.30**

64 Straight Bottom, 9 in. long, 1¾ in. Cutter **.35**

TWO CUTTER

Has two cutters and separate cutter seats, one hollow and one straight. The two forms of cutters in one tool make it a very handy Spoke Shave.

No.   Each
60 Straight Handle, 10 in. long, 1½ in. Cutters **.75**

STANLEY SPOKE SHAVES

EXTRA LIGHT

Designed especially for use in Manual Training Schools, or for any work requiring the use of an extra light Spoke Shave.

No.		Each
X63 Straight Handle, 9 in. long, 1½ in. Cutter		**.45**

DOUBLE IRON

58 Straight Handle, 10 in. long, 2⅛ in. Cutter **.45**

STANLEY UNIVERSAL

The handles are detachable, and either one can be screwed into the top of the stock, enabling the user to work into corners or panels. Two detachable bottoms are furnished, one for straight and the other for circular work. A movable width gauge allows the tool to be used in rabbeting.

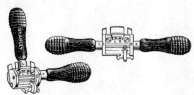

No.		Each
67	Nickel Plated, Rosewood Handle, 9¼ in. long, 1⅞ in. Cutter	**2.05**

ADJUSTABLE CHAMFER

A very convenient tool. Can be adjusted to work chamfers up to 1½ inches (the width of the cutter).

No.		Each
65 Raised Handle, 9½ in. long, 1½ in. Cutter		**.90**

RABBET

Carriage makers, car builders and cabinet makers will find this a very convenient tool for finishing panels, rabbets, etc.

68	Straight Handle, 10¾ in. long, 2⅛ in. Cutter	**1.25**
71	Straight Handle, Brass Frame, 10¾ in. long, 2⅛ in. Cutter, with Gauge	**3.55**

STANLEY RAZOR EDGE

So called from the shape of the cutter, which is hollow ground, giving an exceptionally keen cutting edge. They have an adjustable front, which can be moved up or down, giving the same effect as if the cutter was raised or lowered. The cutter itself is also adjustable, permitting a narrow or wide opening of the mouth.

No.		Each
84 Boxwood Handle, 11 in. long, 2 in. Cutter		**1.40**
85 Boxwood Handle, 12 in. long, 2½ in. "		**1.50**

SPOKE SHAVE IRONS

No.	Each	No.	Each	No.	Each
51	.15	60	.15	67	.35
52	.15	63	.15	71	.40
53	.15	X63	.15	84	.55
54	.15	64	.15	85	.55
55	.15	65	.15	151	.15
58	.15			152	.15

STANLEY (S.W.)

STANLEY HAMMERS

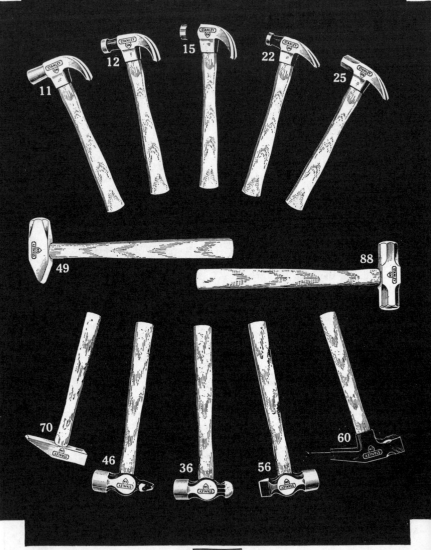

STANLEY HAMMERS

Stanley Hammers are made of a special steel, carefully forged, hardened and tempered.

The Handles of all numbers, including those mahoganized, are made of selected, straight grained, young white hickory.

The improved method of fastening the Head to the Handle, makes it practically impossible for the Head to fly off.

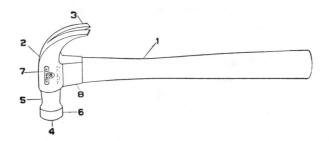

In the illustration above the various parts of a Nail Hammer are clearly indicated, being as follows:

1 Handle, 2 Head, 3 Claw, 4 Face, 5 Neck, 6 Poll, 7 Cheek, 8 Adze Eye.

This will serve to more readily identify the variations in the different numbers of Nail Hammers described on the following pages.

The Claws are of uniform thickness and so formed that they will grip and hold fast at any point of the shank, all sizes and kinds of nails, thus enabling the user to draw them from the toughest kind of wood, even where the head of the nail has been broken off.

The variations in the different numbers lie in the shape of the claw, the shape of the face, whether flat or rounded (the latter called Bell Face), style of the neck and poll, and the general finish.

The Bell Face pattern differs from the Plain Face pattern in that the face of the former is slightly rounded, rendering less liable the possibility of the Hammer Head marring the wood.

The weights given in ounces cover the Head only.

The overall length is taken from the top of the Head to the extreme end of the Handle.

STANLEY HAMMER WEDGE

The offset relation of the teeth on the opposite sides make it impossible for this Patented Wedge to come out as the teeth imbed themselves in the wood without destroying the fibres, thus securely holding the Head to the Handle.

Should it become necessary to tighten the Head it can easily be done by driving home the wedge with a nail set.

STANLEY ADZE EYE, NAIL HAMMERS

STANLEY No. 15

This is a highly finished and an exceptionally fine Hammer.

Red Octagonal Neck, Curved Claw, Bell Face and Round Poll

No.					Each
15	13 Ounces, Size 2,		inches overal		**1.75**
	16 "	" 1½, 13	"	"	**1.85**
	20 "	" 2, 13½	"	"	**1.90**

Curved Claw, Bell Face, Round Neck and Poll

No.					Each
12	5 Ounces, Size 4,	12	inches overall		1.35
	7 "	" 3,	12	"	" 1.40
	10 "	" 2½, 13	"	"	1.50
	13 "	" 2, 13	"	"	1.60
	16 "	" 1½, 13	"	"	1.65
	20 "	" 1, 13½	"	"	2.45

Curved Claw, Plain Face, Plain Neck and Poll

No.					Each
11	5 Ounces, Size 4,	12	inches overall		1.35
	7 "	" 3,	12	"	" 1.40
	13 "	" 2, 13	"	"	1.50
	16 "	" 1½, 13	"	"	1.60
	20 "	" 1, 13½	"	"	1.65
	28 "	" 0, 15	"	"	2.45

Curved Claw, Bell Face, Octagonal Neck, Round Poll, Full Polished

No.					Each
14	13 Ounces, Size 2,	13	inches overall		1.75
	16 "	" 1½, 13	"	"	1.85
	20 "	" 1, 13½	"	"	1.90

Curved Claw, Bell Face, Octagonal Neck, Round Poll, Nickel Plated, Mahoganized Handle

No.					Each
14NM	13 Ounces, Size 2,	13	in. overall		2.00
	16 "	" 1½, 13	"	"	2.10
	20 "	" 1, 13½	"	"	2.20

STANLEY
S.W.

STANLEY AND "VICTOR" ADZE EYE, NAIL HAMMERS

STANLEY

This pattern is designed particularly for ripping off old wood. The peculiar shape of the claw enables the workman to do this more quickly and satisfactorily than with the curved claw pattern.

"VICTOR"

This line of hammers are made of the same grade of steel as the Stanley line, but are not as highly finished. The handles are of straight grained hickory.

Straight Claw, Bell Face, Round Neck and Poll

No.						Each
22	13 Ounces, Size 2,	13	inches overall			1.50
16	"	" 1½, 13	"	"		1.60
20	"	" 1,	13½	"	"	1.65

Curved Claw, Plain Face, Plain Neck and Poll

No.						Each
811	13 Ounces, Size 2,	13	inches overall			1.10
16	"	" 1½, 13	"	"		1.15
20	"	" 1,	13½	"	"	1.20

Straight Claw, Plain Face, Plain Neck and Poll

No.						Each
21	16 Ounces, Size 1½,	13	inches overall			1.60
20	"	" 1,	13½	"	"	1.65

Curved Claw, Bell Face, Round Neck and Poll

No.						Each
812	13 Ounces, Size 2,	13	inches overall			1.10
16	"	" 1½, 13	"	"		1.15
20	"	" 1,	13½	"	"	1.20

CHECKERED FACES

For box making and driving small spikes, some users prefer a hammer having a checkered or corrugated face.

If desired, Nos. 11-16 oz., 11-20 oz., 12-16 oz., 25-16 oz., and 25-20 oz. weights can be so furnished for 25 cents each extra.

Straight Claw, Plain Face Octagonal Neck and Poll

No.						Each
25	13 Ounces, Size 2,	13	inches overall			1.50
16	"	" 1½, 13	"	"		1.60
20	"	" 1,	13½	"	"	1.65

STANLEY
S.W.

STANLEY HAMMERS

RIVETING

This is the style of Hammer commonly used for riveting, although some prefer the Straight or Cross Pein Machinists Hammers. The heads are full polished.

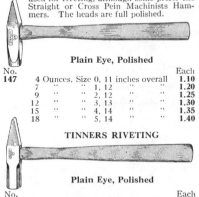

Plain Eye, Polished

No.						Each
147	4 Ounces, Size 0, 11 inches overall					1.10
	7 " " 1, 12 " "					1.20
	9 " " 2, 12 " "					1.25
	12 " " 3, 13 " "					1.30
	15 " " 4, 14 " "					1.35
	18 " " 5, 14 " "					1.40

TINNERS RIVETING

Plain Eye, Polished

No.		Each
75	12 Ounces, Size 2, 13 inches overall	1.30

TINNERS PANEING

These Paneing or Setting Hammers are very popular with all Tinsmiths, as special care is taken to have both ends of the Head well formed, properly beveled, and carefully tempered.

Plain Eye, Polished

No.		Each
70	8 Ounces, Size 1, 12 inches overall	1.25
	12 " " 2, 13 " "	1.30
	16 " " 3, 14 " "	1.35

FARRIERS

These Hammers are all made of the Adze Eye pattern. The Heads are polished, except under the claw, which is blackened.

No. 511 Adze Eye, Curved Claw, Polished

No.		Each
511	7 Ounces, 13 inches overall, Plain Poll	1.40
515	7 " 13 " " Octagon "	1.40

Adze Eye, Straight Claw, Octagonal Poll, Polished

525	10 Ounces, 13 inches overall	1.60
	12 " 14 " "	1.60

BRICKLAYERS

These Hammers are strong and well made and as shown below, can be furnished in the Plain or Adze Eye form. The cutting edge of the Head is specially sharpened and tempered.

Adze Eye, Hand Forged Finish

No.		Each
61	24 Ounces, Size 1, 11 inches overall	1.70
	32 " " 2, 11 " "	1.90

For convenience in carrying or for redressing, Hammer No. 61—24 oz. can be furnished not assembled, the head, handle and necessary wedges being packed in a single box. When so furnished it is identified as No. 161 instead of No. 61.

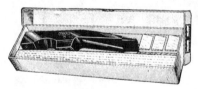

No.		Each
161	24 Ounces. Size 1, 11 inches overall	1.70

Adze Eye, Hand Forged Finish

No.		Each
60	24 Ounces, Size 1, 11 inches overall	1.70

Plain Eye, Hand Forged Finish

No.		Each
160	24 Ounces, Size 1, 11 inches overall	1.45

STANLEY HAMMERS

MACHINISTS

Machinists hammers made with three styles of Peins—the Bell Pein, the one most commonly used, the Straight Pein and the Cross Pein. The two latter are for peining or riveting in corners and places inaccessible to the Ball Pein.

Bell Pein

No.					Each
36	4 Ounces, Size 00000, 10⅜ inches overall				1.20
6	"	"	0000,	12 " "	1.20
8	"	"	000,	13 " "	1.20
12	"	"	00,	14 " "	1.20
16	"	"	0,	14½ " "	1.25
20	"	"	1,	15 " "	1.30
24	"	"	2,	16 " "	1.40
28	"	"	3,	16 " "	1.50
32	"	"	4,	16 " "	1.60
40	"	"	6,	16 " "	1.85
48	"	"	8,	16 " "	2.15
56	"	"	9,	16 " "	2.35

Cross Pein

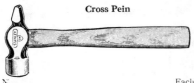

No.				Each
46	16 Ounces, Size 0,	14½ inches overall		1.40
20	"	" 1,	15 " "	1.50
24	"	" 2,	16 " "	1.60
28	"	" 3,	16 " "	1.75
32	"	" 4,	16 " "	1.85

Straight Pein

No.				Each
56	16 Ounces, Size 0,	14½ inches overall		1.40
20	"	" 1,	15 " "	1.50
24	"	" 2,	16 " "	1.60
28	"	" 3,	16 " "	1.75
32	"	" 4,	16 " "	1.85

BLACKSMITHS HAND

These Blacksmiths Hand Hammers are used by the Smith for forging purposes of all kinds. They are very carefully tempered and full polished.

No.				Each
49	26 Ounces, Size 0,	15 inches overall		1.50
32	"	" 1,	16 " "	1.65
42	"	" 2,	16 " "	1.75
48	"	" 3,	16 " "	1.85
56	"	" 4,	16 " "	2.00
72	"	" 5,	16 " "	2.25

ENGINEERS

Engineers Hammers are made in two styles—the Cross Pein and the Double Face pattern. The heads are carefully tempered and full polished.

Cross Pein

No.				Each
48	18 Ounces, Size 0,	14 inches overall		1.40
26	"	" 1,	15 " "	1.50
32	"	" 2,	16 " "	1.65
40	"	" 3,	16 " "	1.75
48	"	" 4,	16 " "	1.85

Double Face

No.				Each
88	24 Ounces, Size 1,	15 inches overall		1.60
38	"	" 2,	16 " "	1.75
48	"	" 3,	16 " "	1.90

STANLEY CARPENTERS CHISELS AND BARS

ATHA  BRAND

These Tools are drop-forged from high grade hexagon steel and will not easily bend or break.

They are attractively finished. Body black baked japan, ends bright red, making them rust-proof. Bits nicely polished.

The cutting edges are specially tempered to a toughness which allows them to cut through nails without difficulty.

RIPPING CHISELS	FLOOR AND CLAPBOARD CHISEL

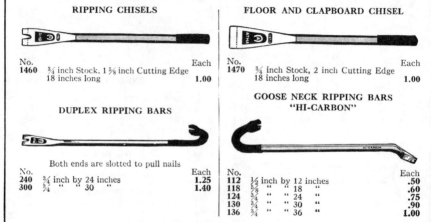

No.		Each	No.		Each
1460	¾ inch Stock, 1⅝ inch Cutting Edge 18 inches long	**1.00**	1470	¾ inch Stock, 2 inch Cutting Edge 18 inches long	**1.00**

DUPLEX RIPPING BARS	GOOSE NECK RIPPING BARS "HI-CARBON"

Both ends are slotted to pull nails

No.		Each	No.		Each
240	¾ inch by 24 inches	**1.25**	112	½ inch by 12 inches	**.50**
300	¾ " " 30 "	**1.40**	118	⅝ " " 18 "	**.60**
			124	¾ " " 24 "	**.75**
			130	¾ " " 30 "	**.90**
			136	¾ " " 36 "	**1.00**

BRICK CHISELS

These Chisels are drop forged in dies from high grade Hexagon Steel which makes them attractive in design and of just the right shape for the purpose they are intended. The body is black japan, the end bright red making them rust proof. Made in three sizes.

No.		Each
1450	3 inch Cutting Edge, 7 inches long	**.90**
	3½ " " 7½ " "	**1.00**
	4 " " 7½ " "	**1.10**

STANLEY
S.W.

ELECTRICIANS CUTTING CHISELS

ATHA  BRAND

This line is used principally by Electricians when installing electric wires or re-wiring old houses.

The tools are forged from a high grade of Hexagon Steel properly tempered and attractively finished: body black japan, ends bright red and blades nicely polished.

TONGUE CUTTING CHISELS

Used for cutting the tongues off floor-boards. For this purpose the blade is made approximately 1-16 in. thick to enable it to enter between the boards without marring the wood.

They are tempered for cutting and are not intended for prying. If used for the latter purpose they are apt to break.

No.							Each
211	½ inch Stock,	7 inches long,	2	inch Bit			.80
212	⅝ " "	8 " "	2½	" "			.90
213	¾ " "	9 " "	3	" "			1.00

OFFSET CUTTING CHISELS

Especially adapted for removing base-boards, moldings, etc. The off-set feature allows for sufficient clearance for the hand.

No.		Each
214	⅝ inch Stock, 11 inches long, 2½ inch Bit	1.50

NAIL CUTTING CHISELS

Used for cutting nails when removing floor-boards, base-boards, molding, etc. Handle is raised or bent to provide clearance for the hand. The end of bar is upset to form a head on which the user can strike to withdraw chisel from wood.

No.		Each
215	⅝ inch Stock, 12 inches long, 1⅛ inch Bit	1.20
216	¾ " " 14 " " 1⅜ " "	1.40

STANLEY CHISELS

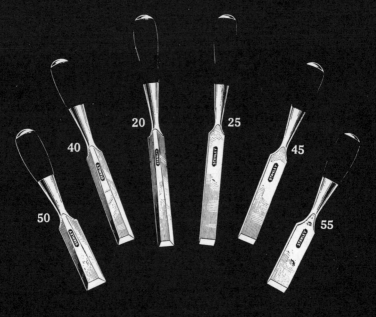

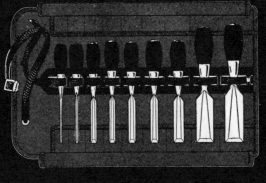

STANLEY "EVERLASTING" CHISELS

The illustrations on the opposite page show the general appearance of Stanley "Everlasting" chisels, which are made in three styles.

FIRMER—The trade name given what might be called the Standard Chisel used in all kinds of ordinary work where such a tool is required. POCKET OR CABINET—which are similar in general appearance to the Firmer line but having handles of a slightly different shape and blades somewhat shorter, and BUTT— which are principally used for sinking in butts, hinges, etc. The blades are shorter than those in either the Firmer or Pocket Chisels, which make them lighter and handier for this work.

"Bevel Edge" chisels are preferable to "Plain Edge," for the reason that they clear themselves easier after a blow and the friction on the sides of the chisel is cut down.

The various sizes manufactured of all numbers are shown on the following pages.

The HEAD, SHANK AND BLADE are of patented construction, having the head, shank and blade forged from one piece of tool steel, as shown in the cut above.

This construction insures great strength and durability and provides for a maximum of efficiency, as a blow on the head of the Chisel is transmitted directly to the cutting edge. Great care is used in the manufacture, especially in the heat treatment of the blade.

THE HANDLE is made from selected hickory and is well finished and fits very snugly into the ferrule. A leather washer is placed between the handle and the steel head to serve as a cushion, thus relieving the handle from shock when the blow is struck.

THE FERRULE is machined from bar steel and is assembled to the Chisel by swaging the ferrule into the double taper in the shank, practically making the shank and ferrule one piece.

The cutting edges of both the Bevel edge and Square edge styles are ground sharp before leaving the factory.

STANLEY "EVERLASTING" CHISELS

Complete details showing the construction of these chisels is given on the preceding page.

BEVEL EDGE FIRMER
Blades 5½ Inches Long

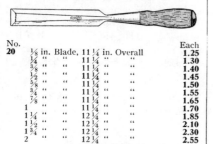

No. 20				Each
1/8 in. Blade, 11 1/4 in. Overall				**1.25**
1/4 "	"	11 1/4 "	"	**1.30**
3/8 "	"	11 1/4 "	"	**1.40**
1/2 "	"	11 1/4 "	"	**1.45**
5/8 "	"	11 1/4 "	"	**1.50**
3/4 "	"	11 1/4 "	"	**1.55**
7/8 "	"	11 1/4 "	"	**1.65**
1 "	"	11 1/4 "	"	**1.70**
1 1/4 "	"	12 1/4 "	"	**1.85**
1 1/2 "	"	12 1/4 "	"	**2.10**
1 3/4 "	"	12 1/4 "	"	**2.30**
2 "	"	12 1/4 "	"	**2.55**

SQUARE EDGE FIRMER
Blades 5½ Inches Long

No. 25				Each
1/8 in. Blade, 11 1/4 in. Overall				**1.20**
1/4 "	"	11 1/4 "	"	**1.25**
3/8 "	"	11 1/4 "	"	**1.35**
1/2 "	"	11 1/4 "	"	**1.35**
5/8 "	"	11 1/4 "	"	**1.45**
3/4 "	"	11 1/4 "	"	**1.50**
7/8 "	"	11 1/4 "	"	**1.60**
1 "	"	11 1/4 "	"	**1.65**
1 1/4 "	"	12 1/4 "	"	**1.80**
1 1/2 "	"	12 1/4 "	"	**2.00**
1 3/4 "	"	12 1/4 "	"	**2.25**
2 "	"	12 1/4 "	"	**2.45**

BEVEL EDGE POCKET
Blades 4½ Inches Long

No. 40				Each
1/8 in. Blade, 9 in. Overall				**1.10**
1/4 "	"	9 "	"	**1.15**
3/8 "	"	9 "	"	**1.25**
1/2 "	"	9 "	"	**1.30**
5/8 "	"	9 "	"	**1.35**
3/4 "	"	9 "	"	**1.40**
7/8 "	"	9 "	"	**1.45**
1 "	"	9 "	"	**1.50**
1 1/4 "	"	10 1/4 "	"	**1.65**
1 1/2 "	"	10 1/4 "	"	**1.90**
1 3/4 "	"	10 1/4 "	"	**2.00**
2 "	"	10 1/4 "	"	**2.25**

SQUARE EDGE POCKET
Blades 4½ Inches Long

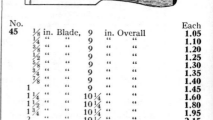

No. 45				Each
1/8 in. Blade, 9 in. Overall				**1.05**
1/4 "	"	9 "	"	**1.10**
3/8 "	"	9 "	"	**1.20**
1/2 "	"	9 "	"	**1.25**
5/8 "	"	9 "	"	**1.30**
3/4 "	"	9 "	"	**1.35**
7/8 "	"	9 "	"	**1.40**
1 "	"	9 "	"	**1.45**
1 1/4 "	"	10 1/4 "	"	**1.60**
1 1/2 "	"	10 1/4 "	"	**1.80**
1 3/4 "	"	10 1/4 "	"	**1.95**
2 "	"	10 1/4 "	"	**2.15**

BEVEL EDGE BUTT
Blades 3 Inches Long

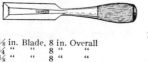

No. 50				Each
1/8 in. Blade, 8 in. Overall				**1.10**
1/4 "	"	8 "	"	**1.10**
3/8 "	"	8 "	"	**1.20**
1/2 "	"	8 "	"	**1.25**
5/8 "	"	8 "	"	**1.30**
3/4 "	"	8 "	"	**1.30**
7/8 "	"	8 "	"	**1.40**
1 "	"	8 "	"	**1.45**
1 1/4 "	"	9 "	"	**1.60**
1 1/2 "	"	9 "	"	**1.80**
1 3/4 "	"	9 "	"	**1.90**
2 "	"	9 "	"	**2.15**

GLAZIERS CHISEL

It has a short stiff blade of the square edge type, 3 inches long and 2 inches wide, which makes it especially adapted for cleaning out old putty and smoothing up and preparing window sashes for the glass.

No. 55		Each
2 in. Blade, 9 in. Overall		**2.05**

[STANLEY] (S.W.)

STANLEY "EVERLASTING" CHISELS

Butt   **SETS OF 6 IN A ROLL**   Pocket

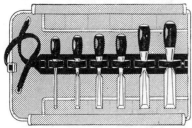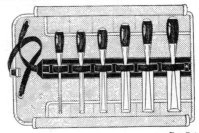

No.				Per Set
120	Butt Chisels, Bevel Edge ¼, ½, ¾, 1, 1¼, 1½ inches wide			**9.50**
110	Pocket "	"	" ¼, ½, ¾, 1, 1¼, 1½ " "	**10.00**
501	Firmer "	"	" ¼, ½, ¾, 1, 1¼, 1½ " "	**11.15**

Butt   **SETS OF 9 IN A ROLL**   Pocket

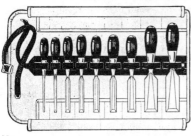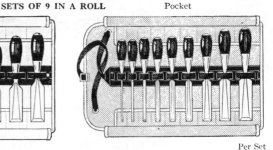

No.				Per Set
220	Butt Chisels, Bevel Edge ⅛, ¼, ⅜, ½, ⅝, ¾, 1, 1¼, 1½ inches wide			**13.35**
210	Pocket "	"	" ⅛, ¼, ⅜, ½, ⅝, ¾, 1, 1¼, 1½ " "	**13.80**
601	Firmer "	"	" ⅛, ¼, ⅜, ½, ⅝, ¾, 1, 1¼, 1½ " "	**15.40**

SETS OF 12 IN A ROLL—Firmer

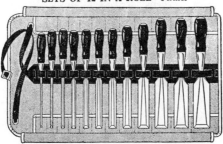

No.				Per Set
320	Butt Chisels, Bevel Edge ⅛, ¼, ⅜, ½, ⅝, ¾, ⅞, 1, 1¼, 1½, 1¾, 2 inches wide			**18.90**
310	Pocket "	"	" ⅛, ¼, ⅜, ½, ⅝, ¾, ⅞, 1, 1¼, 1½, 1¾, 2 " "	**19.60**
701	Firmer "	"	" ⅛, ¼, ⅜, ½, ⅝, ¾, ⅞, 1, 1¼, 1½, 1¾, 2 " "	**22.10**

STANLEY
S.W.

STANLEY SOCKET CHISELS

ONE PIECE SOCKET CHISELS

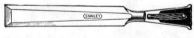

(Sectional View)

Provided with an entirely new locking screw device which holds the handle firmly in the socket. This eliminates the possibility of the handle working loose and dropping out. Hickory handles. The same high quality steel as found in all Stanley Chisels.

Bevel Edge Butt Chisel

No.	Blade	Overall	Each
440	$\frac{1}{8}$ in.	$10\frac{5}{8}$ in.	**1.10**
	$\frac{1}{4}$ "	$10\frac{5}{8}$ "	**1.10**
	$\frac{3}{8}$ "	$10\frac{5}{8}$ "	**1.10**
	$\frac{1}{2}$ "	$10\frac{5}{8}$ "	**1.20**
	$\frac{5}{8}$ "	$10\frac{5}{8}$ "	**1.30**
	$\frac{3}{4}$ "	$10\frac{5}{8}$ "	**1.40**
	$\frac{7}{8}$ "	$10\frac{5}{8}$ "	**1.45**
	1 "	$10\frac{5}{8}$ "	**1.50**
	$1\frac{1}{4}$ "	$11\frac{5}{8}$ "	**1.65**
	$1\frac{1}{2}$ "	$11\frac{5}{8}$ "	**1.90**
	$1\frac{3}{4}$ "	$11\frac{5}{8}$ "	**2.00**
	2 "	$11\frac{5}{8}$ "	**2.25**

Bevel Edge Pocket Chisel

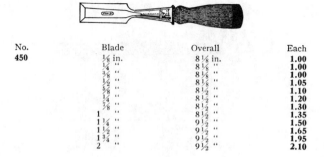

No.	Blade	Overall	Each
450	$\frac{1}{8}$ in.	$8\frac{1}{8}$ in.	**1.00**
	$\frac{1}{4}$ "	$8\frac{1}{8}$ "	**1.00**
	$\frac{3}{8}$ "	$8\frac{1}{8}$ "	**1.00**
	$\frac{1}{2}$ "	$8\frac{1}{8}$ "	**1.05**
	$\frac{5}{8}$ "	$8\frac{1}{2}$ "	**1.10**
	$\frac{3}{4}$ "	$8\frac{1}{2}$ "	**1.20**
	$\frac{7}{8}$ "	$8\frac{1}{2}$ "	**1.30**
	1 "	$8\frac{1}{2}$ "	**1.35**
	$1\frac{1}{4}$ "	$9\frac{1}{2}$ "	**1.50**
	$1\frac{1}{2}$ "	$9\frac{1}{2}$ "	**1.65**
	$1\frac{3}{4}$ "	$9\frac{1}{2}$ "	**1.95**
	2 "	$9\frac{1}{2}$ "	**2.10**

STANLEY
S.W.

STANLEY MITRE BOXES

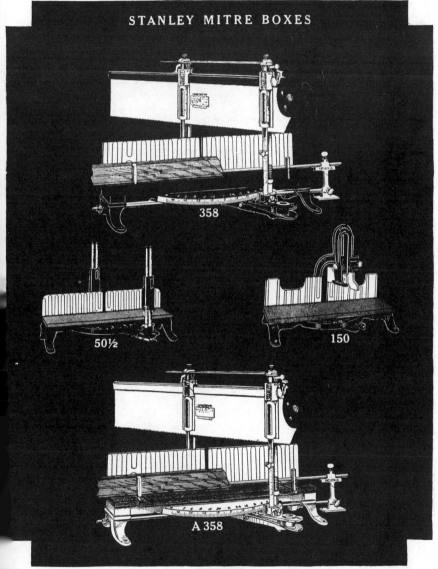

STANLEY MITRE BOXES

Below are described in detail several important features that are of special value on the Stanley Mitre Boxes shown on the following pages.

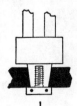

Cut 1 shows the method of tightening the upright in the Stanley Boxes, shown on pages 129 and 130, which is by a large screw drawing a tapered socket into a tapered hole and locking it.

Cut 2 shows the method in the No. 50½ Mitre Boxes, shown on page 131, where the socket fits into a split swivel and is locked by a screw drawing the split swivel together.

In either box, before finally locking the saw guide, care should be taken to set the uprights so that they are the proper distance apart for the working of the saw. Saws vary in thickness and a different setting is required for each saw.

Cut 3 shows the bars set for the narrowest and Cut 4 for widest saw play.

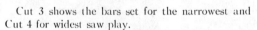

The Swivel Arm on the Stanley Boxes Nos. 240 to 460, has a tapered index pin which engages in holes on the under side of the quadrant. These holes are made at the commonly used angles, allowing 3, 4, 5, 6, 8, 12 and 24 sided pieces to be cut. To set the swivel arm at other angles or to make a slight change of position at a designated angle, the index pin can be held down by inserting a brad in the small hole in the bottom of the pin. The swivel arm can then be set and will automatically fasten at any angle desired.

The Clamping Lever under the front of the swivel arm, may be held up by means of a swinging thumb lever, permitting the saw and swivel arm to be swung to any line of the quadrant or to a line marked on the board to be sawed. When released, the swivel arm automatically locks.

STANLEY MITRE BOXES

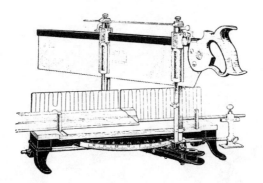

The Back and Frame, Graduated Quadrant and Swivel Arm Bearing are in one piece.

The Saw Guide Uprights, front and back, are graduated in sixteenths of inches, and movable stops can be set to the depth of the cut desired.

The Index Sight Plate, at bottom of front saw guide upright, enables the workman to accurately set the swivel arm to one of the index holes or to any degree of graduation on the quadrant.

Stock Guides hold all ordinary work as well as irregular forms, and can be used as length gauges for duplicating short pieces.

The Length Stop permits of sawing duplicate pieces of practically any length and can be used either right or left hand.

Automatic Catches on the uprights hold the saw up, allowing the use of both hands in placing the work.

The Legs are detachable, and being of malleable iron, are unbreakable. Two cone-pointed screws on the rear legs prevent the Box sliding when in use.

A Tie Bar at the top of the uprights gives great rigidity.

The Two Adjustable Spurs in the back of the frame hold the work from slipping.

The Narrow Opening in the frame is specially adapted for sawing short work.

With each Box is furnished a Back Saw of the size noted in table.

No.	Back Saw	Capacity Right Angle	Capacity Mitre (45°)	Capacity at 30° without Stock Guide	Weight Box only	Each (With Saw)
240	20 x 4	8¼ in.	5½ in.	3½ in.	18 lbs.	22.30
242	22 x 4	8¼ "	5½ "	3½ "	18 "	22.85
244	24 x 4	8¼ "	5½ "	3½ "	18 "	23.35
246	26 x 4	8¼ "	5½ "	3½ "	20 "	23.95
346	26 x 4	9½ "	6½ "	4⅛ "	20½ "	25.95
358	28 x 5	9½ "	6½ "	4⅛ "	23½ "	27.40
460	30 x 6	11 "	7½ "	5⅛ "	28 "	32.75

For Price of Parts see Page 179

STANLEY ALUMINUM MITRE BOX

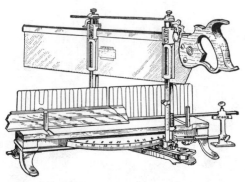

This new Mitre Box is exactly the same in design and variety of adjustments and working features as the regular line of Stanley Mitre Boxes shown on page 129.

The difference lies in the fact that practically all parts are of Aluminum, which provides a Box much lighter in weight and one which will not rust.

The Aluminum Box is made in one size only, having a right angle capacity of $9\frac{1}{2}$ inches, a mitre capacity (45 degrees) of $6\frac{1}{2}$ inches and without stock guides (30 degrees) a capacity of $4\frac{1}{8}$ inches.

With each Box is furnished a 28 x 5 Back Saw.

No.   Each (With Saw)
A358   28 x 5 Saw—Weight Box only, 10 lbs.   **36.00**

Stanley Mitre Box—Knocked Down

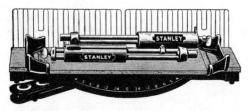

The above cut shows how Stanley Mitre Boxes can be "Knocked Down" allowing them to be readily carried or packed.

All parts are interchangeable. The legs go into sockets and are tightened by a screw.

The Saw Guide Uprights are loosened or tightened by adjustment of only one screw.

For Price of Parts see Page 179

STANLEY MITRE BOXES

These Boxes are strong and accurate, though not having all the refinements of those shown on previous pages.

The back, frame, indexed quadrant and swivel arm bearing are in one piece and accurately machined. The quadrant is indexed for cutting 4, 5, 6, 8, 12 and 24 sided pieces. The swivel arm can be locked at any point desired.

The saw guide uprights can be adjusted to hold the saw without side play, thus insuring great accuracy in working.

Either a back saw or panel saw can be used. In using a panel saw put a nail through the two holes near the top of the rear saw guides to keep the saw in place.

Movable stops are attached to the Saw uprights permitting the saw to cut only to the desired depth. The No. 60½ Box is the No. 50½ with a 20 x 4 Back Saw.

No.	Capacity Right Angle	Capacity Mitre (45°)	Weight Box only	Each
50½ Box only, no saw	7¼ in.	4¾ in.	16 lbs.	10.95
60½ With Saw, 20 x 4	7¼ "	4¾ "	16 "	16.45

For Price of Parts see page 179

STANLEY OPEN FRONT MITRE BOX

The Stanley open front Mitre Box while simple in design and having only a few parts, is very substantially built and has adjustments which make it one of the most convenient moderate priced boxes made.

It will take stock up to 4 inches in height and on account of its open front, boards of extra width can be sawed at any angle between 45 and 90 degrees.

The swivel arm is provided with a latch pivot, which engages in slots in the frame of the ordinary Mitre cuts of 4, 6 and 8 sided frames and the swivel can also be locked at any angle by means of a set screw.

The saw guide can be adjusted for any thickness of saw and adjusted vertically to the base.

The Saw can be adjusted square with the back.

No.		Each
150	No Saw, Weight, Box only, 10 lbs.	6.70

For Price of Parts see Page 180

STANLEY VISES

These are strong, serviceable tools, and on account of their convenient size and many uses to which they can be put, are a valuable addition to the tool kit of any household.

The Screw, (Body, Head and Collar) is of one piece of steel with a square lathe-cut thread working in a malleable nut. A patented, hardened split washer is placed under the head of the screw to take up the wear.

Particular attention is called to the hardened steel jaws on the No. 761, No. 772 and No. 752 lines, which materially add to the life of the vise. Both front and back jaws of all styles are ground to insure that they meet squarely when tight.

Can be furnished in three styles of bases.

CLAMP BASE

These Vises have ample clamping capacity, as they can be clamped to a board or bench up to 2¼ inches thick.

The Clamping Screws are of the vise handle type, which allows the vise to be more easily and securely fastened to the bench than does the ordinary thumb screw. The Clamping Washer has a large bearing surface. They are also provided with holes so that they may be permanently secured to the bench if desired.

Steel Jaws

No.			Each
761	1½ in.	Jaws	2.05
762	1¾ "	"	2.35
763	2 "	"	2.75
764	2¼ "	"	3.15
765	2½ "	"	3.75
766	3 "	"	5.50

Iron Jaws

No.			Each
741	1½ in.	Jaws	1.60
742	1¾ "	"	1.90
743	2 "	"	2.25
744	2¼ "	"	2.70
745	2½ "	"	3.15
746	3 "	"	4.95

SWIVEL BASE
Steel Jaws

The base plate is fastened to the bench, the vise rests on this plate and can be turned to the right or left as desired and firmly locked by means of a clamping nut.

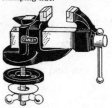

No.			Each
772	1¾ in.	Jaws	2.35
773	2 "	"	2.80
774	2¼ "	"	3.45
775	2½ "	"	4.15
776	3 "	"	5.70

STATIONARY BASE
Steel Jaws

In the stationary base style, the vise itself is permanently secured to the bench in a fixed position.

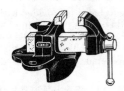

No.			Each
752	1¾ in.	Jaws	2.35
753	2 "	"	2.80
754	2¼ "	"	3.45
755	2½ "	"	4.15

[STANLEY]
(S.W.)

STANLEY DOWELING JIGS

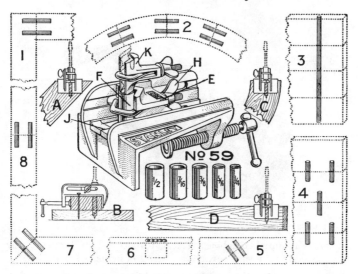

This tool is for the purpose of enabling the user to bore dowel holes in the edge, end or surface of work with ease and accuracy. It will take any thickness of material up to three inches. It is also an excellent bit guide for mortising.

With the Doweling Jig the steel guide is automatically set to guide the bit properly when the Jig is clamped to the work.

A depth gauge "K" is also furnished which can be used with or without the Jig. Where used without the Jig, the gauge should be set with the large end towards the point of the bit, but in using same with the Jig it should be set with the small end down, as shown in the cut.

Fig. A shows the proper way of attaching the Jig when boring dowel holes on mitred or special work.

Fig. B shows the method used in boring dowel holes in the surface of a board. For this work it is necessary that a temporary block be nailed to the board as shown in illustration.

Fig. C shows how the Jig should be attached to the work when doweling segments of circles.

Fig. D the setting of the Jig for all kinds of ordinary doweling.

Figs. 1 to 8 show various forms of work where the Jig can be used to good advantage.

The Jig is made entirely of metal, the working parts being milled true. All parts are nickel plated.

No.   Each
59 with 5 Guides (1 each ¼, ⁵⁄₁₆, ⅜, ⁷⁄₁₆, and ½ inch)   **2.80**
60 " 9 " (1 each ¼, ⁵⁄₁₆, ⅜, ⁷⁄₁₆, ½, ⁹⁄₁₆, ⅝, ¹¹⁄₁₆ and ¾ inch) **4.05**

STANLEY DOWEL AND ROD TURNING MACHINE

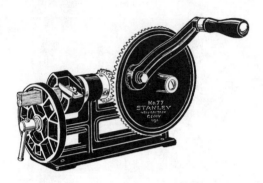

A tool that will appeal to cabinet makers, pattern makers, furniture manufacturers and especially to supervisors and instructors of industrial education.

It will not only cut dowels of varying sizes and lengths to perfect dimensions, but with it one can also form rods of practically any length.

Ready made or stock dowels have a tendency to warp and shrink, making them very unsatisfactory to use where a close fit is desired.

With this machine the workman can cut his dowels when he is ready to use them and furthermore, of the same material as the wood being worked.

It is designed to be operated by hand, and the crank can be adjusted for a long or short throw, giving power or speed to the machine as desired.

One cutter head complete for making dowels or rods $\frac{3}{8}$ inch in diameter is furnished with each machine.

Additional cutter heads with cutters $\frac{1}{4}$, $\frac{5}{16}$, $\frac{7}{16}$, $\frac{1}{2}$, $\frac{9}{16}$, $\frac{5}{8}$, $\frac{11}{16}$ and $\frac{3}{4}$ inches can be furnished if desired. These cutters are adjustable so that the dowels or rods can be made for a tight or loose fit.

A workman whose tool equipment includes one of these machines and a Stanley Doweling Jig can make doweled joints with surprising quickness and accuracy.

No.		Each
77	Doweling Machine, with $\frac{3}{8}$ inch Cutter Head	**12.00**
	Additional Cutter Heads	**1.20**

STANLEY SAW SETS AND SHOOT BOARD
"PISTOL GRIP" ADJUSTABLE SAW SETS

The shape of the Body and Handle enables the user to operate the tool with great ease as the saw set is held in a comfortable and natural position. The saw is held firmly against the gauge while the tooth is being set. The saw teeth are in plain view which enables the user to quickly adjust the tool to the tooth to be set.

They can be readily adjusted to give a greater or less set to the teeth of the saw, according as the saw is to be used for coarse or fine work. As the anvil or part against which the plunger works is graduated, the same adjustment can be easily obtained for duplicate work.

No. 43 is adjustable for thickness of Saw Blade. The Stop Plate should be set to bring the side of the saw flat against the highest point of the anvil and secured by means of the binding screw.

For Back and Panel Saws   **For Cross Cut Saws**

No.		Each	No.		Each
42	Black Finish	2.40	43	Black Finish	4.50
42N	Nickel Plated	3.00			

SHOOT BOARD AND PLANE

For Pattern Makers, Cabinet Makers, Printers, Picture Framers, and Electrotypers. Amateurs will also find this tool very useful. The Board is of ribbed construction, and has an adjustable runway for the Plane, accurately machined. The Swivel can be locked at any angle between zero and ninety degrees. The Swivel is fitted with a sliding back supporting the work to the edge, and with a sliding Back Clamp to hold any shaped work in position. The Plane is especially constructed for the Board, and has Rosewood handle and knob. The cutter has adjustment for depth of cut, also a lateral adjustment, so that a cut giving any ordinary draft to a pattern can be made. Being set on a skew (see page 85) it will make a very smooth, clean cut.

SHOOT BOARD AND PLANE   **PLANE ONLY**

No.		Each	No.		Each
52	22in. long, Plane 15in. long, 2⅜in. Cutter	19.70	51	15 in. long, 2⅜ in. Cutter	7.90

For Prices on Plane Irons and Plane Parts see page 177

STANLEY SCREW DRIVERS

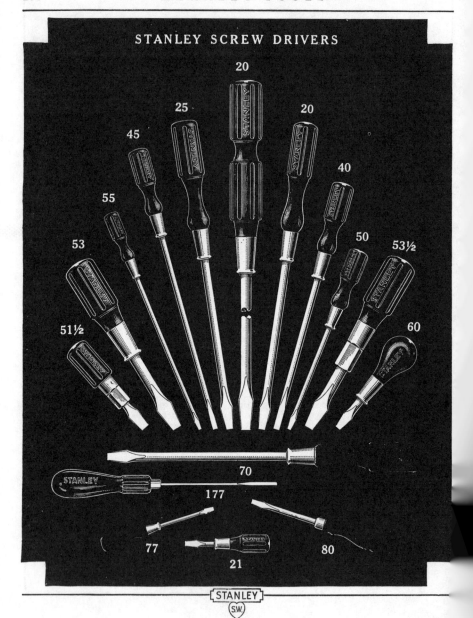

STANLEY SCREW DRIVERS

STANLEY "HURWOOD"

These Screw Drivers are unsurpassed for strength, durability, accuracy of tips, quality of handles and general appearance. All blades are exceptionally well finished and tempered.

THE BLADE, SHANK AND HEAD are formed from one piece of special steel. The shank passes through the handle and ferrule and is pinned, as shown in cut.

THE HEAD has two projecting wings, which together with the pin keep the shank from turning in the handle.

ELECTRICIANS SCREW DRIVERS, so termed, have the head countersunk in the handle and insulated by a non-conducting plug of a hard material.

STANLEY

Stanley Screw Drivers Nos. 70 and 75 (page 142) have projecting wings swedged on the shank and forced into the handle. The shank, handle and ferrule have a pin passing through them, which together with the swedged shank, securely fastens the blade to the handle. The blades are tempered.

No. 80 Screw Drivers (page 143) have two pairs of ears swedged on the ends in the handle securely fastening them.

THE TIPS in both the Stanley "Hurwood" and Stanley lines of Screw Drivers in addition to a full variety of sizes of Standard Tips are made with so-called Cabinet Makers Tips in which the sides of the tip are parallel instead of being tapered. The width of the tip being the same as the diameter of the shank, permits a countersunk screw to be followed up. All tips are carefully hardened and tempered.

STANLEY "HURWOOD" REGULAR SCREW DRIVERS

The blades are of the standard type with proportionate tips and handles. The handles are fluted and stained black

STANDARD HEAD

No.									Each
20	2½ in. Blade	⁷⁄₃₂ in. dia.		6½ in. overall					.30
3	" "	⁷⁄₃₂ "	"	8	"	"			.35
4	" "	¼ "	"	9	"	"			.40
5	" "	⁵⁄₁₆ "	"	10½	"	"			.50
6	" "	⁵⁄₁₆ "	"	11¾	"	"			.60
8	" "	⅜ "	"	15	"	"			.70
10	" "	⅜ "	"	17	"	"			.90
12	" "	⅜ "	"	19	"	"			1.05
18	" "	½ "	"	27¼	"	"			1.65

INSULATED HEAD (ELECTRICIANS)

No.									Each
25	2½ in. Blade	⁷⁄₃₂ in. dia.		6½ in. overall					.30
3	" "	⁷⁄₃₂ "	"	8	"	"			.35
4	" "	¼ "	"	9	"	"			.40
5	" "	⁵⁄₁₆ "	"	10½	"	"			.50
6	" "	⁵⁄₁₆ "	"	11¾	"	"			.60
8	" "	⅜ "	"	15	"	"			.70
10	" "	⅜ "	"	17	"	"			.90
12	" "	⅜ "	"	19	"	"			1.05
18	" "	½ "	"	27¼	"	"			1.65

STANLEY "HURWOOD" CABINET MAKERS
SCREW DRIVERS

In this form of Driver, the sides of the tip are parallel instead of being tapered, the width of the tip being the same as the diameter of the shank. This permits a countersunk screw to be followed up without marring or damaging the work.

The handles are fluted and stained black.

STANDARD HEAD

No.							Each
40	2½ in. Blade	⁷⁄₃₂ in. dia.	6½ in. overall				**.30**
3	" "	⁷⁄₃₂ " "	7½ " "				**.35**
4	" "	¼ " "	9 " "				**.40**
5	" "	¼ " "	10 " "				**.50**
6	" "	¼ " "	11 " "				**.60**
8	" "	¼ " "	13 " "				**.70**
10	" "	¼ " "	15 " "				**.90**
12	" "	¼ " "	17 " "				**1.05**

INSULATED HEAD (ELECTRICIANS)

No.							Each
45	2½ in. Blade	⁷⁄₃₂ in. dia.	6½ in. overall				**.30**
3	" "	⁷⁄₃₂ " "	7½ " "				**.35**
4	" "	¼ " "	9 " "				**.40**
5	" "	¼ " "	10 " "				**.50**
6	" "	¼ " "	11 " "				**.60**
8	" "	¼ " "	13 " "				**.70**
10	" "	¼ " "	15 " "				**.90**
12	" "	¼ " "	17 " "				**1.05**

STANLEY "HURWOOD" SMALL BLADE SCREW DRIVERS

This line of Screw Drivers is designed for light and delicate work. The blades are made of very small stock and the tapered tips of a proportionate size. The handles are short and of small diameter so that they just fit the palm of the hand, permitting the owner to use his thumb and forefinger against the shoulder (near the ferrule) when turning screws requiring delicate adjustment.

The handles are fluted and stained black.

STANDARD HEAD

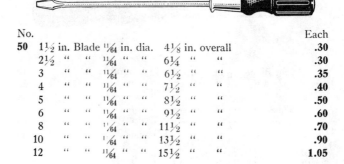

No.							Each
50	1½ in. Blade	¹¹⁄₆₄ in. dia.		4⅛ in. overall			.30
	2½ "	" ¹¹⁄₆₄ "	"	6¼ "	"		.30
	3 "	" ¹¹⁄₆₄ "	"	6½ "	"		.35
	4 "	" ¹¹⁄₆₄ "	"	7½ "	"		.40
	5 "	" ¹¹⁄₆₄ "	"	8½ "	"		.50
	6 "	" ¹¹⁄₆₄ "	"	9½ "	"		.60
	8 "	" ¹¹⁄₆₄ "	"	11½ "	"		.70
	10 "	" ¹ ⁄₆₄ "	"	13½ "	"		.90
	12 "	" ¹¹⁄₆₄ "	"	15½ "	"		1.05

INSULATED HEAD (ELECTRICIANS)

Particularly adapted for light electrical work, as the tip fits the countersink in the porcelain fittings.

No.							Each
55	1½ in. Blade	¹¹⁄₆₄ in. dia.		4⅛ in. overall			.30
	2½ "	" ¹¹⁄₆₄ "	"	6¼ "	"		.30
	3 "	" ¹¹⁄₆₄ "	"	6½ "	"		.35
	4 "	" ¹¹⁄₆₄ "	"	7½ "	"		.40
	5 "	" ¹¹⁄₆₄ "	"	8½ "	"		.50
	6 "	" ¹¹⁄₆₄ "	"	9½ "	"		.60
	8 "	" ¹¹⁄₆₄ "	"	11½ "	"		.70
	10 "	" ¹¹⁄₆₄ "	"	13½ "	"		.90
	12 "	" ¹¹⁄₆₄ "	"	15½ "	"		1.05

{STANLEY}
(S.W.)

STANLEY SPECIAL SCREW DRIVERS

"HURWOOD BABY"

A handy little tool for the vest pocket, only four inches long over all and will work a good sized screw. Same design as the regular "Hurwood," thus insuring strength. The handle is fluted and stained black.

"HURWOOD HANDY"

Especially adapted for Plumbers and for work in places where a longer Driver cannot be used. The handle has a smooth surface and is stained black, while its peculiar shape furnishes a very strong grip.

No.		Each
21	1½ in. Blade, ⁷⁄₃₂ in. dia., 4⅛ in. overall	.30
31	Insulated Head, 1½ in. Blade, ⁷⁄₃₂ in. dia. 4⅛ in. overall	.30

No.		Each
60	1⅝ in. Blade, ⁵⁄₁₆ in. dia. 5½ in. overall	.40

"HURWOOD" MACHINISTS SCREW DRIVERS

These are especially adapted for heavy work where a long driver cannot be conveniently used. Nos. 51½, 52½, 53½ and 54 are made with a hexagon shank for use with a wrench. No. 54 has a long double grip handle. The handles are fluted and stained black.

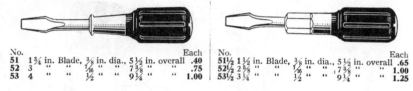

No.									Each
51	1¾ in. Blade,	⅜	in. dia.,	5½	in. overall				.40
52	3	"	"	⁷⁄₁₆	"	"	7⅜	"	"	.75
53	4	"	"	½	"	"	9¼	"	"	1.00

No.									Each
51½	1½ in. Blade,	⅜	in. dia.,	5½	in. overall				.65
52½	2⅝	"	"	⁷⁄₁₆	"	"	7⅜	"	"	1.00
53½	3¼	"	"	½	"	"	9¼	"	"	1.25

Double Grip

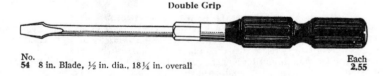

No.		Each
54	8 in. Blade, ½ in. dia., 18¼ in. overall	2.55

"LITTLE MASCOT" SCREW DRIVERS

A small light Screw Driver. The blade is made of one piece of steel carefully tempered with a pair of ears swedged on the end in the handle, securely fastening it. The handle is fluted, stained black, and neatly ferruled.

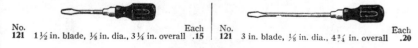

No.		Each
121	1½ in. blade, ⅛ in. dia., 3¼ in. overall	.15

No.		Each
121	3 in. blade, ⅛ in. dia., 4¾ in. overall	.20

STANLEY
(S.W.)

STANLEY SCREW DRIVERS

These Screw Drivers have round steel blades, with two pair of ears swedged on the end in the handle, which, together with a pin riveted through the steel ferrule, handle and shank, prevents it turning. The handles are of hardwood, fluted and stained red.

STANDARD BLADE AND TIP

No.		Blade			Each	No.		Blade			Each
				Overall						Overall	
70	2½ in.	$7/32$ in. dia.		6½ in.	.25	170	2½ in.	$7/32$ in. dia.		6½ in.	.20
3	"	$7/32$ " "		8	.25	3	"	$7/32$ " "		8	.20
4	"	$1/4$ " "		9	.30	4	"	$1/4$ " "		9	.25
5	"	$5/16$ " "		10½	.30	5	"	$5/16$ " "		10½	.25
6	"	$5/16$ " "		11¾	.35	6	"	$5/16$ " "		11¾	.30
8	"	$3/8$ " "		15	.45	8	"	$3/8$ " "		15	.40
10	"	$3/8$ " "		17	.55	10	"	$3/8$ " "		17	.50
12	"	$3/8$ " "		19	.70	12	"	$3/8$ " "		19	.60
15	"	$7/16$ " "		22¾	.80						
18	"	$1/2$ " "		27¼	1.00						

CABINET MAKERS BLADE AND TIP

In this form of Driver, the sides of the tip are parallel instead of being tapered, the width of the tip being the same as the diameter of the shank. This permits of a countersunk screw being followed up without marring or damaging the work.

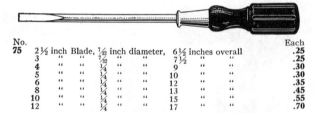

No.								Each
75	2½ inch Blade,	$7/32$ inch diameter,		6½ inches overall				.25
3	"	"	$7/32$ " "	7½	"	"		.25
4	"	"	$1/4$ " "	9	"	"		.30
5	"	"	$1/4$ " "	10	"	"		.30
6	"	"	$1/4$ " "	12	"	"		.35
8	"	"	$1/4$ " "	13	"	"		.45
10	"	"	$1/4$ " "	15	"	"		.55
12	"	"	$1/4$ " "	17	"	"		.70

EXTRA SMALL BLADE AND HANDLE

This line of Screw Drivers is designed for light and delicate work. The blades are made of very small stock and the tapered tips of a proportionate size. The handles are short and of small diameter so that they just fit the palm of the hand, permitting the owner to use his thumb and forefinger against the shoulder (near the ferrule) when turning screws requiring delicate adjustment.

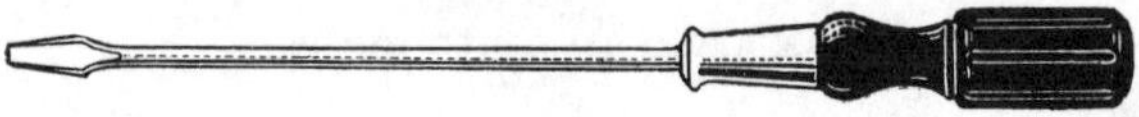

No.								Each
77	1½ inch Blade,	$11/64$ inch diameter,		4⅛ inches overall				.25
3	"	"	$3/16$ " "	6½	"	"		.25
4	"	"	$3/16$ " "	7½	"	"		.30
5	"	"	$3/16$ " "	8½	"	"		.30
6	"	"	$3/16$ " "	9½	"	"		.35
8	"	"	$3/16$ " "	11½	"	"		.45
10	"	"	$3/16$ " "	13½	"	"		.55
12	"	"	$3/16$ " "	15½	"	"		.70

STANLEY SCREW DRIVERS

These screw drivers have round steel blades, with two pair of ears swedged on the end in the handle, securely fastening them. The tips take the standard form throughout, and neat substantial ferrules are used. Handles stained red.

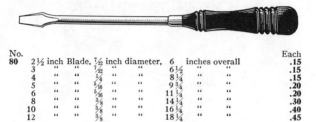

No.								Each
80	2½ inch Blade,	$\frac{7}{32}$ inch diameter,	6	inches overall				.15
3	" "	$\frac{7}{32}$ "	"	6½	"	"		.15
4	" "	¼ "	"	8¼	"	"		.15
5	" "	$\frac{5}{16}$ "	"	9¾	"	"		.20
6	" "	$\frac{5}{16}$ "	"	11¼	"	"		.20
8	" "	$\frac{3}{8}$ "	"	14¼	"	"		.30
10	" "	$\frac{3}{8}$ "	"	16¼	"	"		.40
12	" "	$\frac{3}{8}$ "	"	18¼	"	"		.45

RADIO SCREW DRIVERS

A handy screw driver for light work. The blades are made of small stock and the width of the tip is the same as the diameter of the shank. Handle fluted and stained black.

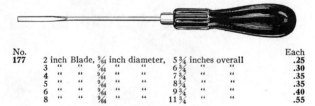

No.							Each
177	2 inch Blade,	$\frac{9}{64}$ inch diameter,	5¾	inches overall			.25
3	" "	$\frac{9}{64}$ "	"	6¾	"	"	.30
4	" "	$\frac{9}{64}$ "	"	7¾	"	"	.35
5	" "	$\frac{9}{64}$ "	"	8¾	"	"	.35
6	" "	$\frac{9}{64}$ "	"	9¾	"	"	.40
8	" "	$\frac{9}{64}$ "	"	11¾	"	"	.55

FLAT BLADE SCREW DRIVERS

These are made of an excellent quality of steel. The No. 64 line have varnished handles, with metallic fastenings. The No. 86 line have polished handles.

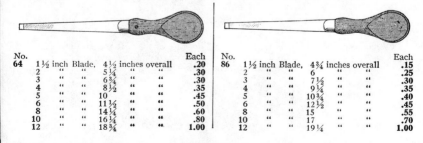

No.					Each	No.					Each
64	1½ inch Blade,	4½ inches overall			.20	86	1½ inch Blade,	4¾ inches overall			.15
2	" "	5¼ "	"		.30	2	" "	6 "	"		.25
3	" "	6¾ "	"		.30	3	" "	7½ "	"		.30
4	" "	8½ "	"		.35	4	" "	9¼ "	"		.35
5	" "	10 "	"		.45	5	" "	10¾ "	"		.40
6	" "	11½ "	"		.50	6	" "	12½ "	"		.45
8	" "	14¼ "	"		.60	8	" "	15 "	"		.55
10	" "	16¼ "	"		.80	10	" "	17 "	"		.70
12	" "	18¾ "	"		1.00	12	" "	19¼ "	"		1.00

STANLEY
S.W.

STANLEY RATCHET SCREW DRIVERS

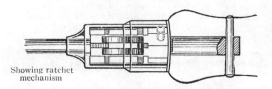

Showing ratchet
mechanism

The Ratchet mechanism (Patented) is the most substantial type and possesses long wearing qualities. All parts are machine made and interchangeable. Handles are securely fastened to the mechanism with tapered steel pins which prevent the handles from turning.

No. 215

An exceptionally attractive and well-made Screw Driver. The blades are of high grade tool steel, carefully hardened and tempered. Cocobolo handles. Sturdy ratchet mechanism.

No.	Blade	Overall	Each
215	2 in. $\frac{7}{32}$ in. dia.	6 $\frac{3}{4}$ in.	**.95**
	3 " $\frac{7}{32}$ " "	7 $\frac{3}{4}$ "	**1.00**
	4 " $\frac{9}{32}$ " "	9 $\frac{1}{8}$ "	**1.15**
	5 " $\frac{9}{32}$ " "	10 $\frac{1}{8}$ "	**1.25**
	6 " $\frac{5}{16}$ " "	11 $\frac{1}{2}$ "	**1.35**
	8 " $\frac{5}{16}$ " "	13 $\frac{3}{4}$ "	**1.55**

No. 216

Designed especially for cabinet makers. The sides of the tips are parallel, enabling the user to follow up a countersunk screw without damaging the work. Knurled rotating Finger Grip assists in starting the screw quickly.

No.	Blade	Overall	Each
216	2 in. $\frac{3}{16}$ in. dia.	5 $\frac{1}{4}$ in.	**1.15**
	3 " $\frac{3}{16}$ " "	6 $\frac{1}{4}$ "	**1.20**
	4 " $\frac{3}{16}$ " "	7 $\frac{1}{4}$ "	**1.25**
	5 " $\frac{3}{16}$ " "	8 $\frac{1}{4}$ "	**1.30**
	6 " $\frac{3}{16}$ " "	9 $\frac{1}{4}$ "	**1.35**

STANLEY "HURWOOD" ICE PICKS AND AWLS

The blade, shank and head are formed of one piece of steel. Two projecting wings under the head, together with a rivet which passes through the steel ferrule, handle and shank, securely fasten the blade in the handle as described in detail on page 137. The handles are stained black. All points are carefully tempered.

ICE PICK

Needle points. No chopping is necessary; simply *push* the point through the ice.

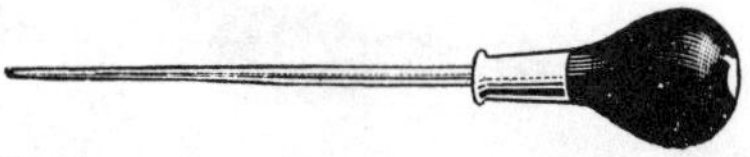

No.		Each
B	Blade $5\frac{1}{2}$ inches, diameter $\frac{7}{32}$ inch, length 9 inches overall, Needle Point	.45

ICE PICK

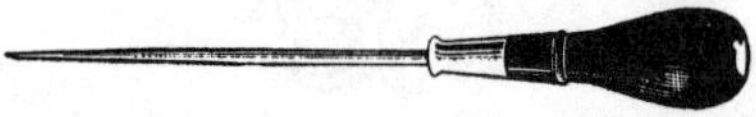

No.		Each
C	Blade $5\frac{1}{2}$ inches, diameter $\frac{7}{32}$ inch, length 9 inches overall, Needle Point	.45

ICE PICK

A hexagonal iron band around the handle will be found convenient for breaking the ice into small pieces, and it prevents the pick from rolling when laid down.

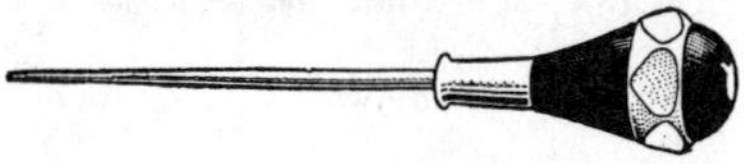

No.		Each
D	Blade $5\frac{1}{2}$ inches, diameter $\frac{7}{32}$ inch, length 9 inches overall, Needle Point, Metal Ring	.75

BELT AWL

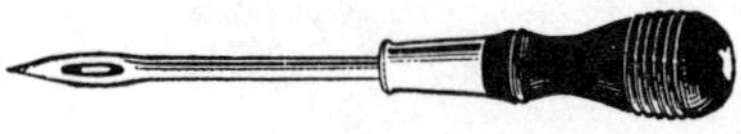

No.		Each
9	Blade $4\frac{1}{4}$ inches, diameter $\frac{1}{4}$ inch, length $8\frac{3}{8}$ inches overall, Eye Point	.40

BRAD AWL

No.		Each
17	Blades 1, $1\frac{1}{4}$, $1\frac{1}{2}$, or $1\frac{5}{8}$ inches. Lengths $4\frac{3}{4}$, 5, $5\frac{1}{4}$, $5\frac{3}{8}$ inches overall, Flat Points	.35

SCRATCH AWL

No.		Each
6	Blade $2\frac{3}{4}$ inches, diameter $\frac{7}{32}$ inch, length $5\frac{7}{8}$ inches overall, Needle Point	.35

SCRATCH AWL

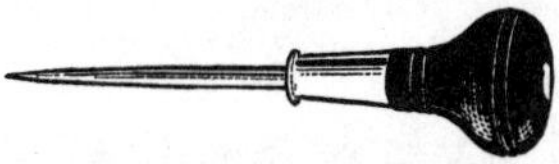

No.		Each
7	Blade $3\frac{1}{2}$ inches, diameter $\frac{1}{4}$ inch, length $6\frac{1}{2}$ inches overall, Needle Point	.40

TINNERS AWL

No.		Each
8	Blade $3\frac{3}{4}$ inches, diameter $\frac{5}{16}$ inch, length $7\frac{1}{2}$ inches overall, Needle Point	.40

STANLEY MISCELLANEOUS TOOLS

AWL HAFTS

This line of Awl Hafts are carefully made of well seasoned wood. Particular attention is called to the X6 Peg Awl, which has a four jaw knurled chuck.

No.		Each
6	Peg Awl, Leather Top, Steel Chuck	.20

No.		Each
X6	Peg Awl, Leather Top, Four Jaw Steel Chuck	.35

No.		Each
6½	Sewing Awl, Steel Chuck	.20

TACK HAMMERS

The head is magnetized.

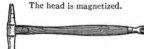

No.		Each
2	4 inch Head, 11½ inch Handle	.20

The head, handle and claw is one piece of malleable iron. The sides of the handle are inlaid with two wooden strips securely riveted in place.

No.		Each
4	4 inch Head, 10¾ inch Handle	.55

UPHOLSTERERS TACK HAMMERS

The head is magnetized and made of highest quality steel. The handle is made from straight grained hickory.

No.		Each
163	4¾ inch head 12 inches overall	1.25

SCRATCH AWLS

The handles are of hard wood, brass ferruled.

No.		Each
1	Blade 3 in. dia., $\frac{5}{32}$ in. Needle Point	.15
2	" 3½ " " $\frac{3}{16}$ " " "	.15

BRAD AWLS

No.		Each
3	Small Flat Points	.20

PATENT PENCIL CLASP

For attaching to a pair of ordinary dividers.

No.		Each
8	1¼ inches long, Nickel plated	.15

CHALK LINE REELS

Made of hardwood and polished. A No. 1 Scratch Awl is furnished with the No. 14 Reel.

No.		Each
11	Length 4 inches, diameter 2¼ inches	.15
12	" 2¾ " " 2 "	.15
14	" 2¾ " " 2 "	.30
	with No. 1 Scratch Awl	

3-ANGLE RULE TOOL

It can be easily attached to any two foot rule that is one inch in width.

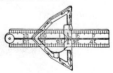

No.		Each
2	Nickel Plated	.90

STANLEY MISCELLANEOUS TOOLS

NAIL SETS

These are made of a high grade of special tool steel, hardened at both ends and blued. The Head is so shaped that there is little possibility of hammer slipping from the tool. The Tips are nicely Cupped and Chamfered, carefully oil tempered and will stand the most severe test under all conditions. Made with either round knurled, or square shanks.

No.					Each
11	$\frac{2}{32}$ in.	Tip 4 in. long			.15
	$\frac{5}{64}$ "	" 4 "	"		.15
	$\frac{3}{32}$ "	" 4 "	"		.15
	$\frac{4}{32}$ "	" 4 "	"		.15
	$\frac{5}{32}$ "	" 4 "	"		.15

No.					Each
11½	$\frac{2}{32}$ in.	Tip 4 in. long			.20
	$\frac{5}{64}$ "	" 4 "	"		.20
	$\frac{3}{32}$ "	" 4 "	"		.20
	$\frac{4}{32}$ "	" 4 "	"		.20
	$\frac{5}{32}$ "	" 4 "	"		.20

CENTER PUNCHES

These are made of the same high grade Steel as are Stanley Nail Sets and are hardened and blued. The Tips are accurately shaped so that the extreme point is always in the center of the tool.

No.				Each
10	$\frac{5}{64}$ in.	Tip 4 in. long		.20
	$\frac{1}{8}$ "	" 4 "	"	.20
	$\frac{5}{32}$ "	" 4 "	"	.20

MACHINISTS CHISELS AND PUNCHES

Forged from a high grade of tool steel. Points and heads highly polished, balance of the tool black japanned.

MACHINISTS CHISELS

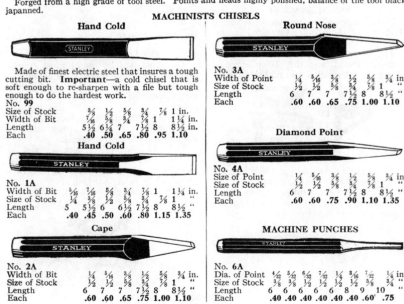

Hand Cold

Made of finest electric steel that insures a tough cutting bit. **Important**—a cold chisel that is soft enough to re-sharpen with a file but tough enough to do the hardest work.

No. 99						
Size of Stock	$\frac{3}{8}$	$\frac{1}{2}$	$\frac{5}{8}$	$\frac{3}{4}$	$\frac{7}{8}$	1 in.
Width of Bit	$\frac{7}{16}$	$\frac{5}{8}$	$\frac{3}{4}$	$\frac{7}{8}$	1	$1\frac{1}{4}$ in.
Length	$5\frac{1}{2}$	$6\frac{1}{4}$	7		8	$8\frac{1}{2}$ in.
Each	.40	.50	.65	.80	.95	1.10

Hand Cold

No. 1A						
Width of Bit	$\frac{5}{16}$	$\frac{7}{16}$	$\frac{5}{8}$	$\frac{3}{4}$	$\frac{7}{8}$ 1	$1\frac{1}{4}$ in.
Size of Stock	$\frac{1}{4}$	$\frac{3}{8}$	$\frac{1}{2}$	$\frac{5}{8}$	$\frac{3}{4}$	$\frac{7}{8}$ in.
Length	5	$5\frac{1}{2}$	6	$6\frac{1}{2}$	$7\frac{1}{2}$ 8	$8\frac{1}{2}$ "
Each	.40	.45	.50	.60	.80	1.15 1.35

Cape

No. 2A						
Width of Bit	$\frac{1}{4}$	$\frac{5}{16}$	$\frac{3}{8}$	$\frac{1}{2}$	$\frac{5}{8}$	$\frac{3}{4}$ in.
Size of Stock	$\frac{1}{2}$		7	7	$7\frac{1}{2}$ 8	$8\frac{1}{2}$ "
Length	6	7	7	$7\frac{1}{2}$	8	$8\frac{1}{2}$ "
Each	.60	.60	.65	.75	1.00	1.10

Round Nose

No. 3A						
Width of Point	$\frac{1}{4}$	$\frac{5}{16}$	$\frac{3}{8}$	$\frac{1}{2}$	$\frac{5}{8}$	$\frac{3}{4}$ in.
Size of Stock	$\frac{1}{2}$	$\frac{1}{2}$	$\frac{5}{8}$	$\frac{3}{4}$	$\frac{7}{8}$	1 "
Length	6	7	7	$7\frac{1}{2}$	8	$8\frac{1}{2}$ "
Each	.60	.60	.65	.75	1.00	1.10

Diamond Point

No. 4A						
Size of Point	$\frac{1}{4}$	$\frac{5}{16}$	$\frac{3}{8}$	$\frac{1}{2}$	$\frac{5}{8}$	$\frac{3}{4}$ in.
Size of Stock	$\frac{1}{2}$	$\frac{1}{2}$	$\frac{5}{8}$	$\frac{3}{4}$	$\frac{7}{8}$	1 "
Length	6	7	7	$7\frac{1}{2}$	8	$8\frac{1}{2}$ "
Each	.60	.60	.75	.90	1.10	1.35

MACHINE PUNCHES

No. 6A								
Dia. of Point	$\frac{4}{32}$	$\frac{5}{32}$	$\frac{6}{32}$	$\frac{7}{32}$	$\frac{1}{4}$	$\frac{5}{16}$	$\frac{7}{32}$	$\frac{1}{4}$ in.
Size of Stock	$\frac{3}{8}$	$\frac{3}{8}$	$\frac{1}{2}$	$\frac{1}{2}$	$\frac{1}{2}$	$\frac{1}{2}$	$\frac{5}{8}$	$\frac{3}{4}$ "
Length	6	6	6	6	6	8	9	10 "
Each	.40	.40	.40	.40	.40	.40	.60	.75

STANLEY MISCELLANEOUS TOOLS

JOINTER GAUGE FOR IRON PLANES

For use in connection with all sizes of Iron Jack or Jointer Planes.

It enables the workman to plane bevels of any angle between 30 and 90 degrees, or to square up the edges of boards with extreme accuracy.

It may be attached to either side of the Plane making it equally adaptable for right or left hand work.

A wood face of any desired size may be attached, increasing the bearing surface of the face of the Gauge.

No.   Each
386 Nickel Plated   **2.35**

BENCH BRACKET

Easily applied. It simply requires that one or more holes be bored in the front of the bench.

The body of the Bracket is made of iron—japanned, and the clamp screw is strong, well threaded and nickel plated.

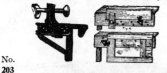

No.   Each
203   **.70**

CORNERING TOOLS

These tools are used by pattern-makers and all wood-workers for rounding sharp edges. They have a different size cutter at each end and their form is such that no depth gauge is required.

No.		Each
28	1/16 and 1/8 inch Cutter	**.40**
29	3/8 " 1/4 " ".	**.40**

CUTTER AND CHISEL GRINDER

A device for holding Plane Irons, Chisels and other similar cutting tools that they may be ground or honed to any desired angle or bevel, insuring an accuracy that is very difficult to obtain when the tool is held in the hand.

The tool to be sharpened is rigidly held in the Grinder and may be given any desired angle by means of the large screw attached to the roller frame, which raises or lowers the main body.

Made entirely of metal.

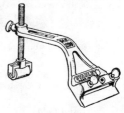

No.   Each
200 Nickel Plated   **1.60**

PORTABLE BENCH DOG

This tool will be found most convenient for all kinds of work requiring the use of a Bench Dog, especially where a well appointed work bench is not available.

One or more can be so placed as to securely hold a board or other work in almost any position required.

Even in connection with a fixed or permanent Bench Dog, it will be found useful to hold steady the other end of a board while being worked.

Made entirely of metal, with well sharpened points and blued finish.

No.   Each
202   **.30**

STANLEY
(S.W.)

STANLEY MISCELLANEOUS TOOLS

CLAPBOARD SIDING MARKERS

This tool can be used with one hand, while the other is employed in holding a clapboard in position. The marking blade is easily adjusted to any thickness of clapboard or siding. The sharp edges of the teeth are parallel with the legs when in position to mark. By moving the tool half an inch, it will mark a full line across the clapboard, exactly over and conforming to the edge of the corner-board.

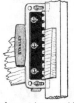

No.		Each
88	8¾ inches long, 4 inches wide	1.10

CLAPBOARD SIDING GAUGE

Two thin steel blades, which form a part of the base of the tool, will slide under the last clapboard already laid. The clapboard can be held any width to the weather, by the graduated scale on the tool. After the tool is released, the mark left is so slight that painting alone will fill it.

No.		Each
89	8¾ inches long, 2½ inches wide	1.20

ROOFING BRACKETS

Made of steel, sturdily constructed, all parts are firmly riveted together. Easily applied and removed.

Shingles can be laid over the bracket and the bracket later removed by driving it upward, disengaging it from the nails.

No loose parts. No nail holes in the roof.

Especially designed for asphalt or other composition shingles. It can also be used in laying regular wood shingles.

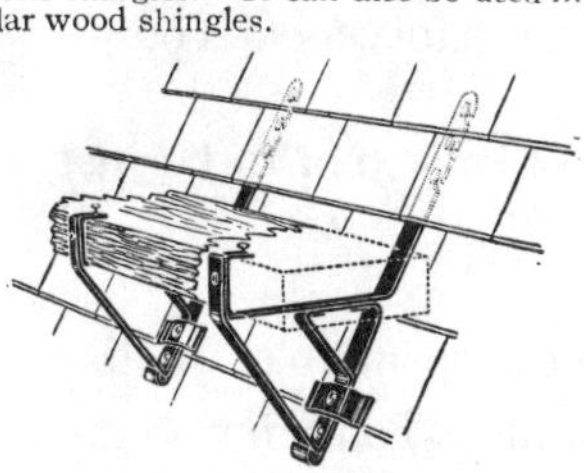

The parts are of spring steel and firmly riveted together. The bracket has two separate bearings on the roof, so formed that any increase of pressure from above increases its stability. The staging boards are held firmly in place by spurs and rails. No loose parts. No nail holes are made in the roof.

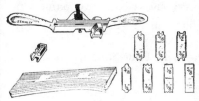

No.		Per Pr.
401	15¾ in. long, 3¾ in. wide	1.00

No.		Each
1	8 inches long, 1 inch wide, Japanned	.80

STANLEY HAND BEADERS

For beading, reeding or fluting straight or irregular surfaces—also adapted for light routering. It is fitted with two gauges; one for straight, the other for curved work. The sample illustrated shows some of the work that can be done.

With each tool are furnished 8 cutters, sharpened at both ends and embracing the following assortment;
6 Single Beads—⅛, 3⁄16, ¼, 5⁄16, ⅜, ½ inch
2 Fluting Tools—¾, ¼ inch
4 Reeding Tools—(2 Beads ¼ inch, 3 Beads 3⁄16 inch, 3 Beads ⅛ inch, 4 Beads ⅛ inch)
2 Routers—⅛ and ¼ inch
1 ⅝-inch Blank, which can be filed as desired

No.		Each
66	11½ in. long, Nickel Plated	1.80
	Extra Cutters	.10

STANLEY

FOUR-SQUARE HOUSEHOLD TOOLS

The following pages illustrate and describe 32 Stanley Tools, built especially for the home.

They are called: "Stanley Four-Square Household Tools."

You will find the size and weight of each tool to be just right for use around the home.

All of these tools have the same dependable quality which carpenters have found in Stanley Tools for many years.

These tools in their attractive individual containers are identified for the household buyer by the quality name "Stanley" and the bright red Four-Square Mark.

Look for the word "Stanley" and the Four-Square Mark!

STANLEY
S.W.

STANLEY

FOUR-SQUARE HOUSEHOLD TOOLS

HOUSEHOLD HAND AXE

Made from one piece tool steel, hand tempered in oil. Cutting edge, polished and honed. Head black lustrous finish, deep etched. Black hickory handle, 18 inches over all. Weight without handle 2¼ pounds.

Each head carefully protected with a cardboard sheath.   Each **1.75**

HOUSEHOLD CHISELS

Socket, pocket bevel edge.   Blades 3¼ inches long.   Black handles, leather capped.

Blade		Each
⅜ inch		**.90**
½	"	**.95**
¾	"	**1.00**
1	"	**1.25**

HOUSEHOLD JACK PLANE

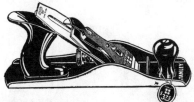

Black hardwood handle and knob.   Sides polished.   Cutter adjustable endwise and sidewise. Length: 11½ inches.   Cutter: 1¾ inches.
Each **3.75**

HOUSEHOLD BOXWOOD RULE

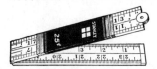

Two Foot.   Four Fold.   1 inch wide.   Round joint. Middle plates. Heavy figures. Graduated in 8ths and 16ths inches   Each **.25**

HOUSEHOLD SCREW DRIVERS

Round steel blades. A rivet through the ferrule, handle and shank securely fastens the blade in the handle.   Black tapered and fluted handles, specially designed to fit the hand.

Blade Length	Over All	Diam	Each
1½ in.	3½ in.	⅛ in.	**.15**
2½ "	6½ "	7⁄32 "	**.30**
4 "	9 "	¼ "	**.35**
5 "	10½ "	5⁄16 "	**.40**

HOUSEHOLD BLOCK PLANE

Black lever cap and sides. Cutter, screw adjustment. Lever screw, lever cam, adjusting wheel and screw, nickel plated.   Length: 6½ inches. Cutter 1⅝ inches.   Each **1.50**

Each packed in an individual container

STANLEY

FOUR-SQUARE HOUSEHOLD TOOLS

HOUSEHOLD HAMMER

Made of a special steel, carefully forged, hardened and tempered. Bell face, round neck and poll, curved claw, which easily pulls any size of nails and brads. Face, poll and top of claw are polished; rest of head black. Black hickory handle, 13 inches over all. Weight without handle, 14½ ounces.

Each **1.00**

HOUSEHOLD PIPE WRENCH
10 inch

Hardened steel jaws. Capacity, ⅛ inch to 1 inch. Black wood handle.

Each **1.25**

HOUSEHOLD
VISE

The jaws are ground and carefully fitted. Width of jaws: 2 inches. Vise screw with square lathe cut thread working in long malleable nut. Patented split washer under head of screw to take up wear. Body of vise, black. This vise will withstand severe usage.

Each **2.50**

HOUSEHOLD "ZIG-ZAG" RULE

Rivet joints, Yellow enamel finish, with black joints and tips. Regular figuring. Graduated in 16th inches on both sides. Length: 4 feet.

Each **.35**

HOUSEHOLD PLIERS

6½ inch. Coppered and nickel plated. Forged from high grade tool steel. Narrow nose. Combination slide joint and shear cutter.

Each **.50**

HOUSEHOLD BIT BRACE

Open ratchet. Nickel plated. Shell, hardwood head, and handle, black. Alligator jaws, 8 inch sweep.

Each **2.00**

Each packed in an individual container

STANLEY

FOUR-SQUARE HOUSEHOLD TOOLS

HOUSEHOLD TRY AND MITRE SQUARE

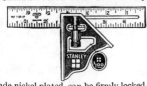

Blade nickel plated, can be firmly locked at any point. Edges machined and squared inside and out. Graduated in 8ths and 16ths. Black iron handle, 7 inch blade, 2⅝ inch handle. **Each 1.00**

HOUSEHOLD LEVEL

Selected Hardwood, carefully seasoned; 2⅜ inches by 1¼ inches stock, 18 inches long. Proved glasses, non-adjustable. Black "Hand-y" grip. **Each 1.25**

HOUSEHOLD AUGER BITS

Solid center, extension lip, double cutter. Correctly tempered. Accurate for size. Highly finished throughout. Shank end of bit, black.

Size in 16ths	Each	Size in 16ths	Each
4	.40	10	.60
6	.40	12	.70
8	.50	16	.90

HOUSEHOLD PUTTY KNIFE

Black, hardwood handle. Crucible steel blade. 1⅜ inches wide, 3¾ inches long. Half elastic. **Each .35**

HOUSEHOLD SAW

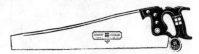

Thin back, highly polished crucible steel blade. Black handle, with four nickel plated brass screws. 24 inch, hand skew-back, 8 point. **Each 2.25**

HOUSEHOLD MILL FILE

8 inch single cut. Each file fitted into black handle, ready for use. **Each 25**

HOUSEHOLD SLIM TAPER FILE

6 inch single cut. Each file fitted into black handle, ready for use. **Each .20**

HOUSEHOLD AWL

A rivet through the ferrule, handle and shank securely fastens the blade in the handle. Black handle. Length over all, 5 inches; blade 1¼ inches. **Each .30**

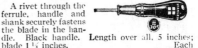

HOUSEHOLD PRY BAR

Drop forged from chisel steel. Black, except face of bit, which is polished. Length: 15 inches, diameter ⅝ inch. **Each .75**

Each package in an individual container

STANLEY
S.W.

STANLEY TOOL CABINET NO. 850

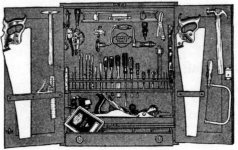

This cabinet is made of oak with a rich dark stain, and well varnished. In the finishing care has been taken to produce a very fine cabinet.

The panelled doors are hung on brass-plated hinges and are securely fastened by a brass lock with key.

The drawer at the base of the cabinet is divided into compartments for holding small tools, nails, screws, etc.

8½ inches deep   29¼ inches high   25⅜ inches wide

Weight 72 lbs.   Price **95.00**

No. 850 contains 48 Tools as follows:

1 Hammer	13 oz.	No. 15	
1 Hammer	4 oz.	No. 147	
1 Saw (Hand)	22 in.		
1 Saw (Rip)	22 in.		
1 Saw (Coping)		No.10D	
with 6 extra Blades			
1 Screw Driver	6 in.	No. 20	
1 Screw Driver	4 in.	No. 40	
1 Screw Driver	4 in.	No. 55	
1 Screw Driver	3 in.	No. 121	
1 Screw Driver	1½ in.	No. 21	
1 Ratchet Screw Driver	5 in.	No. 215	
1 Rule (Zig Zag)	6 ft.	No. 106	
1 Rule (Caliper)	12 in.	No. 32	
1 Plane (Bench)	11½ in.	No. 5¼	
1 Plane (Block)	6 in.	No. S18	
1 Bit Brace	8 in.	No. 921	
1 Expansive Bit (Clark's)			
1 Auger Bit	¼ in.		
1 Auger Bit	⁵⁄₁₆ in.		
1 Auger Bit	⅜ in.		
1 Auger Bit	½ in.		
1 Gimlet Bit		No. 4	
1 Gimlet Bit		No. 6	
1 Screw Driver Bit	¼ in.	No. 26	
1 Screw Driver Bit	⁵⁄₁₆ in.	No. 26	
1 Countersink		No. 24	

1 Bit Gauge			No. 49
1 Chisel		¼ in.	No. 40
1 Chisel		½ in.	No. 40
1 Chisel		1 in.	No. 40
1 Cold Chisel		¼ x 5 in.	No. 1A
1 Cold Chisel		½ x 6 in.	No. 1A
1 Vise		Jaws 1½ in.	No. 741
1 Combination Square		9 in.	No. 21
1 Bevel		6 in.	No. 18
1 Gauge (Marking and Mortise)			No. 98
1 Spoke Shave			No. 151
1 Plumb and Level		18 in.	No.36G
1 Nail Set		²⁄₃₂ in.	No. 11
1 Center Punch		⁵⁄₆₄ in.	No. 10
1 Hand Drill			No. 611
1 Hollow Handle Tool Set			No. 305
Contains one each—Chisel, Reamer, Scratch Awl, Screw Driver, Tack Puller, Belt Awl and six Brad Awls assorted.			
1 Cornering Tool		¹⁄₁₆ x ⅛ in.	No. 28
1 Pair Pliers			
1 Pair Pincers			No. 49
1 Adjustable Wrench		6½ in.	No. G
1 Oil Can			No.1603
1 Carborundum Stone			No. 109
1 Package Corrugated Fasteners			

Plan No. S72 "How to Make a Work Bench" Packed with this Cabinet

STANLEY
(S.W.)

STANLEY TOOL CABINET NO. 851

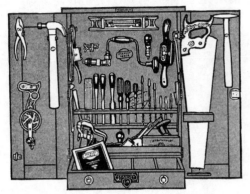

This cabinet is made of oak with a rich dark stain, and well varnished. In the finishing care has been taken to produce a very fine cabinet.

The panelled doors are hung on brass-plated hinges and are securely fastened by a brass lock with key.

The drawer is divided into compartments for holding small tools, nails, screws, etc.

8⅛ inches deep   26⅝ inches high   19½ inches wide

Weight 52 lbs.   Price **65.00**

No. 851 contains 33 Tools as follows:

1 Hammer	13 oz.	No. 15	1 Chisel	¼ in.	No. 40
1 Hammer	4 oz.	No. 147	1 Chisel	½ in.	No. 40
1 Saw (Hand)	20 in.		1 Chisel	1 in.	No. 40
1 Saw (Coping)		No. 100	1 Cold Chisel	½ x 6 in.	No. 1A
with 12 extra Blades			1 Vise	Jaws 1½ in.	No. 741
1 Screw Driver	5 in.	No. 20	1 Gauge (Marking and Mortise)		No. 98
1 Screw Driver	4 in.	No. 40	1 Combination Square	9 in.	No. 21
1 Screw Driver	3 in.	No. 50	1 Bevel	8 in.	No. 25
1 Hand Drill		No. 610	1 Spoke Shave		No. 151
1 Rule (Ziz Zag)	5 ft.	No. 105	1 Plumb and Level	12 in.	No.36G
1 Plane (Bench)	11½ in.	No. 5¼	1 Nail Set	²⁄₃₂ in.	No. 11
1 Plane (Block)	6 in.	No. 60	1 Hollow Handle Tool Set No.		
1 Scraper		No. 80	305—Contains one each—		
1 Bit Brace	8 in.	No. 915	Chisel, Reamer, Scratch		
1 Auger Bit	¼ in.		Awl, Screw Driver, Tack		
1 Auger Bit	⅜ in.		Puller, Belt Awl and six		
1 Auger Bit	½ in.		Brad Awls assorted.		
1 Gimlet Bit		No. 6	1 Pair Pliers		
1 Screw Driver Bit	⁵⁄₁₆ in.	No. 26	1 Carborundum Stone		No. 109
1 Bit Gauge		No. 49	1 Package Corrugated Fasteners		

Plan No. S72 "How to Make a Work Bench   Packed with this Cabinet

STANLEY COMBINATION WORK BENCH AND TOOL CABINET No. 860

All wooden parts are made of spruce. Finished in dark stain on the outside and light stain on the inside. The cabinet, apron and lower shelf are made and finished with the same care that distinguishes the line of Stanley Tool Chests. The top of the bench is made from particularly selected lumber. The steel legs and braces were especially designed and constructed by us in order to produce a sturdy, serviceable work bench.

The cabinet is also equipped with a special hinge hasp and staple so it can be locked. The whole Work Bench is so constructed that it will fold against the back. This is a distinct advantage. When not in use it can be folded back against the wall and out of the way.

The Work Bench is 47½ inches high overall, 48 inches long, and 15¾ inches deep or wide. The height to top of bench when in position is 32¾ inches.

Weight of Work Bench with Tools 108½ lbs.   Price **60.00**

No. 860 contains 34 Tools as follows:

1	Hammer	14½ oz.		1	Auger Bit	1 in.
1	Rule (Zig Zag)	4 ft.		1	Vise	
1	Rule (Boxwood)	2 ft.		1	Pipe Wrench	10 in.
1	Screw Driver	1½ in.		1	Jack Plane	11½ in.
1	Screw Driver	2½ in.		1	Block Plane	6½ in.
1	Screw Driver	4 in.		1	Chisel	⅜ in.
1	Screw Driver	5 in.		1	Chisel	½ in.
1	Saw (Hand)	24 in.		1	Chisel	¾ in.
1	Pair Pliers	6½ in.		1	Chisel	1 in.
1	Awl	5 in.		1	Try and Mitre Square	7 in.
1	Pry Bar	15 in.		1	Mill File	8 in.
1	Bit Brace	8 in.		1	Slim Taper File	6 in.
1	Auger Bit	¼ in.		1	Level	18 in.
1	Auger Bit	⅜ in.		1	Putty Knife	
1	Auger Bit	½ in.		1	Bench Dog	
1	Auger Bit	⅝ in.		2	Bench Brackets No. 203	
1	Auger Bit	¾ in.				

STANLEY TOOL CABINET No. 861

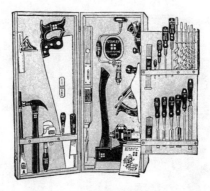

Made of oak, finished in dark stain on the outside and in a light stain on the inside. Joints nailed and glued.   There are three hinges, two catches and a carrying handle.

The hinged panel on the right carrying the small tools, closes inside the front and back making a very compact cabinet.

11¾ inches wide, 7 inches deep, 29 inches high.

Weight 43 lbs.   Price **40.00**

No. 861 contains 32 Tools as follows:

One each of Stanley Four-Square Household Tools

1 Hammer	14½ oz.		1 Auger Bit	¼ in.	
1 Rule (Zig Zag)	4 ft.		1 Auger Bit	⅜ in.	
1 Rule (Boxwood)	2 ft.		1 Auger Bit	½ in.	
1 Screw Driver	5 in.		1 Auger Bit	⅝ in.	
1 Screw Driver	4 in.		1 Auger Bit	¾ in.	
1 Screw Driver	2½ in.		1 Auger Bit	1 in.	
1 Screw Driver	1½ in.		1 Vise		
1 Saw (Hand)	24 in.		1 Pipe Wrench	10 in.	
1 Pair Pliers	6½ in.		1 Jack Plane	11½ in.	
1 Awl	5 in.		1 Block Plane	6½ in.	
1 Pry Bar	15 in.		1 Chisel	⅜ in.	
1 Hand Axe	18 in.		1 Chisel	½ in.	
1 Bit Brace	8 in.		1 Chisel	¾ in.	
1 Chisel	1 in.		1 Mill File	8 in.	
1 Try and Square Mitre Sq.	7 in.		1 Slim Taper File	6 in.	
1 Level	18 in.		1 Putty Knife		

STANLEY
(S.W.)

STANLEY TOOL CABINET No. 862

Made of oak, finished in a dark stain and varnished. Sides set in. Joints nailed and glued. There are three hinges, a lock and a carrying handle.

6¼ inches deep   24 inches high   14 inches wide   Weight 23 lbs.   Price **35.00**

No. 862 contains 20 Tools as follows:

1 Hammer	13 oz.	No. 15	1 Auger Bit	½ in.	
1 Screw Driver	5 in.	No. 20	1 Gimlet Bit		No. 6
1 Screw Driver	3 in.	No. 50	1 Screw Driver Bit	¼ in.	No. 26
1 Rule (Zig Zag)	4 ft.	No. 04	1 Try and Mitre Square	9 in.	No. 21
1 Saw (Hand)	18 in.		1 Nail Set	²⁄₃₂ in.	No. 11
1 Plane (Bench)	8 in.	No. 3	1 Pair Pliers		
1 Chisel	¼ in.	No. 40	1 Hollow Handle Tool Set		No. 306
1 Chisel	¾ in.	No. 40	Contains one each—Chisel,		
1 Spoke Shave		No. 151	Reamer, Scratch Awl,		
1 Bit Brace	8 in.	No. 945	Screw Driver, Tack Puller,		
1 Auger Bit	¼ in.		Belt Awl and six Brad Awls		
1 Auger Bit	⅜ in.		assorted.		
			1 Vise	Jaws 1½ in.	No. 741

1 Package Corrugated Fasteners

STANLEY TOOL CHEST No. 902

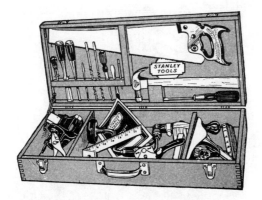

Made of hardwood, finished in a dark stain and varnished. Tops and bottoms set in. Joints nailed and glued. There are three hinges, two catches and a carrying handle.

10¾ inches wide   4⅜ inches deep   25 inches long   Weight **21 lbs.**   Price **25.00**

No. 902 contains 20 Tools as follows:

1 Hammer	13 oz.	No. 12	1 Spoke Shave		No. 51
1 Screw Driver	5 in.	No. 20	1 Bit Brace	**8 in.**	No. 945
1 Screw Driver	3 in.	No. 50	1 Auger Bit	¼ in.	
1 Rule (Zig Zag)	4 ft.	No. 04	1 Auger Bit	⅜ in.	
1 Saw (Hand)	20 in.		1 Gimlet Bit		No. 6
1 Try and Mitre Square	7½ in.	No. 2	1 Screw Driver Bit	⁵⁄₁₆ in.	No. 26
1 Marking Gauge		No. 62	1 Pair Pliers		
1 Plane (Bench)	8 in.	No. 3	1 Awl		No. 6
1 Chisel	¼ in.	No. 50	1 Nail Set	²⁄₃₂ in.	No. 11
1 Chisel	¾ in.	No. 50	1 Vise	Jaws 1½ in.	No. 741

1 Package Corrugated Fasteners

STANLEY TOOL CHEST No. 903

Made of hardwood, finished in a dark stain and varnished.   Tops and bottoms set in. Joints nailed and glued. There are three hinges, two catches and a carrying handle.
11⅜ inches wide   4⅜ inches deep   21½ inches long   Weight 18 lbs.   Price **20.00**

No. 903 contains 17 Tools as follows:

1 Hammer	13 oz.	No. 12		1 Chisel	¾ in.	No. 50
1 Screw Driver	5 in.	No. 20		1 Bit Brace	8 in.	No. 945
1 Screw Driver	3 in.	No. 50		1 Auger Bit	¼ in.	
1 Rule (Zig Zag)	4 ft.	No. 04		1 Auger Bit	⅜ in.	
1 Saw (Hand)	16 in.			1 Gimlet Bit		No. 60
1 Try and Mitre Square	7½ in.	No. 2		1 Screw Driver Bit	¼ in.	No. 26
1 Marking Gauge		No. 62		1 Awl	1¼ in.	
1 Plane (Block)	7 in.	No. 220		1 Vise	Jaws 1½ in.	No. 741
1 Chisel	¼ in.	No. 50				

1 Package Corrugated Fasteners

STANLEY
S.W.

STANLEY TOOL CHEST No. 904

Made of hardwood, finished in a dark stain, and varnished. Tops and bottoms set in. Joints nailed and glued. There are three hinges, two catches and a carrying handle. 11¼ inches wide. 4½ inches deep. 19½ inches long. Weight 15 lbs. Price **15.00**

No. 904 contains 12 Tools as follows:

1 Hammer	10 oz.	No. 12	1 Plane (Block)	5½ in.	No. 102
1 Screw Driver	4 in.	No. 70	1 Chisel	½ in.	No. 50
1 Rule	2 ft.	No. 68A	1 Bit Brace	8 in.	No. 966
1 Saw (Hand)	14 in.		1 Auger Bit	¼ in.	
1 Try Square	4½ in.	No. 20	1 Auger Bit	⅜ in.	
1 Marking Gauge		No. 61	1 Vise	Jaws 1½ in.	No. 741

1 Package Corrugated Fasteners

STANLEY TOOL CHESTS No. 888

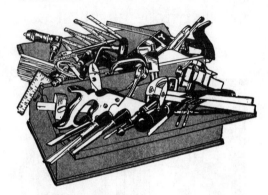

These chests are made of hardwood, stained. They measure 20 inches long, 10½ inches wide and 8 inches deep. The covers are hung on ornamental brass hinges. The sliding drawer inside the chest is for small tools, nails, screws, etc. A brass handle is placed at the top for carrying. There are four assortments, No. 888A, 888B, 888C, 888D, each containing a different assortment of tools.

No.			Price
888A ....Weight 32 lbs.			**35.00**

Contains 32 Tools as follows:

1 Hammer	13 oz.	No. 12		1 Try and Mitre Square	6 in.	No. 2
1 Hammer	4 oz.	No. 147		1 Level	18 in	No. 104
1 Saw (Hand)	16 in.			1 Gauge (Marking)		No. 62
1 Saw (Coping)		No. 100		1 Nail Set	2⁄32 in	No. 11
with 12 extra blades				1 Center Punch	5⁄64 in	No. 10
1 Screw Driver	4 in.	No. 20		1 Hand Drill		No. 611
1 Rule (Zig Zag)	4 ft.	No. 04		1 Hollow Handle Tool Set		No. 302
1 Plane (Bench)	8 in.	No. 3		Contains one each—Gimlet, File, Saw, Chisel, Reamer, Screw Driver, Two Brad Awls and with extra 6½ inch Saw.		
1 Bit Brace	8 in.	No. 945				
1 Expansive Bit (Clark's)						
1 Auger Bit	¼ in.					
1 Auger Bit	⅜ in.					
1 Gimlet Bit		No. 6		1 Adjustable Wrench	8 in.	No. G
1 Countersink		No. 23		1 Adjustable Pipe Wrench	10 in.	
1 Chisel	½ in.	No. 40		1 Pair Pliers		No. 5N
1 Chisel	1 in.	No. 40		1 Pair Pincers		No. 50
1 Cold Chisel	½ x 6 in.	No. 1A		1 Flat Mill File	8 inch with handle	
1 Vise	Jaw 1¾ in.	No. 742		1 Glass Cutter		No. 300
1 Carpenters Steel Square	12 in.	No. 10		1 Sharpening Stone		

1 Package Corrugated Fasteners

STANLEY (S.W.)

STANLEY TOOL CHESTS No. 888

No.   Price
888B...Weight 25 lbs. **25.00**

Contains 18 Tools as follows:

1 Hammer...	13	oz.	No. 12
1 Saw (Panel)...	16	in.	
1 Saw (Coping) with 12 extra blades...........................			No. 100
1 Screw Driver..	4	in.	No. 20
1 Rule (Zig Zag)..	4	ft.	No. 04
1 Plane (Bench)..	8	in.	No. 3
1 Bit Brace..	8	in.	No. 945
1 Auger Bit..	¼	in.	
1 Auger Bit..	⅜	in.	
1 Gimlet Bit...			No. 6
1 Chisel....	¾	in.	No. 40
1 Cold Chisel..............................½ in. x 6		in.	No. 1A
1 Carpenters Steel Square...................................	12	in.	No. 10
1 Hollow Handle Tool Set....................................			No. 302
Contains—1 each Gimlet, File, Saw, Chisel, Reamer, Screw Driver, 2 Brad Awls and with extra 6½" Saw			
1 Adjustable Pipe Wrench....................................	10	in.	
1 Pair Pliers...			
1 Glass Cutter...			No. 300
1 Sharpening Stone...			
1 Package Corrugated Fasteners..............................			

No.   Price
888C...Weight 18 lbs. **15.00**

Contains 12 Tools as follows:

1 Hammer...	13	oz.	No. 12
1 Saw (Panel)...	16	in.	
1 Saw (Coping) with 12 extra blades...........................			No. 100
1 Screw Driver..	4	in.	No. 20
1 Rule (Zig Zag)..	4	ft.	No. 04
1 Cold Chisel.............................½ in. x 6		in.	No. 1A
1 Nail Set...	²⁄₃₂	in.	No. 11
1 Hollow Handle Tool Set....................................			No. 302
Contains—1 each Gimlet, File, Saw, Chisel, Reamer, Screw Driver, 2 Brad Awls and with extra 6½" Saw			
1 Adjustable Pipe Wrench....................................	10	in.	
1 Pair Pliers...			
1 Chalk Line Reel..			No. 14
1 Glass Cutter...			No. 300
1 Package Corrugated Fasteners..............................			

No.   Price
888D...Weight 19 lbs. **15.00**

Contains 12 Tools as follows:

1 Hammer...	13	oz.	No. 12
1 Saw (Panel)...	16	in.	
1 Screw Driver..	3	in.	No. 20
1 Rule (Zig Zag)..	4	ft.	No. 04
1 Plane (Block)..	7	in.	No. 110
1 Bit Brace..	8	in.	No. 945
1 Auger Bit..	⅜	in.	
1 Gimlet Bit...			No. 6
1 Chisel..	½	in.	No. 20
1 Try and Mitre Square.....................................	6	in.	No. 2
1 Gauge (Marking)..			No. 62
1 Bench Bracket..			No. 203
1 Package Corrugated Fasteners..............................			

[STANLEY]
(S.W.)

STANLEY TOOL ASSORTMENT No. 911

Eighteen tools in an attractive cardboard display box.

The following plans are packed with this assortment:

    1 S71 How to Make a Large Tool Chest

    1 S72 How to Make a Work Bench

The display box is 25 inches long, 7 inches wide, 3 inches deep, and is packed in a corrugated board container for protection in handling and shipping.

      Weight 13¾ lbs.   Price **20.00**

No. 911 contains 18 Tools as follows:

1 Saw (Hand)	20 in.		1 Auger Bit	¼ in.	
1 Hammer	13 oz.	No. 12	1 Auger Bit	½ in.	
1 Bit Brace	8 in.	No. 915	1 Gimlet Bit		No. 6
1 Screw Driver	5 in.	No. 20	1 Screw Driver Bit	⁵⁄₁₆ in.	No. 26
1 Screw Driver	3 in.	No. 50	1 Pair Pliers		
1 Rule (Zig Zag)	4 ft.	No. 04	1 Pipe Wrench		
1 Combination Square	9 in.	No. 21	1 Nail Set	³⁄₃₂ in.	No. 11½
1 Gauge		No. 62	1 Plane		No. 3
1 Chisel	¼ in.	No. 40	1 Pair Stanley Hinges with Screws		
1 Chisel	¾ in.	No. 40	1 Package Stanley Wiggle Nails		

STANLEY TOOL ASSORTMENT No. 908

Fifteen tools in an attractive cardboard display box.

The following plans are packed in this assortment:

    1 S70 How to Make a Small Tool Chest

    1 S71 How to Make a Large Tool Chest

    1 S72 How to Make a Work Bench

The display box is 18½ inches long, 7½ inches wide, and 3 inches deep, and is packed in a corrugated board container for protection in handling and shipping.

        Weight 9¾ lbs.   Price **14.00**

No. 908 contains 15 Tools as follows:

1 Hammer	14½ oz.	1 Auger Bit	⅜ in.
1 Rule (Zig Zag)	4 ft.	1 Auger Bit	½ in.
1 Screw Driver	2½ in.	1 File	8 in.
1 Screw Driver	4 in.		
1 Chisel	⅜ in.	1 Pair Pliers	6½ in.
1 Chisel	¾ in.	1 Level	18 in.
1 Try and Mitre Square		1 Saw (Hand)	14 in.
1 Block Plane	6½ in.	1 Package Stanley Wiggle Nails	
1 Bit Brace	8 in.	1 Pair Stanley Hinges with Screws	

STANLEY
(S.W.)

STANLEY TOOL ASSORTMENT No. 906

Twelve tools in an attractive cardboard display box.

The following plans are packed with this assortment:

    1 S70 How to Make a Small Tool Chest

    1 S71 How to Make a Large Tool Chest

    1 S72 How to Make a Work Bench

The display box is 18½ inches long, 7½ inches wide, 3 inches deep, and is packed in a corrugated board container for protection in handling and shipping.

       Weight 6 lbs.   Price **10.00**

No. 906 contains 12 Tools as follows:

1 Hammer	13 oz.	No. 12	1 Try Square	4½ in.	No. 20
1 Rule	2 ft.	No. 68A	1 Marking Gauge		No. 61
1 Screw Driver	4 in.	No. 70	1 Bit Brace	8 in.	No. 965N
1 Chisel	Socket ⅜ in.	No. 440	1 Auger Bit	¼ in.	
1 Chisel	Socket ¾ in.	No. 440	1 Auger Bit	⅜ in.	
1 Saw (Hand)	14 in.		1 Package Stanley Wiggle Nails		
1 Plane (Block)	7 in.	No. 220	1 Pair Stanley Hinges with Screws		

[STANLEY]
(S.W.)

STANLEY TOOL ASSORTMENT No. 909

Eight tools in an attractive cardboard display box.

The following plans are packed with this assortment:

1 S70 How to Make a Small Tool Chest

1 S71 How to Make a Large Tool Chest

1 S72 How to Make a Work Bench

The display box measures 18½ inches long, 7½ inches wide, and 3 inches deep, and is packed in a corrugated cardboard container for protection in handling and shipping.

Weight 7 lbs.   Price **8.75**

No. 909 contains 8 Tools as follows:

1 Hammer	14½ oz.		1 Block Plane	6½ in.
1 Rule (Zig Zag)	4 ft.		1 Bit Brace	8 in.
1 Screw Driver	4 in.		1 Saw (Hand)	14 in.
1 Chisel	⅜ in.		1 Package Stanley Wiggle Nails	
1 Auger Bit	½ in.		1 Pair Stanley Hinges with Screws	

STANLEY
S.W.

STANLEY TOOL ASSORTMENT No. 907

Seven tools in an attractive cardboard display box.
The following plans are packed with this assortment:
    1 S70 How to Make a Small Tool Chest
    1 S71 How to Make a Large Tool Chest
    1 S72 How to Make a Work Bench
The display box is 18½ inches long, 7½ inches wide, 3 inches deep, and is packed in a corrugated board container for protection in handling and shipping.
    Weight 4 lbs.   Price **5.00**

No. 907 contains 7 Tools as follows:

1 Hammer	10 oz.	No. 12	1 Auger Bit	⅜ in.	
1 Rule	2 ft.	No. 68A	1 Marking Gauge		No. 61
1 Screw Driver	4 in.	No. 70	1 Package Stanley Wiggle Nails		
1 Saw (Hand)	14 in.	No. 966	1 Pair Stanley Hinges with Screws		
1 Bit Brace	8 in.				

STANLEY TOOL ASSORTMENT No. 910

Four Tools in an attractive carboard display box. Just the assortment needed to do the many small jobs around the house. It will appeal particularly to the women.
    The display box is 13½ inches long, 5 inches wide, 1¼ inches deep and is packed in a cardboard shell for protection in handling and shipping.
    Weight 2¼ lbs.   Price **2.15**

No. 910 contains 4 Tools as follows:

1 Hammer	14½ oz.	1 Pair Pliers	6½ in.
1 Rule (Zig Zag)	4 ft.	1 Screw Driver	2½ in.

FROGS FOR "BAILEY" AND "BED ROCK" PLANES

From time to time improvements have been made in both the "Bailey" and "Bed Rock" Iron Planes, which necessitated changes in the construction of the Bottom and Frog, making it impossible to use the new style Frog in an Old Style Bottom, or the Old Style Frog in a New Style Bottom.

TO INSURE YOUR ORDER FOR FROGS BEING CORRECTLY FILLED, ALWAYS STATE WHICH STYLE PLANE YOU HAVE.

BAILEY OLD STYLE   BAILEY NEW STYLE

For a time an intermediate style was made having same Frog and Bottom as the latest design, except that there was no Frog adjusting screw, consequently no clip on the Frog.

The latest design Frog or Bottom will be furnished for both the intermediate and new style Planes. If your plane is of the intermediate pattern, remove the steel clip from the Frog and the parts will fit.

The difference in construction of the Frogs and Bottoms in the "Bailey" Planes is shown in the illustration above.

BED-ROCK OLD STYLE   BED-ROCK NEW STYLE

The difference in construction of the Frogs and Bottoms in the "Bed Rock" Planes is shown in the illustrations above.

PRICES OF PLANE PARTS
"BAILEY" IRON PLANES

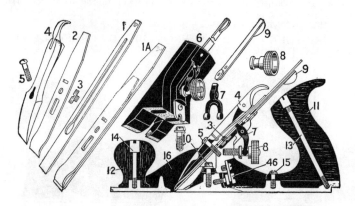

No.	Name of Part	No. of Plane	1 / 2 / 2C	3 / 3C	S4 / A4 / 4 / 4C	4½ / 4½C	S5 / A5 / 5 / 5C	5¼ / 5¼C	5½ / 5½C	A6 / 6 / 6C	7 / 7C	8 / 8C
1A	Double Plane Iron		.90	1.00	1.10	1.25	1.10	1.00	1.20	1.25	1.25	1.30
1	Single " "		.55	.60	.65	.80	.65	.60	.75	.80	.80	.80
2	Plane Iron Cap		.35	.40	.45	.45	.45	.40	.45	.45	.45	.50
3	Cap Screw	.10										
4	Lever Cap	.50					for all numbers					
5	" " Screw	.10										
6	Frog Complete	.70										
7	"V" Adjusting Lever	.10										
8	Adjusting Nut	.20										
9	Lateral Adjusting Lever	.20										
10	Frog Screw	.10										
11	Plane Handle	.40										
12	" Knob	.30										
13	Handle Bolt and Nut	.20										
14	Knob " " "	.20										
15	Plane Handle Screw		....	....	....	.10	.10	.10	.10	.10	.10	.10
16	" Bottom		1.70	2.00	2.00	2.40	2.40	2.40	2.40	3.30	4.70	5.70
46	Frog Adjusting Screw		.10	.10	.10	.10	.10	.10	.10	.10	.10	.10

Add 10 per cent. for Corrugated Bottoms.
Add 30 per cent. for Bottoms and Frogs for Planes A4, A5, A6.
Add 10 per cent. for Bottoms and Frogs for Planes S4 and S5.

STANLEY
S.W.

PRICES OF PLANE PARTS
"BED ROCK" PLANES

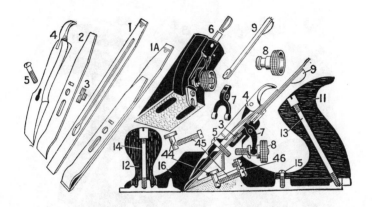

No.	Name of Part / No. of Plane	602	603 603C	604 604C	604½ 604½C	605 605C (05¼	605½ 605½C	606 606C	607 607C	608 608C
1A	Double Plane Iron......	.90	1.00	1.10	1.25	1.10	1.20	1.25	1.25	1.30
1	Single " "	.55	.60	.65	.80	.65	.75	.80	.80	.80
2	Plane Iron Cap........	.35	.40	.45	.45	.45	.45	.45	.45	.50
3	Cap Screw.............	.10								
4	Lever Cap.............	.60								
5	" " Screw.......	.10								
6	Frog Complete........	1.00								
7	"Y" Adjusting Lever...	.10			for all numbers					
8	Adjusting Nut.........	.20								
9	Lateral Adjusting Lever.	.20								
11	Plane Handle..........	.40								
12	" Knob..........	.30								
13	Handle Bolt and Nut...	.20								
14	Knob " " " ...	.20								
15	Plane Handle Screw....	.....	.....	.....	.10	.10	.10	.10	.10	.10
16	" Bottom..........	2.20	2.50	2.50	3.00	3.00	3.20	4.40	6.20	7.00
44	Frog Pin.............	.20	.20	.20	.20	.20	.20	.20	.20	.20
45	" Clamping Screw...	.10	.10	.10	.10	.10	.10	.10	.10	.10
46	" Adjusting " ...	.10	.10	.10	.10	.10	.10	.10	.10	.10

Add 10 per cent. for Corrugated Bottoms.

PRICES OF PLANE PARTS
GAGE SELF-SETTING PLANES

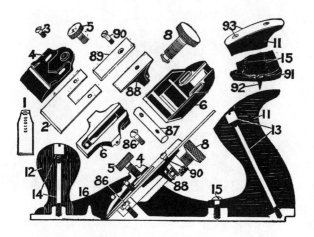

No.	Name of Part	No. of Plane	G3 G3C G4 G4C	G5 G5C	G6 G6C	G7 G7C	G22	G35	G26	G28	G30
1	Plane Iron................		.60	.60	.70	.80	.60	.60	.60	.70	.70
2	Steel Cap................		.35								
3	Cap Screw...............		.10	\} for all numbers							
4	Lever Cap...............		.30								
5	Lever Cap Screw..........		.10								
6	Frog..		*...	*...	*...	*...	.60	.60	.60	.60	.60
8	Cutter Adjusting Screw.....		.30	.30	.30	.30	.30	.30	.30	.30	.30
11	Plane Handle.............		.40	.40	.40	.40	.20	.20	.20	.20	.20
12	Plane Knob..............		.30	.30	.30	.30	.20	.20	.20	.20	.20
13	Handle Bolt and Nut......		.20	.20	.20	.20	....	....	...	....	....
14	Knob Bolt and Nut.......		.20	.20	.20	.20	....	....	...	....	....
15	Plane Handle Screw.......		.10	.10	.10						
16	Plane Bottom.............		*2.70	*3.10	*4.00	*5.40	.80	1.00	1.00	1.40	1.40
86	Frog Screw...............		.10	.10	.10	.10	.10	.10	.10	.10	.10
87	Frog Screw Rod...........		....	....	....	....	.25	.25	.25	.25	.25]
88	Cutter Adjustment Slide....		.25								
89	Clamp Plate..............		.20	\} for all numbers							
90	Clamp Plate Screw........		.10								
91	Handle Base..............		....	....	....	....	.10	.10	.10	.10	.10
92	Handle Base Screw........		....	....	....	....	.10	.10	.10	.10	.10
93	Handle Cap and Screws....		....	....	....	....	.10	.10	.10	.10	.10

*Prices of Bottoms for Iron Planes Include Frogs.

PRICES OF PLANE PARTS

"BAILEY" WOOD PLANES

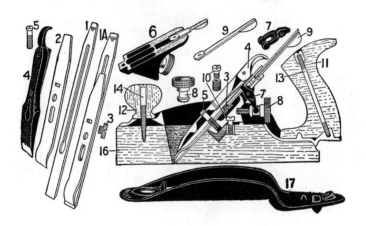

No.	Name of Part	No. of Plane	22	24	35	26	27½	28	31	32	36
1A	Double Plane Iron.........		1.00	1.10	1.10	1.10	1.20	1.25	1.25	1.30	1.25
1	Single " "		.60	.65	.65	.65	.75	.80	.80	.80	.80
2	Plane Iron Cap............		.40	.45	.45	.45	.45	.45	.45	.50	.45
3	Cap Screw................		.10								
4	Lever Cap................		.40								
5	" " Screw..........		.10								
6	Frog Complete.............		.60			for all numbers					
7	"Y" Adjusting Lever.......		.10								
8	Adjusting Nut.............		.20								
9	Lateral Adjusting Lever		.20								
10	Frog Screw and Bushing...		.20								
11	Plane Handle..........		....	.20	.20	.20	.20	.20	.20	.20	.20
12	" Knob..............		.20	.20	.20	.20	.20	.20	.20	.20	.20
13	Handle Bolt and Nut.......		....	.20	.20	.20	.20	.20	.20	.20	.20
14	Knob Screw..............		.10	.10	.10	.10	.10	.10	.10	.10	.10
16	Plane Bottom..............		.80	.80	.80	1.00	1.00	1.40	1.60	1.70	1.00
17	Top Casting..............		.40	.40	.40	.40	.40	.40	.40	.40	.40

STANLEY
S.W.

PRICES OF PLANE PARTS

"BAILEY" AND STANLEY BLOCK PLANES

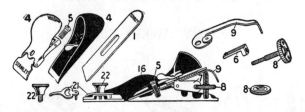

No.	Name of Part	No. of Plane	9½ 9¾	15 15½	16 17	S18 A18 18 19	60 60½	62	61 63	65	65½
1	Single Plane Iron...........		.45	.45	.45	.45	.45	.90	.45	.45	.45
4	Lever Cap.................		.20	.20	.30	.75	.30	.30	.30	.75	.20
5	" " Screw...........		.10	.10	.10	.10	.10	.10	.10	.10	.10
6	Frog Complete.............		....	....	....	....	.20	.20	.20	.20	.20
7	Adjusting Lever...........		.10	.10	.10	.10	....	....	....	....	....
8	" Nut.............		.20	.20	.20	.20	.20	.20	.20	.20	.20
9	Lateral Adjusting Lever.....		.20	.20	.20	.20	....	....	....	....	....
11	Plane Handle...............		.50	.50	....	....	....	.60	....	....	....
16	" Bottom...........		1.40	1.50	1.50	1.50	1.20	3.50	1.00	1.50	1.50
21	Eccentric Plate............		.20	.20	.20	.20	.20	.20	.20	.20	.20
22	Finger Rest Knob..........		.20	.20	.20	.20	.20	.30	.20	.20	.20

Add 30 per cent. for Bottom, for Plane A18.
Add 10 per cent. for Bottom, for Plane S18.

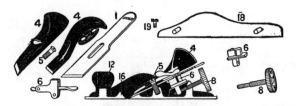

No.	Name of Part	No. of Plane	100 101	102 *103	110	120	130	131	140	203	220
1	Single Plane Iron..........		.10	.20	.30	.45	.30	.45	.50	.45	.45
4	Lever Cap.................		.10	.20	.20	.20	.20	.20	.30	.20	.20
5	" " Screw...........		....	....	....	....	....	.10	.10	.10	.10
6	Frog Complete.............		....	*.30	....	.30	....	.30	.20	.20	.20
8	Adjusting Nut.............		....	....	....	....	....	.20	.20	.20	.20
12	Plane Knob................		....	....	.20	.20	.20	.30	.30	.30	.30
16	" Bottom...........		.20	.40	.50	.60	.70	1.40	1.50	.50	.60
18	Detachable Side...........		....	....	....	....	....	....	.50	....	....
19	Side Screw (Pair)..........		....	....	....	....	....	....	.20	....	..

STANLEY
S.W.

PRICES OF PLANE PARTS

RABBET AND ROUTER PLANES

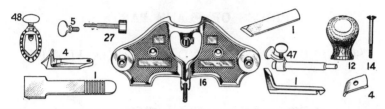

No.	Name of Part	No. of Plane	90 92	93	94	196	98 99	71 71½	75	95	97
1	Single Plane Iron		.60	.60	.60	.50	.40	.60	.40	.40	.90
4	Lever Cap		.30	.30	.30	.20	.20	....	.20	.20	.30
5	Thumb Screw		....	..	....	....	.10	....	....	....	....
12	Plane Knob		....	..	....	....	.30	.30	....	....	.30
14	Knob Bolt and Nut		....	..	....	....	....	.20	....	....	.20
16	Plane Bottom		3.50	4.20	5.00	2.40	1.20	2.00	.60	1.60	2.00
27	Cutter Bolt Adjusting Screw		.40	.40	.40	....	....	....	....	....	....
47	Extra Attachment		....	..	....	....	....	.50	....	....	....
48	Collar		....	..	....	....	....	.50	....	....	....

RABBET, MATCHING AND DADO PLANES

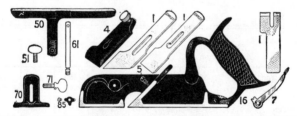

No.	Name of Part	No. of Plane	39	48 49	78 A78	146 to 148	171	190 to 192	239	278	289
1	Single Plane Iron		.40	.40	.40	1.30	.80	.40	.50	.60	.60
4	Lever Cap		.20	.20	.20	.30	....	.20	....	.20	.20
7	Adjusting Lever and Screw		....	....	.20	....	....	....	....	....	....
16	Plane Bottom		2.40	4.00	2.00	3.00	1.80	1.80	3.00	2.00	2.40
50	Fence		1.00	1.00	.50	....	.60	....	.80	.50	.40
51	" Thumb Screw		....	....	.10	....	.10	....	.10	.10	.10
61	Short Arm		....	....	.20	....	.40	....	.20	.20	.20
70	Adjusting Depth Gauge		.40	....	.40	....	....	.40	.40	.40	.40
71	Depth Gauge Thumb Screw		.20	....	.20	....	....	.30	.10	.20	.20
85	Spurs with Screws		.20	....	.10	....	....	.10	.50	.10	.10

Add 30 per cent. for Bottom and Fence for Plane A78.

STANLEY
S.W.

PRICES OF PLANE PARTS

SCRAPER, CHAMFER AND CORE BOX PLANES

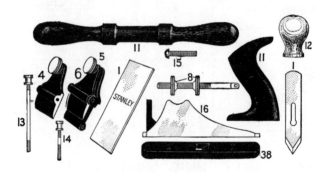

No.	Name of Part	No. of Plane	12	12½	12¼	112	212	85	57
1	Single Plane Iron		.50	.50	.50	.50	.50	.50	.60
4	Lever Cap		.50	.50	.50	.40	.20	.40	.30
5	" " Screw		....	....	....	....	....	....	.10
6	Frog Complete		1.40	1.40	1.20	.70	.20	.60	....
8	Adjusting Nut		.20	.20	.20	.20	....	....	.. ..
10	Frog Screw		....	....	....	....	....	.10	....
11	Plane Handle		1.00	1.00	1.00	.40	....	.50	.20
12	" Knob		....	....	....	.30	.40	.40	.20
13	Handle Bolt and Nut		....	....	....	.20	....	.20	.20
14	Knob " " "		....	....	....	.20	....	.20	.20
15	Plane Handle Screw		.10	.10	.10	....	....	....	....
16	" Bottom		2.40	2.40	1.60	2.40	1.20	2.00	5.00
38	Extra Wood Bottom		....	.50	....	....	....	....	....

PRICES OF PLANE PARTS

CARRIAGE, CIRCULAR, SCRUB, SHOOT AND FLOOR PLANES

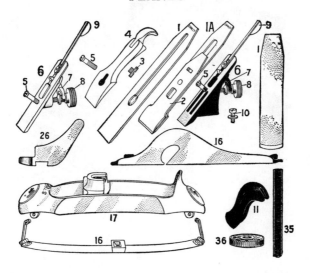

No.	Name of Part	No. of Plane	10	10½	10¼	11	113	20	40	40½	51
1A	Double Plane Iron.........		1.15	1.15	1.15	1.25	1.00	1.00	....	....	1.25
1	Single " "		.70	.70	.70	.80	.60	.60	.40	.50	.80
2	Plane Iron Cap............		.45	.45	.45	.45	.40	.40	....	....	.45
3	Cap Screw...:...........		.10	.10	.10	.10	.10	.10	....	....	.10
4	Lever Cap................		.50	.50	.50	.50	.50	.50	.20	.20	.50
5	" " Screw...........		.10	.10	.10	.10	.10	.10	.10	.10	.10
6	Frog Complete............		.70	.70	.70	.70	.70	.70	....	....	.70
7	"Y" Adjusting Lever......		.10	.10	.10	.10	.10	.10	....	....	.10
8	Adjusting Nut............		.20	.20	.20	.20	.20	.20	....	....	.20
9	Lateral Adjusting Lever.....		.20	.20	.20	.20	.20	.20	....	....	.10
10	Frog Screw...............		.10	.10	.10	.10	.10	.10	....	....	.10
11	Plane Handle.............		.40	.40	.80	.60	....	....	.20	.20	.40
12	" Knob		.30	.30	.60	....	1.00	....	.20	.20	.30
13	Handle Bolt and Nut.......		.20	.20	.20	....	....	....	.20	.20	.20
14	Knob " " "		.20	.20	.20	....	....	....	.20	.20	.20
16	Plane Bottom.............		3.30	3.30	3.00	2.60	1.20	1.20	1.40	2.00	6.00
17	Top Casting..............		....	....	....	....	2.00	3.00	....	....	....
26	Frog Seat................		....	....	....	....	....	1.00	....	....	....
35	Bottom Adjusting Screw....		....	....	....	....	1.00	.50	....	....	....
36	" " Nut......		....	....	....	....	....	.50	....	....	....

STANLEY
S.W.

PRICES OF COMBINATION PLANE PARTS

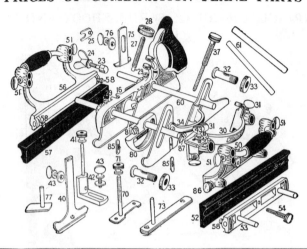

No.	Name of Part No. of Plane	A45 45	46	444	50	55	143
1	Cutters..........................Per Set	7.00	4.00	2.50	3.50	12.00	4.00
16	Main Stock or Bottom.................	5.00	5.00	5.00	2.50	6.00	6.00
23	Cutter Bolt.......................	.30	.30	.30	.30	.30	.....
24	" " Wing Nut..............	.30	.30	.30	.30	.30	.....
25	" " Clip and Screw........	.10	.10	.10	.....	.10	.....
27	" " Adjusting Screw.......	.20	.....	.....	.....	.20	.....
28	" " Wheel.............	.20	.....	.....	.....	.20	.....
30	Sliding Section.....................	3.00	3.00	3.00	.60	1.50	.....
32	Thimble...........................	.....	.....	.....	.....	.30	.....
33	" Check Nut..................	.....	.....	.....	.....	.30	.....
34	Adjustable Bottom..................	.....	.....	.....	.....	2.50	.....
37	" " Screw..............	.....	.....	.....	.....	.40	.....
40	Auxiliary Center Bottom.............	.....	.....	.....	.....	.60	.....
42	Angle Iron and Adjusting Screws......	.....	.....	.....	.....	.60	.....
50	Left Fence.........................	1.50	1.50	2.00	1.50	2.70	2.00
52	Tilting Guard Plate (Wood)...........	.....	.....	.....	.....	.40	.....
53	" Iron with Swivel.............	.....	.....	.....	.....	.80	.....
54	Left Fence Adjusting Screw...........	.....	.....	.....	.....	.40	.....
56	Right Fence........................	.....	.....	2.50	.....	2.00	.....
57	" " Tilting Plate.........	.....	.....	.....	.....	.40	.....
60	Long Arms...................Per Pair	1.00	1.00	1.00	1.00	1.00	1.00
61	Short Arms..................." "	.50	.50	.50	.....	.50	.....
70	Adjusting Depth Gauge...............	.40	.40	.40	.40	.40	.40
73	" Beading Stop..................	.40	.....	.....	.....	.60	.....
75	Slitting Cutter Stop.................	.20	.20	.20	.20	.20	.....
77	Sliding Section Depth Gauge..........	.40	.....	.....	.....	.....	.....
80	Cam Stop.........................	.80	.....	.....	.....	.80	.....
85	Spurs with Screws...................	.10	.10	.10	.10	.10	.....

Screws, Nos. 29, 31, 41, 43, 51, 58, 71, 76, 81, 86 and 87, .20•each.
Add 30 per cent for parts 16, 30 and 50 for Plane A45.

PRICES OF MITRE BOX PARTS

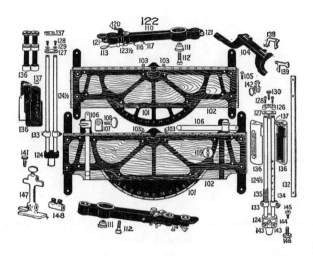

No.	Name of Part	No. of Box	50	50½	240 242	244 246	346 358	460	A358
101	Frame		6.00	6.00	7.00	7.00	8.40	11.20	10.90
102	Frame Board		.60	.60	.60	.60	.60	1.00	.60
104	" Leg		.60	.60	.60	.60	.70	.80	.90
106	Stock Guide		....	....	.50	.50	.50	.50	.65
110	Swivel Arm		1.50	1.50	2.50	2.50	2.80	3.30	3.65
111	" " Bushing		.30	.30	.30	.30	.30	.30	.30
112	" Bushing Screw		.30	.30	.30	.30	.30	.30	.30
113	Index Clamping Lever		.20	.20	.40	.40	.40	.50	.50
122	Swivel Complete (50 and 50½)		2.00	2.00	....	....	....	....	....
123	" " (240 to 460)		....	....	5.00	5.00	5.50	6.00	7.15
124	"T" Base		.50	.50	1.50	1.50	1.50	1.50	1.95
124½	Uprights (each)		.30	.30	.40	.40	.50	.50	.65
126	Saw Guide Cap		....	....	.10	.10	.10	.10	.15
132	" " Tie Bar		....	....	.20	.20	.30	.30	.40
133	Left Saw Guide Stop and Screw		.30	.30	.30	.30	.30	.30	.30
134	Right " " " "		....	....	.40	.40	.40	.40	.40
136	Saw Guide Cylinder		1.50	.50	.70	.70	.70	.70	.90
137	" " " Plate		.10	.10	.10	.10	.10	.10	.10
138	Trip Lever (back)		....	....	.30	.30	.30	.30	.30
139	" " (front)		....	....	.30	.30	.30	.30	.30
141	Leveling Screw		....	....	.20	.20	.20	.20	.20
142	Trip Clamp and Screw		....	....	.30	.30	.30	.30	.30
146	"T" Base Clamp Screw		....	....	.20	.20	.20	.20	.20
147	Length Stop Stand		....	....	.50	.50	.50	.50	.65
148	" " Coupling		....	....	.20	.20	.20	.20	.25

Parts Nos. 103, 105, 107, 108, 109, 114, 115, 116, 117, 119, 120, 121, 123½, 127, 128, 129, 130, 135, 143, 144, 145, 149, **.10** each.

PRICES OF PARTS No. 150 MITRE BOX

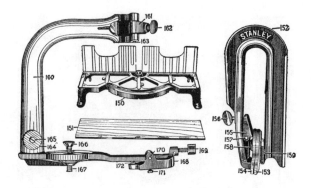

No.	Name of Part	Each
150	Frame..	**3.00**
151	Frame Board...	**.60**
152	Saw Yoke..	**1.25**
153	Right Saw Guide...	**.25**
154	Left Saw Guide..	**.25**
155	Saw Guide Lever...	**.15**
156	Saw Guide Thumb Screw......................................	**.10**
157	Saw Guide Pin...	**.10**
158	Saw Guide Spring..	**.10**
159	Saw Guide Adjusting Screw...................................	**.10**
160	Swivel..	**1.50**
161	Yoke Clamping Lever...	**.10**
162	Yoke Clamping Lever Thumb Screw.............................	**.10**
163	Yoke Clamping Lever Pin.....................................	**.10**
164	Roller..	**.10**
165	Roller Screw..	**.10**
166	Swivel Pivot Screw..	**.10**
167	Swivel Pivot Check Screw....................................	**.10**
168	Latch...	**.25**
169	Latch Fastening Screw.......................................	**.10**
170	Latch Pivot Screw...	**.10**
171	Latch Pivot Set Screw.......................................	**.10**
172	Latch Spring..	**.10**

[STANLEY]
(S.W.)

PRICES OF BIT BRACE PARTS

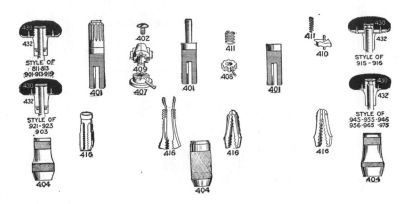

All parts listed can be readily put into the Brace by the user. Other parts can be supplied if required, but should any piece be wanted that is not shown, it is better that the Brace be returned to the factory for repairs. Some parts having the same name differ in design in the different Braces. We show different cuts bearing the same number to illustrate the different designs. Heads and quills are shown in section to make difference of construction clear. **Always give the number of the Brace when ordering repairs.**

No.	Name of Part	811	813	901	903	913	915	916	919	921	923
401	Chuck Body	.70	.80	.70	.70	.80	.50	.40	....	.70	.80
402	Plug Screw	.20	.20	.20	.20	.20	....	....	.20	.20	.20
404	Shell	1.80	1.80	1.00	1.00	.80	.70	.70	....	.80	.80
407	Clutch Gear	.50	....	.50	....	....	....	....	....	.50	....
408	Ratchet Gear	....	....	....	....	....	.30	....	....	....	....
409	Clutch	.80	....	.80	....	....	.30	....	....	.80	....
410	Pawl with Pin	....	.40	....	.40	.40	.30	....	.40	.20	.40
411	Clutch Spring	.20	.10	.20	.10	.10	....	....	.10	.20	.10
416	Jaws	.50	.50	.50	.50	.50	.40	.40	.50	.50	.50
430	Head	.70	.70	.70	.70	.70	.30	.30	.70	.70	.70
432	Quill	.90	.90	.90	.60	.90	.80	.80	.90	.60	.60

No.	Name of Part	924	945	946	955	956	965	965N	966	975	975N
401	Chuck Body	.50	.50	.40	.50	.40	.50	.50	.40	.50	.50
402	Plug Screw	....	....	....	....	....	....	....	....	....	....
404	Shell	.80	.70	.70	.60	.60	.60	.70	.60	.60	.70
407	Clutch Gear	....	....	....	....	....	....	....	....	....	....
408	Ratchet Gear	....	.30	....	.30	....	.30	.30	....	.30	.30
409	Clutch	....	....	....	....	....	....	....	....	....	....
410	Pawl with Pin	....	.30	....	.30	....	.30	.30	....	.30	.30
411	Clutch Spring	....	....	....	....	....	....	....	....	....	....
416	Jaws	.50	.30	.30	.30	.30	.20	.20	.20	.20	.20
430	Head	.70	.30	.30	.30	.30	.30	.30	.30	.30	.30
432	Quill	.60	.40	.40	.30	.30	.30	.40	.30	.30	.40

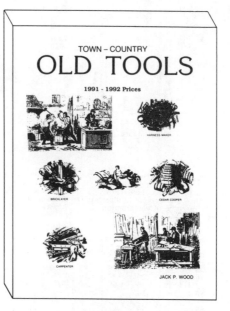